MATERIALS HANDLING

Materials Handling

JOHN R. IMMER

Director, Work Saving International;
Formerly Professor of Industrial Management,
The American University

New York   Toronto   London

McGRAW-HILL BOOK COMPANY, INC.

1953

MATERIALS HANDLING

Library of Congress Catalog Card Number: 52–7439

PREFACE

Since the beginning of the Second World War the movement of materials has been recognized as one of the most important determinants of modern production. At this time more efficient methods of materials movement made possible the huge increases in production of war material which was necessary for the defense of the country. It was soon realized that not only was production increased by improved methods of handling but total production costs were drastically reduced. As the factories of the nation returned to normal peacetime activity, this cost-saving aspect of materials handling made it the number one tool of the postwar production executive. In the face of rising labor and material costs it was often the only way by which production costs could be restrained.

It is not surprising then that there has been a strong demand from industry for university courses in materials handling. This demand has increased to a point where no industrial engineering program today is complete without at least one course in the fundamentals of materials handling. Not only college and university students but handling engineers with a lifetime of experience in the industry have felt the need for a general textbook which would bring together the more significant organizational, cost, and managerial aspects of the subject. Yet, such a general textbook could not be written until the companies themselves developed the techniques, methods, and philosophy of handling to a point where generalizations on these aspects could be made.

This text is a direct product of these developments. It is also the product of the complete cooperation accorded by the companies that have made important advances in the growing science of materials handling. Without this cooperation and the willingness to share the results of months or years of costly research, this text in its present form would not have been possible. Countless other individuals spent considerable time and effort in providing the author with a complete description of a method or an idea which could be only very briefly described in this text. Rather than present a collection of personal ideas, the author has sought to present in an organized form the best practices and ideas of materials handling as they have developed to the present time.

Special mention should be made of the invaluable review and assistance of the manufacturing research division of the International Harvester Company and of the Hoover Company in England. The author is also indebted to help on the managerial aspects of handling given by C. G. Chantrill of C. G. Chantrill & Partners (Management Engineers), London.

The following acknowledgments are also made: Chap. 31, Air Cargo Handling, cooperation and review by the members of Air Cargo, Inc.; Chap. 32, Railroad and Truck Handling, review and suggestions by C. E. Beauprie, Secretary, Freight Claim Division, Association of American Railroads; Chap. 33, Ship and Barge Handling, assistance of International Cargo Handling Coordination Association and review by Paul Amundson, editor of World Ports; Chap. 34, Handling Bulk Materials, review by R. B. Kern, Public Relations Department, Link-Belt Company.

JOHN R. IMMER

WASHINGTON, D.C.
January, 1953

CONTENTS

PART VI. ORGANIZATION

PART VII. SPECIAL HANDLING PROBLEMS

APPENDIX

PART I

INTRODUCTION

CHAPTER 1

INTRODUCTION

Materials handling is the means by which the goal of greater efficiency may be attained not only in industry but wherever materials must be moved. It offers the greatest opportunity today for the reduction of production costs. Because of increased efficiency in materials handling, countless firms within recent years have increased production within their existing premises, have maintained unit costs in spite of rising material costs and wage rates, and have been able to perform other miracles in cost reduction.

The handling of material is big business. A recent editorial points out how big it really is.[1]

Industry can save $2 billion a year by doing a better job of materials handling:

Let's review our arithmetic:

Start with $35 billion—1950's wage bill in manufacturing.

Take a quarter of this—say, $8 billion. That's a conservative estimate of the portion of wages spent for handling. (Many plants spend up to 40 per cent; one plant reports 60 per cent!)

Now, say, industry can cut its handling costs 25 per cent. Take 25 per cent of $8 billion—and there's your 2-billion target.

But this is not all of the story by any means. The amount spent in the transportation industries and the physical costs of merchandising, wholesaling, and other distributive functions should be added to the estimate of $8 billion. The handling costs in the mining and other extractive industries, agriculture and food processing, and the construction industry should be added also. The total of these costs of handling constitutes one of the largest single cost items in economic life today.

There are other effects of materials handling that are equally important. Because of its importance in affecting cost structures it has become the determining factor in the competition of industries and of individual firms. When a company's principal competitor halves his processing cost with a new handling system, the company must devise an equally efficient system in order to survive in a highly competitive market.

[1] *Factory Management and Maintenance*, June, 1950, p. 81.

A striking example of how these costs can affect the economy of a country was afforded recently in New Zealand where dock strikes increased handling and shipping costs. Even the temporary imposition of a surcharge of 50 per cent for all shipping seriously threatened the national economy.

The proposed 103-mile conveyor belt between Lake Erie and the Ohio River offers potential savings to the Ohio steel industry of millions of dollars a year.[2]

Such figures seemed to promise the rejuvenation of Ohio's entire steel industry. Although the state stands second in steel production with 20 per cent of the national output, Ohio mills, especially those in the landlocked Youngstown area, have been hard pressed to compete with river-front and lake-front plants elsewhere. . . . Furthermore, since the Youngstown mills, producing half of Ohio's output, work under the added handicap of f.o.b. mill prices which require a customer to pay the freight from Youngstown to his plant, the area of their market has become even more restricted. For them Riverlake (the conveyor project) held the prospect of low rates, stabilized costs, and broader markets.

1. What Is Materials Handling?

Materials handling is the preparation, placing, and positioning of materials to facilitate their movement or storage. It includes every consideration of the product except the actual processing operation and, in many instances, is included in this as an integral part of the process.

If for no other reason, this broad interpretation of the subject is dictated by the fact that maximum economy in materials handling is achieved only by the consideration of what happens to the product from its very first movement as a raw material to its final place of consumption. Any other interpretation of materials handling will result in a restricted outlook and will prevent a company from obtaining the maximum benefits and savings which the efficient movement of materials can provide. The movement of materials should be minimized; handling should be eliminated as far as possible.

2. Importance of Materials Handling

Within recent years a number of figures have been developed to show the amount of materials handling involved as a part of the total production process. Naturally enough, these percentages vary considerably from one industry to another. Their main value in each case is to point out the importance of the handling function. Obviously the importance of the function is greater in those industries where there is a high ratio of

[2] Rise of the Rubber Railroad, *Fortune*, April, 1951, p. 120.

handling cost to the total processing cost than in those activities in which the ratio is considerably smaller.

The importance of materials handling to American industry was pointed out in the objective study made in 1949 by a British team sent to this country by the Anglo-American Council on Productivity. In the introduction of their report it is noted: [3]

Previous British teams investigating productivity in their counterpart industries in the United States have repeatedly drawn attention to the degree to which in America the handling of materials is mechanized. A common theme running through their reports has been that greater output is obtained by freeing the operators to concentrate on maximum utilization of their productive equipment. This was an impressive feature of observations in both small and large size American firms in many industries.

From the standpoint of the national economy, the cost involved in the movement and handling of materials assumes gigantic proportions. Within industry, the cost of moving materials from one workplace to another is often more than the processing cost itself. When the cost of the transportation of raw materials, of partly finished assemblies and parts, and of the finished product is added, the result is one of the largest single items of expense in the total economy.

From the standpoint of the individual company, materials handling can be the millstone that plunges the firm into bankruptcy or retires it to a second-place position in the competitive picture. On the other hand, efficient materials handling may be the means of launching a new business (by extending services and products at the lowered production cost thus made possible) or the sole means of continuing corporate existence in the face of restricted price levels and rising costs.

From the standpoint of labor, improved methods of materials handling offer the greatest prospects for higher wages and better working conditions. Since wages are dependent upon productivity, it is to the interest of labor to assist management in lowering production costs and increasing output. At the same time, the decrease in heavy lifting and "man handling" of materials has removed a large part of the hazard and fatigue from many production jobs. The efficient plant is the safe plant, and efficient movement of materials is the best safeguard for the worker's welfare.

The importance of materials handling from all these standpoints is summed up in the conclusions of the British Productivity Team: [4]

[3] "Materials Handling in Industry," productivity report published by the Anglo-American Council on Productivity, London, 1950, p. 1.
[4] *Ibid.*, p. 43.

We found a general awareness on the part of both management and labour that standards of living in the United States could only be improved by increased production at the same or lower conversion cost. In view of the fact that salaries, wage rates, and material costs have risen in recent years, it was realized that reduction in price of goods manufactured could only be effected by

  a. Improved manufacturing methods giving higher productivity per man-hour, at the same or lower cost.

  b. Reduction in costs of servicing the manufacturing and processing departments.

3. Scope of Materials Handling

The problem of moving materials with the lowest expenditure of time and effort is definitely not restricted to the industrial plant. Although the greatest development in this field and a large share of the techniques and methods of analysis developed to date have come out of industry, there has already been a wide application to other fields of activity. It is very important, then, that both the beginning student and the experienced materials-handling engineer be aware of these broader applications and have an idea of the possibilities inherent in these techniques which are commonly ascribed to the intra-plant movement of materials.

  a. *Industrial Materials Handling.* The movement of materials within the confines of a factory takes on a new significance with the increase in size of the individual production unit. The importance of this function in the determination of production costs has led manufacturing companies to set up separate divisions and company-wide coordinating committees.

Industry still has the greatest interest in the problem of moving and storing materials. To date it has been the main source of methods of analysis and organizational procedures. It also is the area in which the majority of materials-handling engineers will find employment. Although the specific handling problems in the various industries may be extremely varied, the principles and the methods of approach will be the same.

The primary function of a manufacturing plant is to produce a given product. Raw materials are fed into the productive unit and are transformed, changed in shape and size, and assembled together to emerge at the end of the process as the finished product. The primary purpose of materials movement is to provide an uninterrupted flow of materials to, through, and from these processes.

  b. *Transportation Industries.* In the transportation industries the movement of materials is the primary consideration. The main cost considerations are the fixed equipment and overhead, consisting of terminal loading points and rolling stock. In each industry the handling required to get materials from the manufacturer's dock to the rolling stock at the point of shipment and from the rolling stock to the consignee often constitutes a major part of the total cost. In the barge industry, for example, this

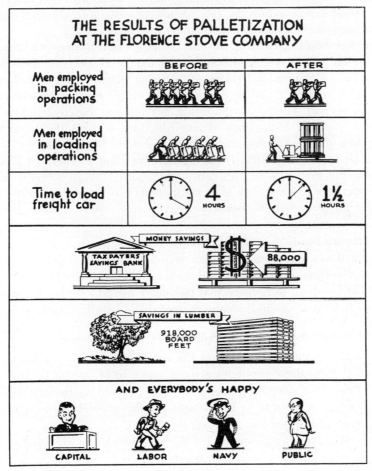

Fig. 1. Pictorialized results of a change in materials handling at the Florence Stove Company at Gardner, Mass. (*The Palletizer.*)

cost in 1949 represented approximately one-half of the total operating costs of the industry.

In these industries, therefore, more efficient movement of materials is, in many cases, necessary to the continued health of the industries concerned and is of considerable interest, to the national economy as a whole. The maintenance of high standards of living depends upon the low cost of the transport of materials as well as upon efficient production.

c. Merchandising and Warehousing. The cost of receiving, processing, storing, and delivering of the materials and products being sold forms a substantial part of the operating cost of modern merchandising units. The restriction of gross operating margins can be reconciled to higher labor and capital expenses only by the introduction of more efficient methods for the movement and handling of these materials.

The warehousing industry is based almost entirely upon the handling and storage of materials. Although a change of 10 per cent in handling costs may be important to a manufacturing plant, to the warehouse it may be a matter of life or death. Many supplementary functions performed as part of the warehousing service are based entirely upon efficient handling techniques. These functions include the breaking of bulk, packaging, wrapping and crating, and order filling.

d. Extractive Industries. In these industries the problem of handling and moving materials has long been recognized as an integral part of their operations. A number of developments have wide application and can be adapted within industry, particularly where similar handling problem are involved.

e. Process Industries. The handling function as such has long been recognized in the process industries as one of the most important aspects. It is not surprising, then, to find in these industries a well-developed system of handling or to learn that the entire manufacturing or extracting process is built upon and designed around the handling system.

4. Who Solves the Handling Problem?

From the foregoing section on the scope of materials handling it is obvious that all these problems are not going to be solved by specialists in the field. One purpose of this text is to provide an understanding of the subject and a guide to the solution of the problem in an extremely wide range of application.

There is a growing tendency for the merchandising, distributing, and transporting industries to hire trained industrial engineers as a part of their operating staff. Whether or not a firm has personnel with this training they are still faced with the problem of analyzing their own materials movement and handling.

In the final analysis, the solution of any handling problem lies in getting the necessary information together and ascertaining from that the basic relationships involved. There is no substitute for plain common sense. The accumulated experience of other companies in solving similar problems can, however, serve as an invaluable guide in accomplishing this rational analysis.

In this materials-handling age every production man must have a knowledge of its fundamentals. In fact, there are few economic activities today in which this knowledge is not almost a prerequisite to success. Materials handling is a necessary part of the education of every student of business and engineering, regardless of his age or the number of years of experience he has had.

In addition to a general understanding of the subject, industry now needs specialized knowledge. The emergence of the "materials-handling engineer" is a phenomenon of recent years. At first there was a tendency to apply the term to men specializing in specific types of conveyor systems. Since the end of the Second World War, however, the term has gradually acquired a wider connotation.

5. The Materials-handling Engineer

The first requirement of the materials-handling engineer is that he be familiar with the techniques and methods of industrial engineering. It must be kept in mind that materials handling is simply one specialized aspect of this broader field. A thorough knowledge and understanding of time and motion study, production and material control, and industrial processes is a basic requirement for the intelligent analysis of the materials-handling problem. It goes without saying that the materials-handling engineer should be familiar with all the aspects and methods of making a plant layout.

His further training falls into two separate classifications, the first of which is the primary purpose of this text.

a. Understanding the Function and Organization of Materials Handling. Any thoroughgoing analysis of a materials-handling problem affects a wide variety of other functions and processes within the company. It also raises a number of questions in regard to the use, application, and maintenance of the equipment to be used. It involves the use of a large number of managerial, accounting, and engineering techniques. In sum and substance, the materials-handling analysis which adequately covers a given problem is simply a production analysis with emphasis put upon the materials-handling aspect.

This understanding of the nature of the movement of materials is a prerequisite to any use or consideration of specific types of equipment. With this grasp of these fundamental relationships to all the other aspects of production, the student of materials handling and the practicing materials-handling engineer is able to proceed intelligently to the application of specific types of materials-handling equipment. Without this background, there is the danger that the installation may be technically adequate but

PALLETIZED UNIT LOADS vs LOOSE CARGO

THE FOLLOWING CHART COMPARES TWO CARGO HANDLING METHODS AT EACH OPERATION IN A
TYPICAL SHIPMENT OF SUPPLIES FROM NAVY CONTRACTOR TO POINT OF USE. THE NUMBER OF
MAN-HOURS REQUIRED TO HANDLE 100 TONS OF PALLETIZED CARGO (77 PALLET LOADS) IS
COMPARED WITH THE NUMBER OF HOURS REQUIRED TO HANDLE
THE SAME AMOUNT OF LOOSE CARGO (4080 SEPARATE
PACKAGES). THE FIGURES USED ARE BASED ON TIME
STUDIES CONDUCTED BY MATERIALS HANDLING OFFICERS
IN THE UNITED STATES, GUAM, PEARL HARBOR AND
TRINIDAD. IDEAL WORKING CONDITIONS ARE ASSUMED

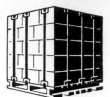

·10 MAN-HOURS

OPERATION	PALLETIZED	LOOSE CARGO
LOADING PALLET AT CONTRACTOR'S	15 MAN-HOURS	NO MAN-HOURS
STRAPPING PALLET AT CONTRACTOR'S	35 MAN-HOURS	NO MAN-HOURS
LOADING CAR AT CONTRACTOR'S	8 MAN-HOURS	50 MAN-HOURS
UNLOADING CAR AT SUPPLY DEPOT	9 MAN-HOURS	24 MAN-HOURS
STOWING AT SUPPLY DEPOT	9 MAN-HOURS	30 MAN-HOURS
ISSUING AT SUPPLY DEPOT	6 MAN-HOURS	30 MAN-HOURS
LOADING CAR AT SUPPLY DEPOT	8 MAN-HOURS	50 MAN-HOURS

FIG. 2. Palletized unit loads vs. loose cargo. (*Official U.S. Navy photograph.*)

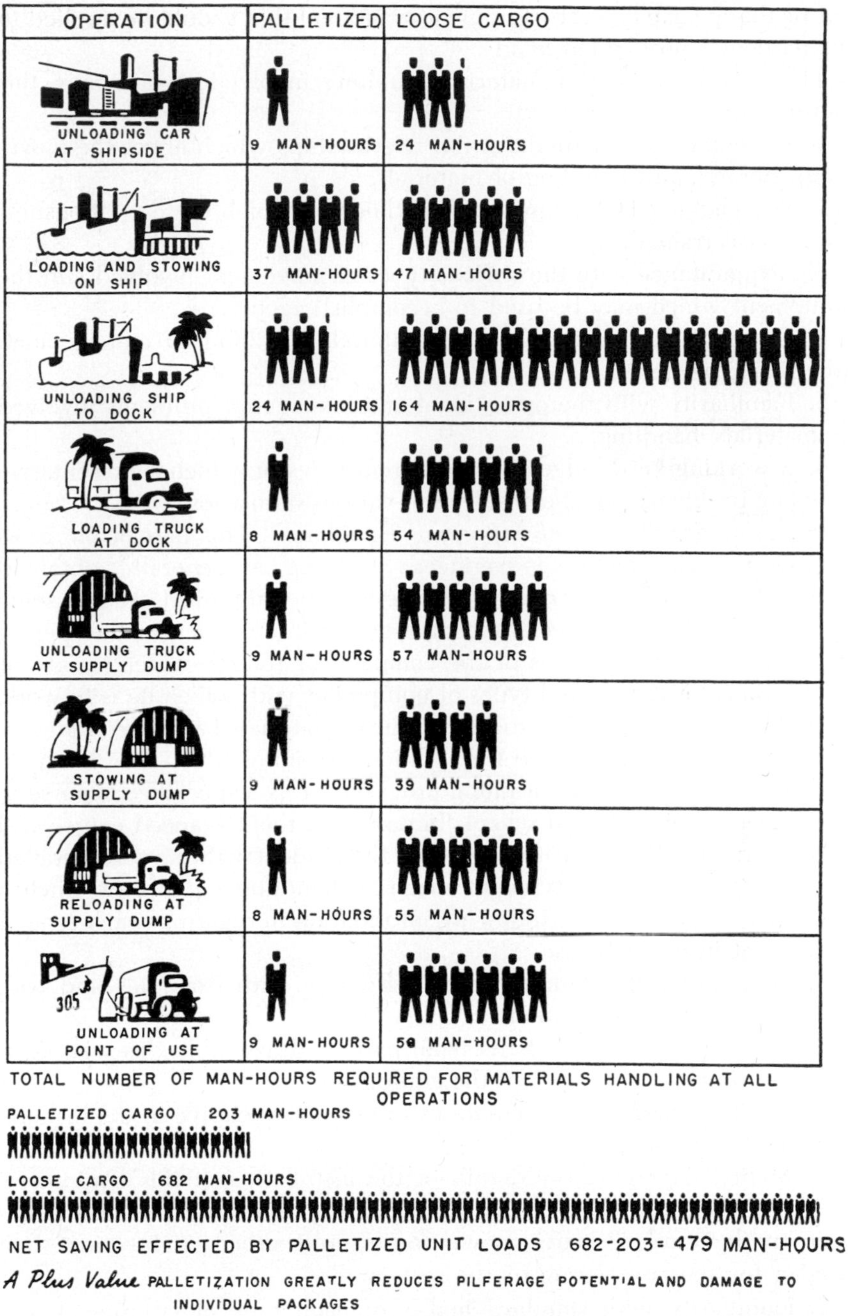

OPERATION	PALLETIZED	LOOSE CARGO
UNLOADING CAR AT SHIPSIDE	9 MAN-HOURS	24 MAN-HOURS
LOADING AND STOWING ON SHIP	37 MAN-HOURS	47 MAN-HOURS
UNLOADING SHIP TO DOCK	24 MAN-HOURS	164 MAN-HOURS
LOADING TRUCK AT DOCK	8 MAN-HOURS	54 MAN-HOURS
UNLOADING TRUCK AT SUPPLY DUMP	9 MAN-HOURS	57 MAN-HOURS
STOWING AT SUPPLY DUMP	9 MAN-HOURS	39 MAN-HOURS
RELOADING AT SUPPLY DUMP	8 MAN-HOURS	55 MAN-HOURS
UNLOADING AT POINT OF USE	9 MAN-HOURS	50 MAN-HOURS

TOTAL NUMBER OF MAN-HOURS REQUIRED FOR MATERIALS HANDLING AT ALL OPERATIONS

PALLETIZED CARGO   203 MAN-HOURS

LOOSE CARGO   682 MAN-HOURS

NET SAVING EFFECTED BY PALLETIZED UNIT LOADS   682-203= 479 MAN-HOURS

A Plus Value PALLETIZATION GREATLY REDUCES PILFERAGE POTENTIAL AND DAMAGE TO INDIVIDUAL PACKAGES

FIG. 2. (Continued.)

not be the specific type of equipment or method that should be applied to the particular problem at hand.

The various aspects of materials handling involved in obtaining this picture are:

1. Understanding of fundamental relationships which affect the movement, storage, and handling of materials.

2. Knowledge of techniques and methods by which these relationships may be ascertained.

3. Acquaintance with the various types of movement involved and the equipment which may be used to accomplish each type.

4. Grasp of the relationships of materials handling to management, labor, and the public.

5. Familiarity with the operational and managerial problems involved in materials handling.

6. A working knowledge of the different ways by which representative handling problems have been solved in various industries.

b. Training in Technical Aspects of Equipment. This part of the prospective materials-handling engineer's training is generally obtained within the specific industry in which he is to be employed. At this stage he will embark upon a specialized course of training either for the specific types of handling problems of the company or for the wider variety of applications for the limited types of equipment with which he is to work.

With the increasing demand for trained materials-handling engineers there has developed the need for additional training which may be given under individual company training programs or as a specialized course in the university or technical school. In any case, this advanced course will be concerned primarily with providing the student with a more detailed knowledge of the main types of materials-handling equipment. Such a course should provide the following information in regard to each type of equipment in common use:

1. Advantages and limitations of use along with examples and case studies of specific installations.

2. Working knowledge of the main parts and assemblies as well as of the operating characteristics of the equipment.

3. Ability to make any calculations or estimates relative to the installation of the equipment.

4. Ability to prepare the details of the installation of this equipment, including the knowledge of the type of information required and familiarity with standard parts, power units, and other engineering data needed for the completion of the system.

5. Familiarity with standard makes of each type of equipment and ability to discuss intelligently the differentiating aspects of each make.

This includes a working knowledge of manufacturers' catalogues and of the sources for additional information.

QUESTIONS

1. Discuss the effects of materials handling on the national economy.
2. Define materials handling.
3. What types of economic activity are concerned with materials handling?
4. How are materials-handling problems solved? Who solves them?
5. What is meant by "materials-handling engineer"?
6. What specific aspects are involved in obtaining an understanding of materials handling?
7. What kind of training and background should the materials-handling engineer have?
8. What should be considered in an advanced course of this subject?

PROJECTS FOR FURTHER STUDY

1. Prepare a report on the editorial comments in regard to materials handling and packaging in technical magazines of recent issue.
2. Interview local representatives of equipment companies for their ideas on the background needed for selling equipment.
3. Contrast the attention given to materials handling in two widely divergent industries. One way to do this is by reference to the trade journals of the respective industries. Before writing the report, talk with local representatives of these industries, if possible.

CHAPTER 2

HISTORY

The movement of materials or the creation of place utility has always constituted a serious challenge to man's ingenuity and inventiveness. The problem of moving heavy objects was one which confronted the ancients. With the increased use of iron and steel at the beginning of the modern era, the movement of heavy weights became an increasingly important activity.

From the standpoint of materials handling, history can be divided into two periods:

1. *Man handling era (pre-1900). Materials moved by man power where possible.* Although many kinds of cranes, hoists, and other lifting devices were used extensively in this period, they were for the most part restricted to the movement of material too heavy for handling by man power. It will be seen that the dates are not all-inclusive for these two periods, as evidenced by the fact that many companies today still regard materials-handling equipment in this manner.

2. *Machine handling era (post-1900). Movement of materials by mechanical means where possible.* The revolutionary idea which developed shortly after the turn of the century was that, although certain materials, because of their limited weight and size, could be moved by man power, mechanical equipment could and should be used for their movement. The rise of this concept represents the birth of modern materials handling.

1. History of Materials Handling

Although history from the standpoint of materials handling can be divided into the two main periods previously described, each of these, in turn, falls naturally into two very unequal subdivisions. It must be kept in mind that the problem of moving materials is by no means a new one. The periods into which the history of handling are divided do not automatically or completely start or stop with the dates given. As with most great developments, there have been numerous pioneers far in advance of their time. At the same time, history (and the present is no exception) is replete with examples of firms using the methods and attitudes of previous periods.

a. The Ancient World. Some of the handling feats of the ancients would provide a test for the most modern of materials-handling equipment. Well-known examples are the construction of the pyramids in ancient Egypt and the erection of the obelisks in Egypt and Rome. Of lesser renown are the stones of the Stonehenge, which was erected in southern England circa 1500 B.C. These stones, weighing 8 to 12 tons and standing nearly 15 feet high, were supposedly quarried in South Wales, floated around Land's End and up the river Avon (not the river of Stratford fame), and then moved by sled 3 miles over land to the present site.

In the Western Hemisphere, one of the marvels of ancient engineering is a pre-Inca temple near Cuzco, Peru. Individual stones of this temple weigh up to 20 tons and were quarried from the bottom of the valley over 2,000 feet below the temple site. The problem of moving these stones was further complicated by the fact that the builders apparently were not aware of the principle of the wheel. (One explanation is that the stones were raised by means of a series of locks on canals, of which many evidences have been discovered.)

b. The Period from 450 to 1900. Although a number of types and varieties of handling equipment were developed within this period, the problem still remained, namely, the moving of materials unsuited for movement by man power. There were a number of outstanding exceptions to this, however.

Eli Whitney, in 1800, undertook the mass production of muskets. It was recorded that not only were standardized parts used, but that workbenches were arranged so that the parts could be passed from one worker to another, thus simplifying the materials-handling problem. About the same time, Thomas Jefferson reported the use of a similar method of manufacture in a factory in France which had been developed at the beginning of the eighteenth century: "In 1785 LeBlanc in France produced muskets with interchangeable parts." [1] In 1770, Josiah Wedgwood also became aware of the importance of layout in affecting handling costs and experimented with various ways of moving materials.

In the foundry of the firm of Boulton and Watt, erected in 1796, various types of swinging jib cranes and other lifting devices were included. Some of the earliest pictures drawn of this plant show some of the larger jib cranes fitted with small carriages which supported the hoisting block and provided greater flexibility in the movement of heavy parts. By 1860, an overhead traveling bridge crane had been installed to provide complete coverage of the working area.

[1] Lewis Mumford, "Technics and Civilization," p. 90, Routledge and Kegan Paul, Ltd., London, 1934.

The jib crane has a long and venerable history. Several types were described in Agricola's "De Re Metallica," written in 1556 and used as the standard text in metallurgy for nearly two hundred years. This treatise was translated into English by Herbert Hoover and printed in 1912 with the original illustrations. These woodprints showed a number of the other methods used in elevating and transporting materials.

The wheelbarrow appeared as the main piece of equipment for horizontal movement, although a type of four-wheel cart was also used. No

FIG. 3. Wheelbarrows were for centuries the main means of moving materials around the shop floor. This style, depicted in 1550, has been shown in other drawings three centuries later with almost no change in construction. (*G. Agricola, "De Re Metallica," p. 519, Dover Publications, Inc., New York, 1951.*)

fixed-track equipment was shown, although a drawing of a timber railway with a truck being drawn along it was shown in a contemporary work by Sebastian Münster ("Cosmographia Universalis," 1550).

The problem of hoisting materials was always a serious one in early mining operations. Agricola described a number of devices used for this purpose. One was a simple windlass turned by a crank. Agricola noted, "All windlass workers, whatever kind of a machine they turn, are necessarily robust, so that they can sustain such great toil." One type of windlass was equipped with a flywheel to steady its operation. Gearing was used in some types to transmit power to the windlass, the source of power being two men on a treadwheel or a horse-drawn whim. Iron was frequently used for journals and sockets but never for wheels or axles.

Water was raised from the mines by means of an elevating conveyor formed of a chain of metal dippers. These were of standard size and shape and could be replaced with little difficulty. The chain was formed of large metal links which were also replaceable. The high mechanical advantage necessary to permit it to be worked by one man made it extremely slow in operation. The weight of the machine also limited the height of the lift.

FIG. 4. The earliest type of fixed-track vehicle. (*G. Agricola, "De Re Metallica," p. 343, Dover Publications, Inc., New York, 1951.*)

Suction pumps and various types of force pumps were also used. The most successful solution found to the problem of raising water was the ball-and-chain system. Balls made of horsehair with a sewn covering were fastened at 6-foot intervals. These were drawn through a vertical pipe, and the water was discharged at the upper end. Agricola stated that a water wheel 24 feet in diameter would draw water from a 210-foot shaft. These wheels were powered by human treadwheels or by a horse-drawn whim.

c. *The Period from 1900 to 1940.* This period marks the beginning of the use of materials-handling equipment for moving materials which were formerly moved by man power. It also marks the beginning of modern systems of production based upon the conveyorized machine or assembly line.

In his book "Secrets of Industry," Lewis C. Ord describes the methods used in the fabrication of wooden freight cars in the 1890's at the

FIG. 5. Revolving jib crane with movable crab was the forerunner of the modern traveling bridge crane. There was little difference between this crane shown in 1550 and the one used in the Soho Foundry of Boulton, Watt & Company in 1800. (*G. Agricola, "De Re Metallica," p. 514, Dover Publications, Inc., New York, 1951.*)

Canadian Pacific Railway Company shops. At first, the same gang built the complete freight car from wheel trucks to roof. A second method—prompted by the need for greater production and the shortage of skilled help—utilized gangs with special functions. Thus, the underframe gangs would move from one rail car to another, to be followed, in turn, by flooring, framing, and roofing gangs. In this second method, more men would be put to work at one time. This, plus the higher output rate, resulted in reduced production costs, despite increased cost of controls, supervision, and materials handling.

The third step was a method of continuous assembly which was adapted a few years later by Henry Ford in his first assembly line. With

FIG. 6. Interchangeable links and buckets of standardized size and shape were featured in this sixteenth-century model of a chain-bucket conveyor. (*G. Agricola, "De Re Metallica," p. 175, Dover Publications, Inc., New York, 1951.*)

this development, the men remained in one permanent location, and the cars were moved past them. This was a truly significant development and marked the transition to modern progressive assembly methods.[2]

In operation, a six-track shop, with four erecting tracks and two supply tracks, would build eleven freight cars per day on each working track, single

[2] Lewis C. Ord, "Secrets of Industry," p. 18, George Allen & Unwin, Ltd., London, 1944.

shift operation, and a nine-hour day. The cars on each track were pulled forward one position every forty-five minutes. From the time the trucks (bogies) were run into one end of the shop until they came out the other end completed, ready for painting, took just a little over seven hours. That was the start of mass production.

In May, 1913, operations were started on the first progressive assembly line at the Ford Motor Company. Within a short time a number of other production assembly lines had been set up on various types of conveyors. During the First World War a number of companies changed over to the new type of layout, which involved some type of fixed-path equipment. This remained the main production technique for mass production until the outbreak of the Second World War.

During the 1920's, a number of other companies changed over to a conveyorized type of operation, both for movement of materials through the machine shop and through the assembly process. The idea of a complete kit of parts accompanying the chassis or main framework during the complete assembly process was also developed at the beginning of this period. Packard Motor Car Company, as well as Hudson and Velie, also used the method at this time. In the late 1930's, the system was adopted by the Standard Motor Car Company of Coventry, England, which has used it in one way or another up to the present date. It is interesting to note that the system was taken out of the Packard plant in the late 1920's and later replaced after the Second World War.

d. Post 1940. With the beginning of war production for the Second World War, both materials handling and plant layout entered an advanced stage in their development and in their recognition by management as a means of increasing production. Many managements which had previously been hesitant about making large investments in materials-handling equipment now found themselves faced with the primary objective of production regardless of cost. Firms having large cost-plus contracts for war materials were completely freed from their former hesitation in making such capital expenditures. In many instances the corresponding reduction in production costs resulting from the introduction of this equipment was strictly a by-product to the more important problem of getting the materials produced.

The economies and advantages resulting from the use of this handling equipment and of the systems based upon it were large contributing factors to the phenomenal increase in the use of this equipment in the immediate postwar years. The increased attention given to improving the efficiency of materials movement and handling by industrial and non-industrial firms has played an important part in the increased production of the United States within these years.

2. Future of Materials Handling

Although a tremendous amount of material in the form of books (most of which describe the operation and application of specific types of equipment) and articles in technical and nontechnical magazines has been printed, the subject, as a whole, is only now beginning to assume a definite shape. The principles outlined in the following chapter are the result of an evolutionary process. Although most of the specific techniques and methods outlined in this text have been developed within the last ten years, some of them were being used successfully in a small number of companies thirty or forty years ago.

The place of materials handling in the organization has changed rapidly since 1948 and, indeed, the most important trend (that of centralization of control over materials-handling activities) is largely a development of 1950 and 1951.

Of the immediate future of materials handling, the following may be noted:

1. Materials handling is an accepted part of managerial and engineering education. As such, it is a subject of extreme importance to every student of production methods.

2. Materials handling offers the best prospects for increased production and lowered production costs within the near future. As such, it commands the attention of every executive responsible for these functions.

3. Materials handling is a recognized professional activity. As such, definite requirements and basic principles have been recognized and accepted.

4. Materials handling will have an increased application to a wide range of activities outside the normal range of a plant or factory. In many places the application of these techniques has only just begun.

QUESTIONS

1. Explain the justification for dividing history into two periods from a materials-handling standpoint.

2. Discuss the characteristics of handling under the "man handling era."

3. Discuss the characteristics of handling under the "machine handling era."

4. Trace the historical development of the crane.

5. Who are the oldest equipment manufacturers? (Check advertisements in old technical magazines.)

PROJECTS FOR FURTHER STUDY

1. Write a report on the following:

   a. Materials handling in the building of the pyramids.
   b. Methods of handling used in the Middle Ages.
   c. Handling in the early days of the iron and steel industry.

2. Examine a number of the oldest industrial magazines obtainable for descriptions of handling methods.

3. Give a report on the handling methods recounted in "De Re Metallica" (see translation by Herbert Hoover published in 1912 and republished in 1950).

CHAPTER 3

PRINCIPLES

1. Importance of Principles

As a subject becomes more complicated and involved, the need increases for the recognition of guiding principles. It is not too surprising to note that many of these principles have been recognized and practiced for a good many years. The 10 principles formulated by Harold Coes in 1925 were incorporated in a more comprehensive list of 27 general rules in the "Cost and Production Handbook," which first appeared in 1934. Other authors on the subject have since that time pointed out other basic relationships involved in materials handling.

These basic principles of materials handling as developed to date fall naturally into the four major classifications:

1. Planning principles
2. Operating principles
3. Equipment principles
4. Costing principles

In addition to these general principles, there are numerous other fundamental relationships both in the movement of materials and in the installation and operation of equipment. Many of the examples and case studies which follow were chosen with the aim of pointing out these relationships.

To the student, these principles provide a convenient framework for the mass of information, examples, techniques, and methods which follow. They also serve as a test of the value of these examples and a means of realizing in a practical form why and how the methods illustrated are so effective.

To the general public these principles help to explain the phenomenal and often fantastic savings reported as the result of new handling methods. Even to the experienced materials-handling engineer there is a bit of wonder at headlines such as the following:

"How overhead handling saved the cost of a new warehouse ($400,-000)."

"Production increased three times with no increase in space."

"New warehouse cuts handling costs in half."

These savings are generally the result of a very carefully planned program. The principles provide the layman (as well as the student) with a guide as to how such things can be accomplished by methodical analysis.

To the busy executive, these principles provide a valuable guide in the decisions he is called upon to make regarding production and materials handling. He wants to know (in a nutshell) what his company should do to improve its handling. In addition, he has a responsibility to see that his company is kept abreast of every development that is going to help production and lower costs. Materials handling is currently one of the most promising fields in this respect.

To the materials-handling engineer, these principles have the greatest value of all. They become part of the criteria by which every handling and materials-movement problem can be considered. They provide a rule for his everyday work. Whether the problem is a simple one or an extremely complex one, the clue to the answer will be found in these principles. In addition to the general principles listed, he gradually develops other rules of specific application to the plant or company in which he is working.

2. Planning Principles

Efficient handling is the result of planning. It involves a recognition of the fundamental relationships of materials movement and storage, an understanding of their effects on costs and production, and a knowledge of the methods of achieving the most efficient relationship of these cost factors.

a. Plan Handling for Over-all Economy. One of the most pronounced trends in industry today is the increased recognition and utilization of this principle. This is reflected in the many top-management committees which have been formed in recent years to coordinate the handling and movement of materials. Most of the larger industrial firms today have such a committee in one form or another.

b. Sell the Philosophy of Handling to the Organization. Workers as well as management need to be made "handling conscious." This may be done as part of a motion-study program, a work-simplification program, or by a special materials-handling program. It may also be accomplished by giving emphasis to materials handling as part of a suggestion program. The important thing is to make everybody aware that *motion is money* and that every unnecessary movement adds unnecessarily to the cost of the product.

c. Revise Layout to Reduce Handling. In all except some of the most recently constructed factory buildings, one of the prime problems of mechanized handling is how to overcome the defects of poor layout. A number of expensive mechanical handling systems could be done away with simply by improving the flow of the product.

An improved layout will reduce a large amount of the movement required for materials in process. By planning the location of successive operations so that the material at the completion of one operation is prepositioned for the beginning of the next, a large amount of handling can be eliminated.

d. Delegate Responsibility to One Man. Materials handling cuts across every manufacturing and production division of the company. Even in a medium-sized company it involves a large number of otherwise unrelated activities (except of course their interest in the end product). Sometimes the interests of the shipping department seem to be diametrically opposed to those of the press department when a method of handling is involved.

The first principle of handling (planning for over-all economy) requires that all the functions and responsibilities be centered under one man and that man be directly accountable to the production executive of the firm. In even the smallest firms, materials handling must be recognized as a separate function and some one individual given responsibility for it.

e. Utilize the Third Dimension. Increased costs for industrial construction have forced many companies to investigate other means of getting production space. One of the most effective was found to be the utilization of "air rights." By increasing the stacking height of goods from 5 feet to 10 feet, one company doubled the amount of cubic space available for storage. This saved the cost of a new warehouse. At the Mengel Company, Louisville, Ky., 1,100 feet of overhead trolley conveyor replaced a warehouse for temporary storage of finished furniture. The Minnesota Mining and Manufacturing Company, St. Paul, Minn., added 50,000 square feet of storage space within an existing building by suspending rolls of abrasives from the ceiling. A new building of this size would have cost the company $400,000 at that time.[1]

The increased output of modern machine tools creates a problem in the movement of the materials being machined. Congestion in the working areas can often be relieved by transporting materials overhead. Many companies have achieved complete overhead movement for all their materials within the production areas.

f. Utilize Live Storage. This is often referred to as "storage on the move." It frequently combines the functions of storage and of movement of materials. Live storage refers primarily to the fact that no handling is needed to put the materials into motion again. This was an outstanding

---

[1] John R. Immer, "Layout Planning Techniques," p. 284, McGraw-Hill Book Company, Inc., New York, 1950.

characteristic of the River Rouge plant of the Ford Motor Company when first put into operation in 1918. Since that time, many other trolley conveyor systems have been installed to keep materials on the move. Other types of conveyors, such as roller, wheel, and belt, are also used for the same purpose.

3. Operating Principles

Within recent years a number of fundamental relationships in the day-by-day operation of materials-handling systems and methods have been recognized. Some of these are disarming in their simplicity but just as effective in their ability to speed up the movement of materials. The value of each of these principles is attested to by the number of case studies and examples of their successful application in industry upon which this text is based.

a. Efficient Handling Is Safe Handling. There is no room in the modern plant for unsafe practices. Yet, according to a recent survey, 22 per cent of all industrial accidents are connected with handling. Although mechanization decreases the number of accidents, their severity tends to increase. This calls for a recognition of the conditions that permit them to happen and a rigid enforcement of safety regulations as further protection for all concerned.

b. Avoid Rehandling. From the standpoint of minimum movement of materials, it would be desirable always to move them directly from the receiving dock to the location of the first operation to be performed on them. In practice, it is seldom that this ideal can be attained for a number of practical reasons. Nevertheless, any rehandling is a loss to the company. In one company, each movement of the materials in process is given an operation number; any other movement appears under an "excess movement" account.

c. Move in Unit Loads. This is one of the most important principles in modern handling. Although of recent development, the basic principle has been known for centuries as the "lazy man's load." It is quicker to move a number of items as a unit than it is to move them individually. With the use of pallets, skids, and strapping the problem of unitizing materials was largely solved. The limitations of weight and size of the load to be moved has also been sharply reduced by improvements of unit-load carriers such as fork trucks, cranes, and straddle trucks.

d. Use Gravity Where Possible. This is still the cheapest way of moving materials. A simple chute between machines is often all that is needed for straight-line production on a series of machine operations. Chutes and passing boards at a slight incline have long been one of the chief handling mediums in the garment trade. In other industries, circular parts are easily rolled to the site of the next operation. These gravity devices, being simple, also often have the added advantage of lightness and flexibility of use. This is of particular importance in the smaller manufacturing plants where production runs are inclined to be fairly short.

e. Where Gravity Will Not Suffice, Use Mechanical Means Where Practical. Where the desired movement of materials cannot be accomplished by the use of gravity, some means of mechanical movement should be considered. Where heavy weights are involved or much time is spent in the movement of materials, some mechanical assistance should be provided. In jobs where a high fatigue factor is encountered, extra attention should be given to the lifting and movement of materials as a possible cause of fatigue and loss of production.

f. Establish Schedules and Procedures for Maintenance of Equipment. There is no more vivid testimony to the value of a fork truck to production than the outcry that arises when that truck is suddenly removed from use for a few hours for maintenance service. This dependence on handling equipment necessitates very careful scheduling of all maintenance in order to provide this vital care without affecting production. Without such a schedule the pressure exerted for the constant use of the equipment may easily result in a complete absence of even the most rudimentary care. This results in excessive repair costs and eventually in loss of the use of the equipment.

Conveyors, cranes, and hoists require periodic inspections as well as normal greasing and lubrication. The only way of ensuring that this is done at the proper intervals is by the maintenance of inspection and lubrication records. If these records consist of check sheets filled in at the time of inspection, a closer control is provided. Any discrepancies noted should receive proper attention. This requires a definite procedure for completion of the action similar to that described in Chap. 26.

4. Equipment Principles

With the many varieties of equipment available today for the handling and movement of materials, it is sometimes difficult to see any hard and fast rules in the relationships of their use and operation. Because of this number there is an even greater need for definite principles to guide both the student and the experiencd materials-handling engineer.

a. Select Proper Equipment for the Job. Each type of handling equipment has its proper range of uses—no one of them is adequate for all handling problems. It is necessary, then, to know for each type of equipment its various advantages, the type of material it can handle, its operating characteristics and abilities as well as its limitations, the types of materials which it is not adapted to handle, and special peculiarities in its operation.

This problem of proper selection is simplified by eliminating at the beginning the types of equipment not suited to the handling problem under consideration. The Equipment Characteristic Sheet (Fig. 159) simplifies this task. This process narrows the field and permits a more detailed study of the most suitable types.

b. *Integrate the Equipment into the Plant Handling System.* As noted above, no one type of equipment is adequate for all the handling problems of a plant. In fact, most industrial plants employ a surprisingly large variety of types in even the most standardized operations. This means, then, that one responsibility of the materials-handling engineer is to evolve the most efficient combination of all these types in order to move materials through the plant at the desired volume and at the lowest cost.[2]

c. *Coordinate the Operation of Materials-handling Equipment.* The most efficient utilization of the various types of equipment found in most industrial plants requires a close coordination of their operation. Two rules for this coordination are: [3]

When two or more pieces of materials-handling equipment are used, coordinate their operation.

When two or more persons are engaged as a unit in handling materials, synchronize their work so that they will always be occupied; avoid arrangements where some of them are required to wait for others to complete their part of the work.

This may be accomplished by a close control over all personnel and equipment engaged in the handling and moving of materials. This implies a scheduling of such functions and a means of maintaining close contact with all personnel engaged in this work. In order to accomplish this, plants have used pneumatic-tube systems, intercommunication and inter-plant telephone systems, telautograph, loudspeaker, and even two-way radio systems.

d. *Reduce Terminal Time of Power Units.* In industrial handling this is important. In the transportation industry it often means the difference between profit and loss. It costs a large cargo ship, for example, over $1,000 per day for every day it is in port. The loading and unloading time then becomes a very substantial part of the total cost of water transport.

---

[2] For examples of the variety of handling equipment used in a large-scale plant, refer to the list of the General Electric Company in L. P. Alford and J. R. Bangs, "Production Handbook," The Ronald Press Company, New York, 1945; see also the Westinghouse Electric Corporation's classification of equipment, Immer, *op. cit.,* p. 328.

[3] Alford and Bangs, *op. cit.,* p. 938.

The same principle is applied to the use of fork trucks when waiting time is involved. It is economy to reduce to a minimum the waiting time of a $6,000 fork truck, for example, by using trailers costing $150 each. Similarly, a few thousand dollars invested in loading equipment may drastically reduce the loading time of an airplane costing several hundred thousand dollars. It should be noted that the new "super" cargo planes have several pieces of handling equipment built into them, such as hoists, overhead bridge cranes, roller conveyors, and ramps lowered and raised by electric motors.

e. Standardize Equipment and Method. There is a strong tendency for large industrial plants to standardize on one make of equipment and even on one or two types and sizes as much as possible. In many cases this is done after several years of experimentation in which a number of manufacturer's products have been tried out. This is true especially of industrial trucks.

The advantages of the principle accrue also to the maintenance and repair of equipment. By restricting the types, varieties, and makes of equipment, it is easier to keep an adequate supply of parts and accessories on hand. Maintenance personnel also become more familiar with lubricating requirements and the replacement of parts.

Standardized parts and accessories are a necessity in every type of materials-handling equipment. Production techniques—if they are to keep abreast of the latest developments and ideas—are never static. Layout is subject to continuous changes in a progressive plant. Changes in the product (style, model, new sizes, etc.) cause changes in the flow of production. Trolley conveyors, though a fixed piece of equipment provided for a specific layout requirement, should be composed of standardized sections of track as well as chain links, carriers, etc.

f. Select Equipment for Flexibility. Even in the most standardized processes the possibility of change must always be kept uppermost in mind. Larger plants can often obtain flexibility by having available a wide variety of equipment. The smaller plant has to obtain this flexibility in the limited pieces it can afford to operate. In a small grocery warehouse, portable conveyor sections are often preferable to a permanent installation, even where the path of flow is fixed at the moment. The many accessories which have been developed for use with the fork truck all widen its usefulness by increasing the flexibility of the equipment.

5. Costing Principles

Although cost accounting has occupied an important niche of its own for some time—and there is even a well-developed handbook [4] for the

---

[4] Theodore Lang, editor, "Cost Accountants' Handbook," The Ronald Press Company, New York, 1945.

subject—much work still remains to be done before industry as a whole has available adequate methods of costing handling operations.

a. Know Your Handling Costs. This is easier said than done. A number of handling operations can be costed by the setting up of proper account numbers (see Chap. 20). This may be adequate for most inter-departmental movement (except for small plants). What happens to the movement of these materials within the department constitutes one of the most insidious cost elements with which management has to contend.

Handling is a part of every operation and is often the most difficult part to standardize and measure. Although this part of materials movement is (in larger plants at least) more often the concern of the methods engineer than of the materials-handling engineer, neither can afford to disregard the work of the other. Time study and an accurate measure of the handling element is the only way by which the cost of this type of handling can be isolated and thus controlled. The compilation of these elements of current time studies often reveals an astonishingly high cost of handling.

b. Select Equipment for Lowest Over-all Handling Cost. This principle assumes that handling costs are known. This is not always a valid assumption. In order to accomplish the objective of this principle, it is often necessary to determine the handling cost with the various types of equipment under consideration. With other operating costs as a guide this may not be so difficult a task as it may seem at first. In any case, it is a very important step in securing the best equipment for a given task or job.

c. Amortize Equipment within a Reasonable Length of Time. Where handling equipment is being introduced into a department or an operation for the first time, it is often not difficult to pay for the equipment within a fairly short period of time. Management has, in many instances, given the materials-handling department considerable freedom in the purchase of equipment as long as it is amortized within a specified period. Although an extreme case, in one company the handling engineers could purchase any piece or system of equipment as long as it would pay for itself within 3 months. Even with this extreme limitation, they were able to justify heavy expenditures for fork trucks and other handling devices. In other instances, periods of 6 months to 1 year are fairly common for such directions from management.

This policy "skims the cream off the top" of handling improvements and is a vivid example of how costly the older methods of handling must have been. As improvements are made, it becomes more difficult to effect such savings and longer amortization periods must be allowed. This policy is also affected by legal provisions for writing off equipment.

The big danger in a policy of short-amortization periods is that longer term savings may be overlooked. The Ford Motor Company, for example, has long since adopted a policy of lowest handling cost for its handling-equipment purchases regardless of the time required to pay for itself. The purchase of more durable types of equipment has been found to be much more economical in the long run than less durable types which tend to be purchased under a limited investment policy.

Gradually, management is adopting a policy of amortization periods which more closely approximates the life expectancy of the equipment. As many pieces of equipment have performed satisfactory service for 10, 15, or 20 years, this policy must be tempered by the legal allowances for taxing purposes and the period of expected usage.

QUESTIONS

1. Discuss the development of the principle of materials handling.
2. Explain the purpose served by the principles and the reason for their importance.
3. List the planning principles, and discuss briefly the importance of each.
4. Discuss the application of the operating principle.
5. The equipment principles outline the most effective way of obtaining maximum benefit from the use of equipment. Explain.
6. Outline briefly the main elements of each of the costing principles.
7. With which groups of principles will each of the following be most interested? (Explain your answer.)

    a. The materials-handling engineer.
    b. Management.
    c. The factory manager.

PROJECTS FOR FURTHER STUDY

1. Prepare a report on the development of materials-handling principles. Pay particular attention to publication date of each source of information.
2. Obtain an example of the use and operation of each principle in

    a. Planning group.
    b. Operating group.
    c. Equipment group.
    d. Costing group.

PART II

MOTION AND TIME STUDY

CHAPTER 4

WORK SIMPLIFICATION

The reduction of handling costs starts within the work area itself. The development of modern production techniques is a story of the gradual elimination of nonproductive activities of the operator. This permits him to concentrate on those activities that will add direct value to the product.

1. Handling within the Work Area

The handling of materials within the work area does not involve such great distances but it is largely handling entirely by hand and is a highly repetitive operation. Furthermore, as reaching distances increase, other parts of the body are brought into use, which contributes to the accumulation of fatigue.

a. Classification of Hand Motions. Hand motions have been classified into five types: [1]

1. Finger motions
2. Motions involving fingers and wrist
3. Motions involving fingers, wrist, and forearm
4. Motions involving fingers, wrist, forearm, and upper arm
5. Motions involving fingers, wrist, forearm, upper arm, and shoulder; this class necessitated a disturbance of the posture

The lowest classification of the above requires the least time and effort and should be used whenever possible.

b. Balance Work. It has been found that fatigue is lessened if the work of the two hands can be balanced. These motions should be made simultaneously and, if possible, in opposite directions. This in itself will often speed up an operation.

c. Pre-position. Materials brought into the work area should be deposited or left in a position to permit their quickest and easiest positioning to the final work place, whether it is an assembly operation or a machine operation. Some assembly operations, for example, can be performed on a moving conveyor, which means that the worker does not have to position the assembled part at all. Where the piece being worked upon is

[1] Ralph M. Barnes, "Motion and Time Study," 3d ed., p. 216, John Wiley & Sons, Inc., New York, 1949.

heavy, this positioning may become a very important item. In machine operations, materials being transported on roller conveyors, for example, may be positioned level with the bed of the machine. The operator in this case simply rolls the new part into the work area as needed.

2. Work-simplification Programs

The pattern for work-simplification programs installed in a large number of industrial plants by Allan H. Mogensen [2] consists of the following five steps:

1. Pick a job to improve.[3]
2. Make a process chart.
3. Challenge every detail.
4. Work out a better method.
5. Apply the new method.

The principles involved in this program for improving methods are to eliminate, combine, change, and simplify. The personnel affected must then be sold on the program.

At the Richmond, Ind., plant of the Belden Manufacturing Company, a program for development of new methods was expected to double the dollar volume of cost reductions. In one year reductions of $200,000 in product cost were effected.

Considerable care was given to the organization of the material for the program which was based upon the following principles: [4]

1. Participation in the program, so far as practical, should extend to all levels of management.
2. Program participants should be fully informed as to the long-range importance of the program both to themselves and to the company.
3. The training aspect of the program should take a minimum of the participant's time.
4. The instruction pattern should be such as to appeal to a practical shop man. (This was accomplished by the elimination of textbooks and quizzes.)
5. Each participant should understand that success in reducing costs is dependent upon ability to solve problems; the program should provide a systematic plan for the application of the principles of problem solving.

The training program was based upon sessions of 2½ hours each. One hundred five members of management (approximately 10 per cent

[2] Allan H. Mogensen, Carry Out a Methods Improvement Program, *Factory Management and Maintenance*, July, 1949, p. 66.

[3] For a discussion of the problem of picking a job, see G. Z. Wollam, How to Organize for Cost Production, *Factory Management and Maintenance*, May, 1949, p. 66.

[4] Charles Winkelman, Putting 105 Men to Work on Cost Reduction, *Factory Management and Maintenance*, July, 1949, p. 70.

of the entire plant personnel) were invited to participate. A portfolio of procedure forms was made available for each member. The individual sessions were organized on the following points: [5]

Session 1

 a. Introduction by the plant engineer.

 b. Importance of cost reduction to the participant and to the company.

 c. Statement of the program objective: To reduce costs by teaming up job know-how with an effective procedure for improving methods.

 d. Outline of the supervisory responsibilities of the participants and how these obligations could be better discharged through methods improvements.

 e. Sample cost-reduction problem of the "before" stage of a manufacturing operation presented on movie film. Members asked both to record the details of the operation and to suggest improvements.

Session 2

 a. Report of the various individual approaches uncovered in the problem analysis made on the previous day. Based on the variance disclosed in these approaches to solving the particular cost-reduction problem, the need was outlined for an organized method of observing problem details and a reliable method of solving problems.

 b. Procedure instruction for making right- and left-hand operation analysis.

 c. Analysis made of the cost-reduction problem introduced in Session 1, using the program procedure for right- and left-hand operation analysis.

 d. Group instructed in the use of right- and left-hand analysis chart in the development of the improved methods.

 e. Movie film shown, illustrating how the problem was solved in actual practice.

 f. Review of the two approaches to solving the cost-reduction problem: (1) the individual approach of the members; and (2) the systematized approach introduced in the program.

Session 3

 a. Various applications of right- and left-hand analysis pointed out.

 b. Participants introduced to the program's procedure for process analysis.

 c. Simple operations, such as examining a book, performed by selected group members, while the group made a process chart of the operation.

 d. Participants asked to make an analysis of an operation or of a process, using the program procedures, before the next session.

Session 4

 a. Applications for process analysis outlined.

 b. Analysis of flow of materials explained.

 c. Experiences of group members in the use of the program's analysis procedures discussed.

 [5] *Ibid.*

Session 5

   a. Procedure introduced for computing product cost and methods improvements.

   b. Entire program and its systematized procedures reviewed.

   c. Cost and methods improvement proposals made by program participants reviewed.

3. Operation Analysis

   The first step in analyzing an operation is to break it down into subdivisions. This may be done in various degrees of detail. The following classification is most commonly used:

   1. Element breakdown provides the simplest breakdown of an operation and consists of a more or less related group of activities which can be easily and accurately identified. Their length will depend upon the time cycle of the complete operation, purpose of the study, and the importance of the operation.

   2. Basic motions are shown on operation analysis charts. In the simplest form they consist of two symbols only: operation and transportation. Other charts use symbols for four types of motions: operation, move, storage, and inspection. In further variations, the action of a foot or the movement of the eyes may also be indicated.

   3. Basic motions are shown on prepared-symbol charts. Symbols for the four basic motions of movement outlined above are preprinted on a special form with a separate column for the right and left hands. While taking the study, the observer has only to connect lines from one symbol to the other as the action progresses.

   4. Micromotion study is used for the more detailed analysis. This is a system devised by Frank B. and Lillian M. Gilbreth for the detailed study of motions in an operation. A moving picture is taken of the operation at regular camera speed. Later in his office, the analyst studies the motions by moving the film one frame at a time.

   In the earlier experiments a special electrically controlled clock, called a microchronometer, was used. This was calibrated to show time in 1/2,000 of a minute. Later, speed control on cameras and use of a speed of 1,000 frames a minute, made the clock unnecessary as the analyst could count frames to get his time-lapse interval.

   In addition to viewing the operation at a slower speed, the analyst has available a set of symbols by which he can record on paper the nature of the elements involved in the study. These are called therbligs and simply represent elements of motion common to all operations. By these operations in general can be described.

Fig. 7. Origination of the problem. Methods analysis at Oldsmobile.

Fig. 8. Studying the problem. Methods engineer making an act breakdown chart. (*Oldsmobile.*)

5. Memomotion. The idea of ascertaining time lapse by counting frames of film has been extended by Prof. Marvin Mundel of Purdue

	METHODS ENGINEERING DEPT.						Sheet 1 of 4
(144)	OLDSMOBILE DIVISION						
	ACT BREAKDOWN						

Operation Name __FINISH GRIND ALL CRANK-PINS AND CHECK ALL__

Operation No. __340__   Act Breakdown No. __1__   Film No. __101__

Before [X]   After [ ]   Engineer __Fozdar__

Part Names and Numbers __#559432: Crankshaft - Rocket Engine__

Step No	LEFT HAND	Object	Act	Proc.	Act	Object	RIGHT HAND
1	From previous operation, walk 10-12 feet	A-Frame	G		G	A-Frame	Assist LH
2	In front of machine	"	P		P	"	"
3	WAIT		W		G	Identification Hammer	From table
4	WAIT		W		P	"	Stamp identification on (3) Cranks
5	WAIT		W		D	"	On Table
6	From hook on machine	Hook	G		G	Hook	Assist LH
7	Under #1 Crank	"	P		P	"	"
8	From A-frame	Crank	G		G	Crank	"
9	In fixture on machine	"	P		P	"	"
10	From under crank	Hook	G		G	Hook	"
11	Under hook on machine	"	P		P	"	"
12	WAIT		W		G	Socket Wrench	From table
13	WAIT		W		P	"	On clamp nut-RH end
14	WAIT		W		P	"	To tighten nut
15	WAIT		W		D	"	On table
16	On machine	Shift Lever	G		G	Hammer	From machine tray
17	In position to clamp LH end	"	P		P	"	Hammer shaft in position if necessary
18	"	"	P		D	"	On machine tray
19	On machine	Traverse Wheel	G		G	Feed Wheel	On machine
20	Operate to locate #6 pin in position	"	P		P	"	Operate to guide grinding wheel in position

Fig. 9. The act breakdown chart. (*Oldsmobile.*)

University. He has taken exposures at 100 frames per minute or a frame per second to provide the same pictorial presentation the time-study man generally obtains on a regular type of time study (see Chap. 6).

4. Development of Handling Method; Analysis at Oldsmobile

The analysis of a handling method by engineers of the Oldsmobile Division of General Motors Corporation is a good example of the type of planning and study that will go into a change in handling where high production of a standard product is involved. The number of the total units involved will more than justify the time and expense of such a study. One notable feature is the amount of coordination required by and between all the parties who may be affected by these changes.

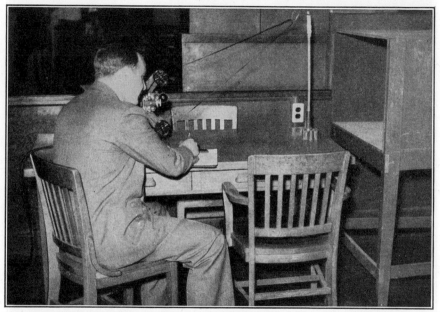

Fig. 10. Micromotion study made of complex operation. (*Oldsmobile.*)

Manufacturing operations at Oldsmobile consist of:

1. Machining and automatic processes
2. Manual operations, such as those in the press plant, paint plant, and motor car assembly plant

A recent analysis of both these types showed that over half the work in the entire division was manual. The methods-engineering department has the responsibility for "planning the manual part of the operation." The following case study shows the step-by-step development of a new workplace arrangement.

a. Origination of Problem. Problems for methods analysis originate from one of the following sources:

a. Management   c. Methods department
b. Production supervision   d. Employees suggestion plan

The problems range from a simple bolt-and-washer assembly to a very complex problem involving the analysis of an entire department such as the crankshaft department.

FIG. 11. Full-sized model of proposed fixture is prepared in experimental laboratory. (*Oldsmobile.*)

Figure 7 shows the method engineer talking with the foreman of the crankshaft department, who has a problem. The A frames used for handling the shaft between operations are not satisfactory. The operator has to make an 80-degree turn to pick up the shaft and replace it after performing the operation. Also, after every three shafts, he has to reverse the frame to get access to the other three shafts. After finishing the six pieces, he has to push the frames to the next operation in order to move up another frame from the previous operation. This amounts to considerable unproductive time and effort. The frames take up a lot of floor space and make good housekeeping difficult.

   b. Study of Problem. Figure 8 shows the method engineer making an act breakdown chart. In doing so, he learns the fine requirements of the operation, which he cannot do from his desk in the office. He must get

Fig. 12. New method reviewed with engineering supervisor. (*Oldsmobile.*)

a complete picture of the job and its elements as well as the quality and quantity standards of the operation.

   c. Act Breakdown Chart. Figure 9 is part of a typical act breakdown chart made on the job. All pertinent information concerning the operation is recorded on this form. Various acts required to complete the job cycle are recorded. These acts are:

(G) Get	(H) Hold
(P) Place	(W) Wait
(D) Dispose	

The operation is thus broken down into various elements which the engineer can then study separately. Additional remarks, if any, are noted on the chart or on a separate sheet attached to it.

d. Micromotion Study. The use of micromotion depends upon the complexity and length of the job cycle and the number of operations involved in completing the job. This particular problem involved a

Fig. 13. Final review with layout supervisor and factory superintendent. (*Oldsmobile.*)

change in the handling methods and a complete revamping of the layout of the crankshaft department. Therefore it was not felt necessary to make a micromotion study. It should be noted that most improvement jobs at Oldsmobile do not necessitate such a study.

e. Mocking Up. The engineer will gather additional information, depending upon the size and type of the job. He will obtain drawings of the layout which show the different positions of the operators and the related machines.

In this particular example it was found that there were 26 different operations performed on the crankshaft before it was ready for delivery to the engine assembly line. Allowing for the float between operations, about 2,500 shafts should be on the line at one time.

A number of suggestions and alternatives were prepared to take these things into consideration. These were reviewed in numerous discussions and meetings by everyone concerned and alternative plans were considered. Finally, one method was adopted.

A full-sized model is made of the proposed fixture. Figure 11 shows the method engineer experimenting with this mock up for the first time.

Fig. 14. The new fixtures are installed. (*Oldsmobile.*)

The crankshafts are carried on a hanger suspended from a trolley which in turn travels along a monorail. Shafts are within the most favorable motion area. (The Oldsmobile standard work area level is 38 inches above floor.) Hangers are pivoted on swivel from the trolley, making it easier for the operator to turn them around. It also takes very little effort to move them after the operation is completed. The floor is left free of material and can be kept clean easily.

f. Preliminary Review. After the rough edges are taken off the new method, the engineer reviews it with his supervisor. They then determine what additional work will be done. If a change in tooling is involved the production engineer and the process engineer are called in. After all the planning personnel have had an opportunity to contribute

their ideas, the foreman of the department concerned is asked to review
the method. This had been found to be very advantageous because the

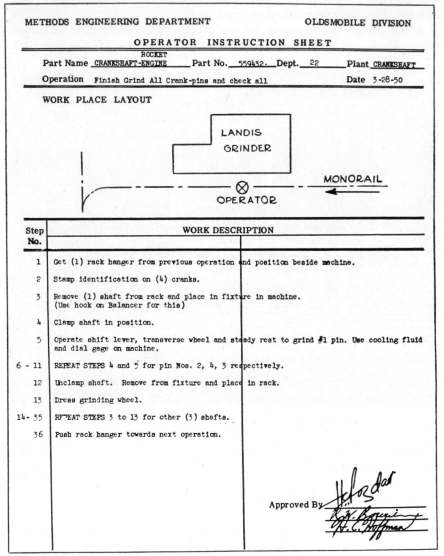

METHODS ENGINEERING DEPARTMENT   **OLDSMOBILE DIVISION**

OPERATOR INSTRUCTION SHEET

Part Name <u>CRANKSHAFT-ENGINE</u>   Part No. <u>559432 </u> Dept. <u>22</u>   Plant <u>CRANKSHAFT</u>

Operation Finish Grind All Crank-pins and check all   Date 3-28-50

WORK PLACE LAYOUT

LANDIS GRINDER

MONORAIL

OPERATOR

Step No.	WORK DESCRIPTION
1	Get (1) rack hanger from previous operation and position beside machine.
2	Stamp identification on (4) cranks.
3	Remove (1) shaft from rack and place in fixture in machine. (Use hook on Balancer for this)
4	Clamp shaft in position.
5	Operate shift lever, transverse wheel and steady rest to grind #1 pin. Use cooling fluid and dial gage on machine.
6 - 11	REPEAT STEPS 4 and 5 for pin Nos. 2, 4, 3 respectively.
12	Unclamp shaft. Remove from fixture and place in rack.
13	Dress grinding wheel.
14- 35	REPEAT STEPS 3 to 13 for other (3) shafts.
36	Push rack hanger towards next operation.

Approved By

Fɪɢ. 15. Operator instruction sheet prepared by the methods engineer. (*Oldsmobile.*)

foreman must operate the new method, and he will be more interested
in promoting it if he has had a hand in its development. In Fig. 12 the
foreman and the engineer are reviewing the new method in the laboratory.

g. *Final Review*. At this stage, the layout department is called in. The members of this department determine the facilities and additional equipment needed to put the new plan into effect and then prepare a layout. This preliminary layout is again discussed with everybody concerned, and finally a three-dimensional layout is prepared. In Fig. 13 the general methods supervisor is reviewing the new method with the

FIG. 16. The operator is performing the job with the new method. (*Oldsmobile.*)

layout supervisor and the production superintendent. They will prepare a schedule for the installation and decide whether to buy needed facilities from outside sources or to fabricate them at Oldsmobile.

h. *Installation*. The new facilities and equipment have been ordered by the plant layout department and arranged or installed by the plant engineering department. Sometimes it is advantageous to install an experimental line as a final check on the method.

i. *Operator Instruction Sheet*. In the meantime, the methods engineer prepares an operator instruction sheet. Essentially, this is a simple work description of the sequence to be followed in performing the operation. It is approved by the methods engineer, the foreman, and the plant superintendent before it is placed on the machine. This procedure ensures that the new method is clearly understood by everyone and further induces the cooperation of operating personnel.

j. Operation. In Fig. 16 the operator is now performing the job after having been trained in the new method by his foreman. The methods engineer is checking the method to see that everything works as planned.

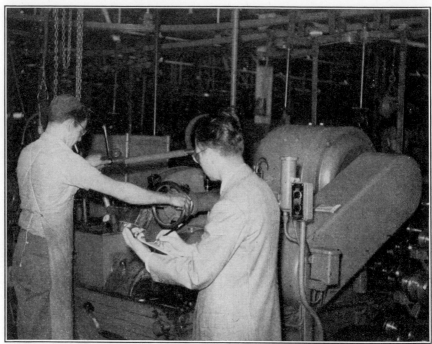

Fig. 17. The final step in the job improvement is the time study taken on the new method. (*Oldsmobile.*)

k. Time Study. This is the last stage in the process of job improvement. In Fig. 17 the time-study man is making a study on the new method so that a change in standard can be put into effect. This also provides a test on the extent of the savings or improvement effected by the new method.

QUESTIONS

1. Explain the importance of pre-positioning materials within the work area.

2. What steps are involved in a work-simplification program?

3. Outline a training program for methods improvement.

4. Explain the different ways in which operations are subdivided for analysis.

5. Explain the procedure for analysis of a handling problem at Oldsmobile.

6. What is the importance of the classification of hand motions?

7. How does handling within the work area affect handling between operations?

8. How does handling between operations affect handling within the work area?

9. What principles were involved in the methods program at Belden?

PROJECTS FOR FURTHER STUDY

1. Discuss the effects of different types of handling equipment on handling within the work area.

2. How do measurements of the body affect the placing of materials in the work area?

CHAPTER 5

METHODS OF SHOWING FLOW

To show the flow of materials in modern production processes, it is necessary to present a large amount of factual data. To permit its analysis, this data must be presented in a clear, concise way which will show and emphasize the flow of materials. The form of presentation then becomes very important to any consideration of materials movement.

A number of methods have been developed to show the flow of materials. Each of them has a particular application, and the materials-handling engineer must be able to select the appropriate method or technique for the problem at hand.

1. Operation Sequence List

The simplest method of ascertaining the course followed by materials is to list the operations performed on them and then note where this is done. This may be sufficient to show the flow where the number of operations is limited and everyone is familiar with the process.

If many of these lists are to be prepared, it will be advisable to prepare a standard form. This is especially desirable if a comparison of various lists is to be made. Information to be included on a simple form may include operation number and description, where performed, distance in feet for all travel (or in inches for movement within the work area), and present method of movement or type of equipment involved.

2. Process Charts

"A process chart is a graphic representation of events and information pertaining thereto occurring in a series of actions or operations." [1] The chart is a means of showing graphically the relationships between operations without regard to the distance or space actually involved. As such it is an effective means of simplifying the presentation and showing just those factors pertinent to that problem. This is especially important in an analysis of a production problem from a materials-handling standpoint.

The two types of process charts are operation process charts and flow

---

[1] "Operation and Flow Process Charts," American Society of Mechanical Engineers, 1947, p. 3.

ORIGINAL GILBRETH PROCESS CHART SYMBOLS

Stores Requisitioned	Inspection for Quality
Stores Bought	Inspection for Quantity
Stores Received	Inspection for Quantity and Quality (Quantity most important)
Several kinds of Components—Not Desirable to List Individually	Inspection for Quality and Quantity (Quality most important)
Worked Materials Requisitioned	Over-inspection for Quantity
Worked Materials Ordered	Over-inspection for Quality
Worked Materials on Hand	Insp. for Quan. on Exception Principle
Merchandise in Storage ready to Ship	Insp. for Qual. on Exception Principle
Storage as part of Process	Over-insp. for Quan. on Exception Principle
Permanent File of Documents or Materials	Over-insp. for Qual. on Exception Principle
Temporary File of Documents or Papers	Insp. for Quan. and Oper. performed simultaneously
(38) Operation Symbol	Insp. for Qual. and Oper. performed simultaneously
(38) Moved by Operator performing Oper. No. 38	Insp. for Quan. and Qual. and Oper. performed simultaneously. (Quan. most important)
(M) Moved by Man	Insp. for Qual. and Quan. and Oper. performed simultaneously. (Qual. most important)
(m) Moved by Boy	
MOB Moved by Messenger Boy	
(E) Moved by Elevator	A single Dept. used more than once
(T) Moved by Pneumatic Tube	Broken lines indicate process outside of the Dept. Charted —used on Dept'l Charts
(C) Moved by Conveyor	Process within the Department is connected with closed line
(G) Gravity	
(C) Belt	
(K) Moved by Truck	
(K) Electric Truck	
(P) Information by Telephone	
(L) Moved by Mail	

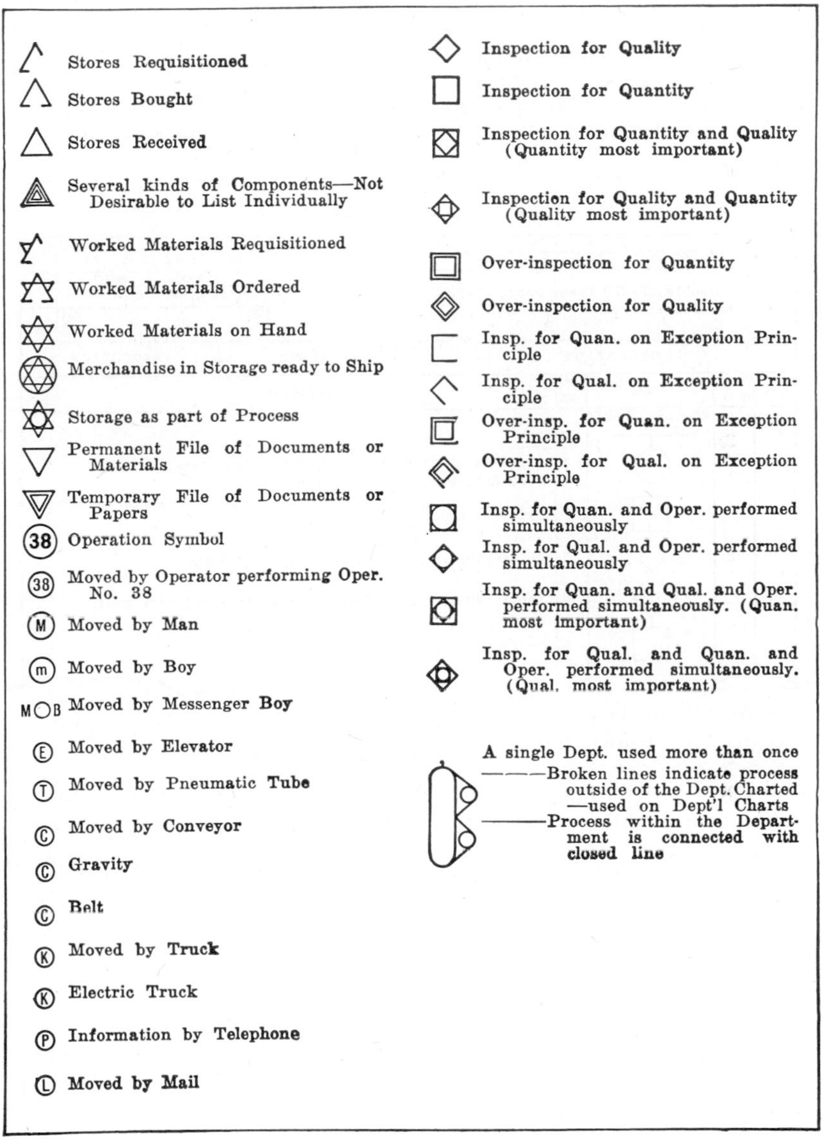

FIG. 18. Original Gilbreth process chart symbols. (*Ralph M. Barnes, "Motion and Time Study,"* 3d ed., p. 29, *John Wiley & Sons, Inc., New York,* 1949.)

process charts. The operation process chart includes only the basic information required to show the relationships of the various operations. The flow process chart includes additional information to provide a more detailed analysis of the process.

a. Operation Process Chart: [2]

An operation process chart is a graphic representation of the points at which materials are introduced into the process and of the sequence of inspections

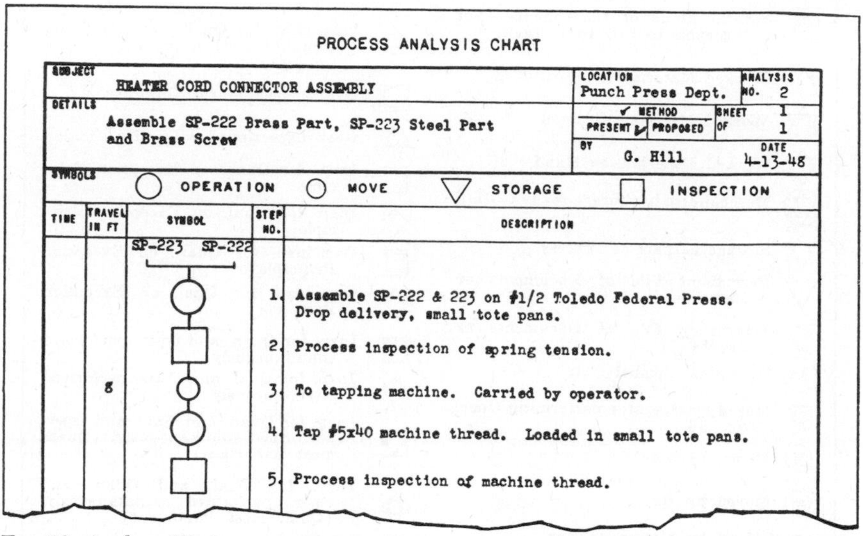

Fig. 19. Analyst fills in appropriate symbol and other information on special form for process analysis. (*Belden Manufacturing Company.*)

and all operations except those involved in material handling. It includes information considered desirable for analysis such as time required and location.

The first such chart, developed by Frank B. and Lillian M. Gilbreth, employed four basic symbols. These were used to represent the four types of activities or events by which movement of the product could be adequately described. These symbols and the commonly used adaptations are:

○ *Operation.* The large circle, to indicate an operation, often has the operation inserted as ⑥. Symbols may also be combined, such as ▢, an inspection with an operation.

○ *Transportation.* The small circle to represent movement may be used with a wide variety of other symbols to indicate the mode or method of movement such as ©, ⓚ, or ⓔ.

[2] *Ibid.,* p. 4.

□ *Inspection.* The square, either vertical or inclined, may also indicate the type of inspection involved.

▽ *Storage.* Temporary storage is indicated by ▽ or by ▿. Delay is also shown by this symbol or a special symbol such as ⊃. Storage may also be indicated by △.

PROCESS ANALYSIS SHEET

SUBJECT HEATER CORD CONNECTOR ASSEMBLY					LOCATION PUNCH PRESS DEPT	ANALYSIS NO. 1
DETAILS Assemble SP-222 Brass Part, SP-223 Steel Part and Brass Screw					✓METHOD PRESENT✓ PROPOSED BY G. Hill	SHEET 1 OF 1 DATE 4-13-48

TIME	TRAVEL IN FT	IS IT A OPERATION ○	MOVE ○	STORAGE ▽	INSPECTION □	RECORD ONLY ONE SUBJECT IN AN ANALYSIS ✓ CLASSIFICATION DESCRIPTION ✓ IT CAN BE	ELIMINATED	COMBINED	SEQ CHANGED	CAN IT BE ? SIMPLIFIED
1		✓				Assemble SP-222 & SP-223 on #1/2 Toledo Federal Press. Production count by meter. Drop delivery, small tote pans.	X	X	X	X
2					✓	Process inspection of spring tension.	X	X	X	X
3	8		✓			To tapping machine. Carried by operator.	✓			
4		✓				Tap #5x40 machine thread. Loaded in small tote pans.	X	X	X	✓
5					✓	Process inspection of machine thread.	X	X	X	X
6	36		✓			To scale. Carried by general man.	✓			
7					✓	Weigh count for pay.	✓			
8	40		✓			To screw assembly machine. Carried by general man.	✓			
9		✓				Assemble screw. Drop delivery in small tote pans.	X	X	X	X
10					✓	Process inspection for loose screws.	X	X	X	X
11	40		✓			To scale. Carried by general man.	✓			
12					✓	Weigh count for pay.	✓			
13				✓		Temporary. Accumulate for large tote pan quantity.	✓			
14				✓		Dumped in large tote pan by general man.	✓			
15					✓	Weigh count for billing.	✓			
16					✓	Final inspection.	X	X	X	X
17	124	3	5	1	7	TOTAL				
18										
19						IMPROVEMENT POSSIBILITIES 1. Install counting meters on machines to eliminate				
20						weigh count for pay and billing. 2. Move machines side by side and install roller conveyor				
21						between machines to eliminate carrying tote pans. 3. Drop delivery into large tote pan at assembly screw				
22						operation to eliminate dumping operation by general man. 4. Make Right- and Left-Hand Operation Analysis of				
23						tapping operation to simplify.				
24										

Copyright 1946 by Charles Winkelman

TUMBLE TURN SHEET FOR INSTRUCTIONS

Fɪɢ. 20. Analyst checks appropriate column and recommendations for its improvement. (*Belden Manufacturing Company.*)

The important thing to remember about charting symbols is to use the symbols that will serve the purpose of the specific analysis. For that reason, a number of variations in process charting are found in industry today. The engineer, confronted with a particular problem, will not hesitate to devise his own if it will facilitate or clarify his analysis. Figure

SUBJECT CHARTED **75# Rolled Barley**			
OPERATION **Rolled Barley Cut-In**			
CHARTED BY **C. Small**			
CHART NO **1** SHEET **1** /OF **1**			
DATE **8-16-48**			
DEPT. **Feed Mill**			
PLANT **Vallejo**			

FLOW PROCESS CHART

CAN I ELIMINATE?
CAN I COMBINE?
CAN I CHANGE SEQUENCE?
CAN I SIMPLIFY?

SUMMARY	PRES.	PROP.	SAVE
OPERATIONS	2	1	1
TRANSPORTS	3	1	2
INSPECTIONS	0	0	0
DELAYS	1	0	1
STORAGES	1	1	0
TIME	4.52	2.0	2.52
DISTANCE	100	150	-40

DIST. IN FEET	TIME IN MIN.	OPER.	TRAN.	INSP.	DELAYS	STORE	PRESENT □ / PROPOSED □ DESCRIPTIONS	NOTES
							(Present--Hand Transport)	
	.75						Packed, check weighed, tied & stacked	Six sacks per load
	1.87						Waits on truck	
95	.8						Trucked to cut-in area	
							Stacked on floor	
							Stored ahead of cut-in	
15	0.1						Carried to hopper	
	1.0						Opened, dumped & fed-in	
							(Proposed--Conveyor Transport)	
150	1.0						Transported to bin	Conveyor system
							Stored in bin	
							Fed-in	Adjustable slide on feeder
150	2.0						TOTAL	

FIG. 21. Simplified analysis chart in which analyst draws line connecting the appropriate symbol. (*General Mills, Inc.*)

18 shows some of the variations used by the Gilbreths in their original charting work. In an effort to standardize the symbols used for charting, the American Society of Mechanical Engineers has adopted the symbols shown in Fig. 22.

b. Flow Process Chart: [3]

A flow process chart is a graphic representation of the sequence of all operations, transportations, inspections, delays, and storages occurring during a process or procedure, and includes information considered desirable for analysis such as time required and distance moved.

[3] *Ibid.,* p. 11.

In addition to the information contained in the operation process chart it shows storage and operation time, distance traveled, and other details of the process.

The same basic smbols for process charting are used and in addition several others may be employed. Flow diagrams may be used with

FLOW PROCESS CHART

SUBJECT CHARTED __RELIEF VALVE BODY__ CHART NO. __1021__
DRAWING NO. __A-520612__ PART NO. __16150__ CHART TYPE _____
CHART BEGINS __Barstock Storage__ CHARTED BY __J. Smith__
CHART ENDS __Assembly Department Storeroom__ DATE __9-9-43__

◯ OPERATION   ⇨ TRANSPORTATION   SHEET NO. __1__ OF __1__ SHEETS
□ INSPECTION   D DELAY   ▽ STORAGE   COST UNIT __1 Valve Body__

DIST. MOVED FT.	UNIT OPER. TIME Hr.	UNIT TRANSP TIME Hr.	UNIT INSPEC TIME Hr.	DELAY TIME Hr.	STOR-AGE TIME Hr.	CHART SYM-BOLS	PROCESS DESCRIPTION OF _Proposed_ METHOD
						▽	Stored in bar stock storage until requisitioned
10	.0002					①	Bars loaded on truck upon receipt of requisition from machine shop (2 men)
210		.0002				⇨1	Moved to #301 machine
10	.0002					②	Bars unloaded to bar stock rack near #301 machine
				4.00		D1	Delayed awaiting for operation to begin
8	.0550					③	Drill, bore, tap, seat, file, cut off
				2.00		D2	Delayed awaiting drill press operator
20		.00002				⇨2	Moved to drill press by operator
8	.0350					④	Drill 8 holes

FIG. 22. Flow process chart showing subdivision of time column into each class of event. (*"Operation and Flow Process Charts," p. 15, The American Society of Mechanical Engineers,* 1947.)

them to provide a complete analysis. Flow process charts may be divided into (1) free-drawn and (2) prepared forms.

Free-drawn charts follow the general form of the operation process chart except that a smaller part of the process is considered at a time and this in much greater detail. Assembly and disassembly processes may be shown as well as alternate processes.

Of the printed or prepared forms, one type provides columns for the information to be included and the analyst draws in the appropriate symbol for each activity. The other type has all the symbols preprinted so the analyst makes a check or draws a line from one symbol to the

	Symbol	Discussion		Symbol	Discussion
Man:			**Equipment:** cont.		
		If team or gang indicate number			carboy type
walks					drum type
lifts, picks up			dolly		
carries			truck slide		
lowers, puts down			dock plate		
shoves, pulls			**Railway equipment:**		
rolls something			railroad bed		
Equipment:			flat car		
highway truck		Body type	box car		
highway truck		tractor-trailer type	refrigerator car		
hand truck		skid or pallet	hopper car		inside dumping
low-lift pallet or platform truck		power industrial, walkie	tank car		
high-lift pallet or platform truck		power industrial, walkie	**Unit load accessories:**		
high-lift fork truck		power industrial, riding	tote box		
low-lift fork truck		power industrial, riding	skid bin		
high-lift fork truck		one trailer attached	pallet or skid		
low-lift fork truck		two trailers attached			10 packages on pallet
hand truck, warehouse trailer		platform, 6 wheel, 4 wheel			2 pallets
tractor trailer		industrial, four trailers	pallet or skid		2,000 pounds on pallet
conveyor		gravity, dead roller			2 pallets weighing 2,000 pounds with 10 packages on each pallet
conveyor		powered	pallet rack		
escalator		passenger or freight	**Containers:**		
elevator		automatic	tank		
monorail			drum		
drag line		overhead, floor	gas cylinder		
crane		overhead, movable	box, carton		
		yard	bag		
hoist		stationary	carboy		
pump			**Access ways:**		
pipe line			dock		
hand truck		2-wheeler-general	aisles		10 feet wide
		bag or box type, 2 bags			

FIG. 23. Table of "handligs," symbols developed for use in materials-handling analysis. (*W. W. Phillips, R. E. Pigg, and W. J. Greer.*)

next. Both types are used where the flow of one material or item is being charted.

3. Symbols for Materials-handling Analysis

A number of efforts have been made to provide a type of shorthand for the analyst. The Yale and Towne Manufacturing Company devised for use in process charts and flow diagrams the following: ∿ yard or road, ⌒ bridge, ◿ ramp up, ◺ ramp down, ⊐⊏ doorway, ∧ elevator up, and ∨ elevator down. These symbols are used primarily for flow diagraming rather than as a description short cut on the process chart.

To be successful, a system of this type must be easy to remember and easy to use. The first can be accomplished by the use of initials of the equipment represented or by symbols which automatically call that equipment to mind. In order to facilitate their use, both initials and symbols must be easily and quickly drawn. The symbols developed by W. W. Phillips, R. E. Pigg, and W. J. Greer satisfy these conditions (Fig. 23).

These symbols are used both with the flow chart (Fig. 24) and with the flow diagram (Fig. 25) for analysis of materials flow. The example given is the unloading and storing of bottles. The material being charted consists of cases of bottles. From its temporary storage place in a truck to its permanent storage place on pallets, every handling, transportation, delay, and storage procedure is recorded in sequence.

In addition to the conventional flow-chart analysis, additional information is indicated by means of the "handlig" symbols. On line 2, the symbol ⊊ indicates that a man picked up the box, carried it, and placed it on the pallet. On line 5, it is shown that the material on the pallet was delayed and that there was room for 22 cases of bottles on the pallet. The same method of conveyance applies to additional lines until a different symbol is used. Lines 7, 8, and 9 indicate that the pallet was carried to and put on a tractor-trailer train by the fork lift truck. Lines 9 and 10 indicate that the pallet was carried to the storage area by the tractor-trailer train. A ramp is also indicated on the route. In line 12, the pallet was picked up by the fork truck (∟) and placed in temporary storage. This same information is shown on the flow diagram. In addition, it is pointed out that space for 60 pallet loads is available in the area (◬).[4]

4. Flow Diagrams

The spatial relationships of the various areas are indicated by flow diagrams. These indicate the direction of movement as well as show the

[4] Adapted from W. W. Phillips and R. E. Pigg, Materials Handling Charts, *Modern Materials Handling*, October, 1948, p. 35.

various places where each individual operation is performed. They may be drawn to scale or may consist of a simple freehand drawing executed with no regard to scale. In other instances, freehand or ruled drawings may be drawn without rigid adherence to scale but may approximate the scale generally used in the plant for layout drawings.

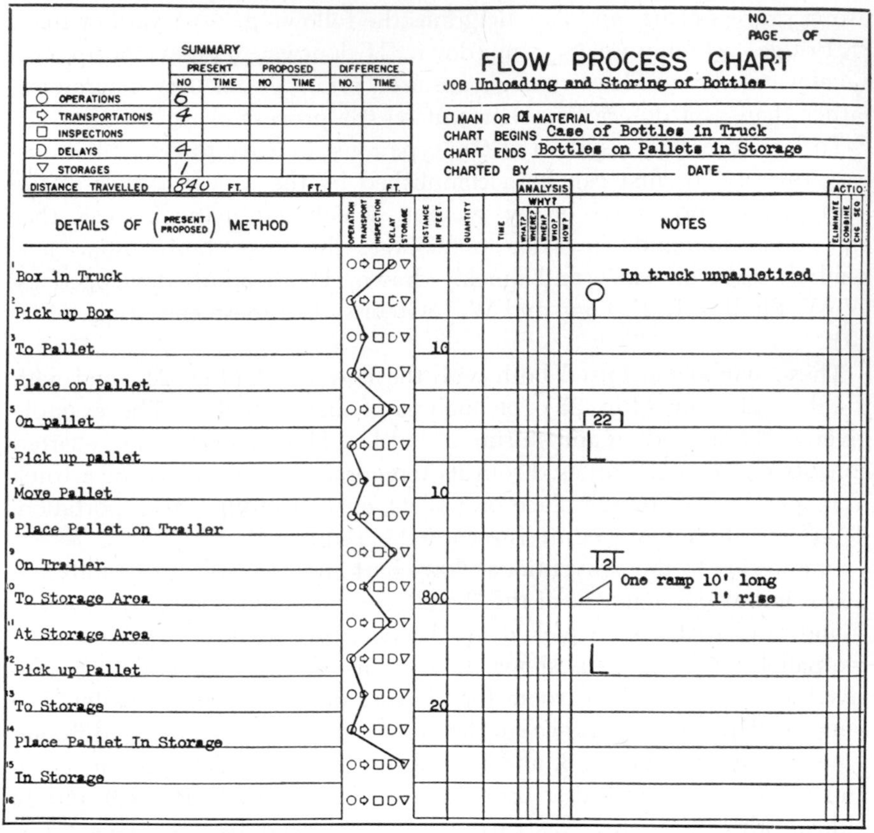

FLOW PROCESS CHART

NO. _____
PAGE ___ OF ____

JOB Unloading and Storing of Bottles

☐ MAN OR ☒ MATERIAL _____
CHART BEGINS Case of Bottles in Truck
CHART ENDS Bottles on Pallets in Storage
CHARTED BY _____ DATE _____

SUMMARY

	PRESENT		PROPOSED		DIFFERENCE	
	NO	TIME	NO	TIME	NO	TIME
◯ OPERATIONS	6					
⇨ TRANSPORTATIONS	4					
☐ INSPECTIONS						
D DELAYS	4					
▽ STORAGES	1					
DISTANCE TRAVELLED	840 FT.		FT.		FT.	

DETAILS OF (PRESENT/PROPOSED) METHOD	Chart symbols	DISTANCE IN FEET	NOTES
Box in Truck	◯⇨☐D▽		In truck unpalletized
Pick up Box	◯⇨☐D▽		
To Pallet	◯⇨☐D▽	10	
Place on Pallet	◯⇨☐D▽		
On pallet	◯⇨☐D▽		22
Pick up pallet	◯⇨☐D▽		
Move Pallet	◯⇨☐D▽	10	
Place Pallet on Trailer	◯⇨☐D▽		
On Trailer	◯⇨☐D▽		2
To Storage Area	◯⇨☐D▽	800	One ramp 10' long 1' rise
At Storage Area	◯⇨☐D▽		
Pick up Pallet	◯⇨☐D▽		
To Storage	◯⇨☐D▽	20	
Place Pallet In Storage	◯⇨☐D▽		
In Storage	◯⇨☐D▽		
	◯⇨☐D▽		

FIG. 24. Flow process chart showing use of handligs in description. (*Modern Materials Handling, October,* 1948, *p.* 36.)

a. Single-story Layouts. Where movement on the same horizontal plane is involved, flow diagraming is simple. If such studies are made very often or if this is an accepted part of the engineering analysis of production in the plant, it is advisable to have standard forms prepared.

In one company the layout-planning department makes available for such studies copies of the latest floor arrangements for each floor. Another company, the Carr, Adams & Collier Company of Dubuque, Iowa, printed floor plans of each floor to speed up flow-analysis work. The appropriate job method sheet is obtained for the part to be diagramed. A process chart is prepared from this, and finally the flow of each part is developed. As there are a large number of parts to each product, a separate flow diagram is used for each part with a different color for each chart. These may also be combined on a single chart to show the complete travel of the product.

General Mills, Inc., with a large number of widely scattered installations, uses a printed form for flow diagrams. This form includes only

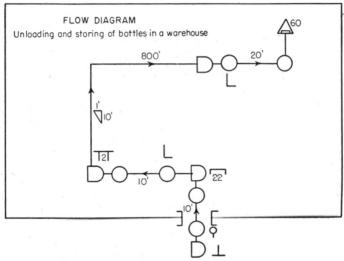

FIG. 25. Flow diagram for the unloading and storing of bottles in a warehouse. (*Modern Materials Handling, October,* 1948, *p.* 36.)

the basic information for the identification of the study. The analyst draws in the building outline or other information as well as the lines to show the flow of the product (Fig. 27).

b. Multi-floor Flow Diagrams. With the attention given to the over-all aspects of the movement of materials within the plant, the need has increased for visual methods of showing the relationships of one floor to another. When conveyors are being considered, it is often necessary to know how the location of that equipment is going to affect layout on each floor.

In order to show the direct relationships of spots located over each other, these diagrams are generally presented in the form of isometric drawings. With this type, it is possible to connect points directly over each other on the manufacturing floors with a straight vertical line in the drawings. This is particularly important where it is desired to connect operating positions on various floors with conveyors or elevators.

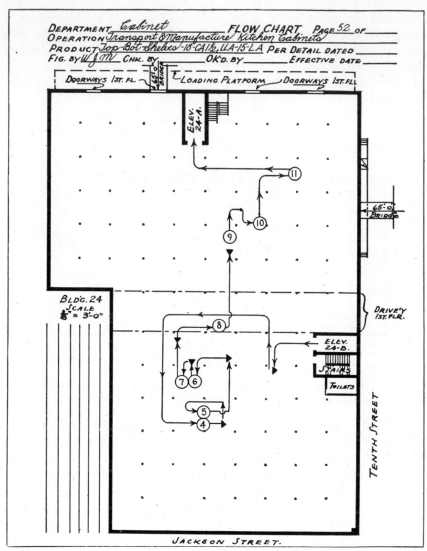

FIG. 26. Travel on one floor shown on printed form. (*Carr, Adams & Collier Company.*)

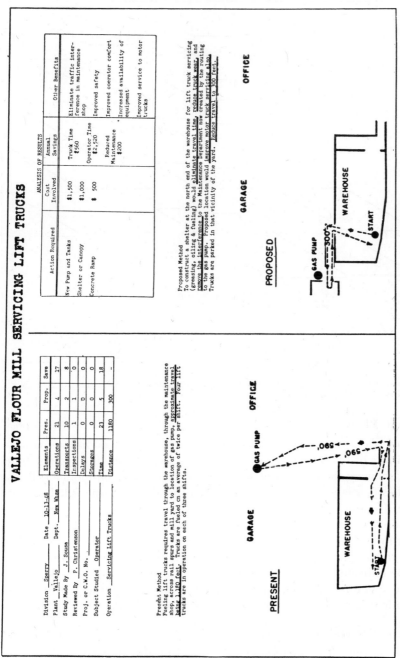

VALLEJO FLOUR MILL SERVICING LIFT TRUCKS

Division _Sperry_   Date _10-13-48_
Plant _Vallejo_   Dept. _New Whse_
Study Made By _J. Sousa_
Reviewed By _P. Christenson_
Proj. or C.W.O. No. _____
Subject Studied _Operator_
Operation _Servicing Lift Trucks_

Elements	Pres.	Prop.	Save
Operations	21	4	17
Transports	10	2	8
Inspections	1	1	0
Delays	0	0	0
Storages	0	0	0
Time	23	5	18
Distance	1180	300	-

Present Method
Fueling lift trucks requires travel through the warehouse, through the maintenance shop, across rail spurs and mill yard to location of gas pump, approximate travel being 1180 feet. Trucks are fueled on an average of twice per shift. Four lift trucks are in operation on each of three shifts.

PRESENT

Proposed Method
To construct a shelter at the north end of the warehouse for lift truck servicing (greasing, oiling & fueling) would eliminate travel time, reduce truck wear and remove the interference to the Maintenance Department now created by the routing to the gas pump. Proposed location would improve motor truck servicing also. Trucks are parked in that vicinity of the yard. Reduce travel to 300 feet.

PROPOSED

Action Required	ANALYSIS OF RESULTS		Other Benefits
	Cost Involved	Annual Savings	
New Pump and Tanks	$1,500	Truck Time $560	Eliminate traffic interference in maintenance shop
Shelter or Canopy	$1,000	Operator Time $2,520	Improved safety
Concrete Ramp	$ 500	Reduced Maintenance $200	Improved operator comfort
			Increased availability of equipment
			Improved service to motor trucks

Fig. 27. Prepared form ensures uniformity in presenting essential information on a proposed methods change. (*General Mills, Inc.*)

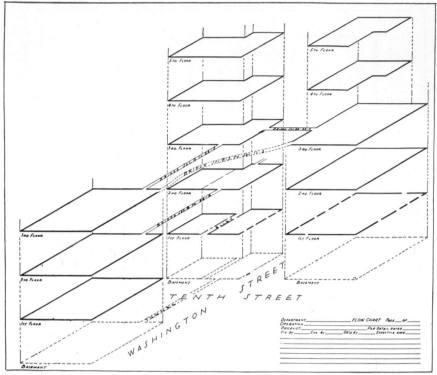

FIG. 28. Printed forms of multi-story building speed-up flow charting. (*Carr, Adams & Collier Company.*)

5. Flow Plans

Flow plans are drawn to the scale commonly employed in the plant for blueprints of the building. In fact, it generally consists of a regular blueprint, showing the position of workplaces or machines on the floor. It also includes permanent features such as fixed handling equipment. Lines are drawn from one machine to another to show the sequence of operations and also to indicate the space required for the travel of the materials being moved. It is particularly valuable in showing the flow of materials through a department. The quantity or volume of materials in movement can be indicated by making the movement lines heavy or light according to the quantity involved. A separate line drawn for the movement of individual parts also indicates the traffic in each aisle.

6. Templets and Scale Models

The movement of materials in a plant can also be shown by the use of templets and scale models. Where major layout changes may be indicated as the major part of the solution of a materials-handling problem, some means of visual presentation can be profitably employed.

Flow on a templet layout can be shown by a number of means, chief of which is the use of thread or string. Different colors may be used to represent different products or types of conveyors. The color scheme may also be developed with the use of strips of cardboard.

The same methods of showing flow may be used with scale models. Colored thread and string are just as effective. One company draws flow lines on transparent plastic overlay sheets, which are then placed over the model to show the movement of materials. One advantage of this method is the ease of changing the lines in order to consider what would happen to the materials movement under different layouts. This same company found that a situation could often be improved by the movement of one or two machines.[5]

QUESTIONS

1. List and describe the various types of process charts.
2. Compare the four basic charting symbols with those developed by the ASME.
3. Discuss the difference between free-drawn and prepared types of flow process charts.
4. Describe and chart some handling method taken from elsewhere in the text, using the handlig symbols.
5. Discuss the problem of flow diagrams for single-story layouts.
6. Discuss the problem of flow diagrams for multi-story layouts.
7. How can templets be used to show the flow of materials?

PROJECTS FOR FURTHER STUDY

1. Prepare a flow diagram of the example given on page 53.
2. Prepare a flow diagram of the example given on page 55.
3. Using a work sheet similar to that shown in Fig. 24, observe a handling operation in a local plant or warehouse. Use handligs for the description.
4. Report on the ASME study, "Operation and Flow Process Charts."

[5] John R. Immer, "Layout Planning Techniques," p. 368, McGraw-Hill Book Company, Inc., New York, 1950. See also Chap. 19, Templets, and Chap. 20, Use of Scale Models.

CHAPTER 6

TIME STUDY AND STANDARD TIMES

Analysis of materials handling involves more than the determination of the flow of materials, important as that is. The really important thing to the production engineer or the factory manager is the cost of that handling. The cost consists of the capital equipment, the amount of space required by the equipment or the handling process, and the labor outlay required to accomplish a given movement or transport. The equipment will be selected for its ability to move the materials in the desired manner, quantity, and speed at the lowest cost. The extra space required or saved by the method will be added to or deducted from this cost.

The other quantity in the analysis is the element of time. This must be measured and ascertained before the economies of any handling method can be firmly established. Time study, and the process of analysis that goes along with it, then becomes one of the most valuable tools available to the materials-handling engineer.

1. Time Study for Materials Handling

Time study performs two main services for materials-handling studies. First, it provides an analysis and breakdown of the elements that go to make up an operation. Second, it provides an accurate measurement of the importance of handling elements in terms of time required for their performance.

If the operation being studied is strictly a handling operation, time study will provide a form for the orderly array of the elements of the operation. It will put the problem on paper so that an analysis may be made more easily. If the operation being studied is a regular production operation, the isolation of the handling elements will reveal the importance of this type of activity. Unfortunately, in the time-study and cost records of most manufacturing companies much of the time and cost of materials handling is concealed within the framework of "production operations" and not revealed in its true extent.

Time study is invaluable in computing the costs of handling by various methods and in calculating the savings resulting from new methods. An example of this is provided by the changes recently made in a department filling customer's orders. Orders were filled on the second floor and placed on skids for removal to the shipping department on the first floor. Handling costs were high, and because the elevator was old there was constant threat of a breakdown which would delay customer's orders.

Time studies were made with the results shown in Table 1. Distances traveled were measured by the time-study man. From these studies, the

TABLE 1. OPERATION TIME VALUES AND DISTANCE INVOLVED *

Opera-tion No.	Operation description	Unit	Distance, feet	Standard, minutes
1	Obtain empty skid for wrapper........	Skid	70	0.24
2	Unload corrugated box from table, and place on skid.....................	Box	10	0.22
3	Move loaded skid to "out bay".......	Skid	80	0.70
4	Move loaded skid onto elevator.......	Skid	50	0.50
5	Elevator travel to first floor..........	2 skids	..	0.30
6	Move loaded skid to "in bay" in shipping department.................	Skid	50	0.50
7	Move loaded skid to area adjacent to dispatcher's scale...................	Skid	70	0.70
8	Unload box from skid and place on dispatcher's scale....................	Box	6	0.14
9	Dispose of empty skid...............	Skid	18	0.11

* *Flow*, March, 1948, p. 22.

costs of handling by this method were ascertained (Table 2). The installation of a gravity wheel conveyor and a gravity chute to move these orders to the first floor provided a savings for this operation of $2,749 per year (Table 3). The cost of installation is shown in Table 4.[1]

The Cadillac Motor Car Division of General Motors Corporation recently set up its materials-handling functions on a time standard basis. Among the benefits listed for this program are: [2]

1. A reduction in handling time
2. A definite measure of performance
3. The most efficient and economical method for doing each job (through methods improvement)

[1] $711.00 Investment Saves $2,749.00, *Flow*, March, 1948, p. 22.
[2] C. D. Dernier, Time Standards . . . Yardstick for Material Handling, *Flow*, November, 1948, p. 25.

TABLE 2. DETAIL OF MATERIALS-HANDLING COST REDUCTIONS *

Opera-tion No.	Operation eliminated	Occur-rence per day	Minutes	
			Per occ.†	Per day
1	Obtain empty skid.........................	60	0.24	14.40
2	Move carton from wrapping table to skid.....	1,000	0.22	220.00
3	Move loaded skid to elevator "out bay"......	60	0.70	42.00
4	Move loaded skid into elevator.............	60	0.50	30.00
5	Elevator travel to 1st floor (2 skids per trip) ‡	30	0.30	9.00
6	Move loaded skid to elevator "in bay" on shipping floor.........................	60	0.50	30.00
7	Move loaded skid to dispatching area........	60	0.70	42.00
8	Lift carton from skid to dispatching scale.....	1,000	0.14	140.00
9	Move empty skid to stock pile.............	60	0.11	6.60
	Total minutes...........................	....	....	534.00

* *Flow*, March, 1948, p. 22.

† $\dfrac{534 \text{ minutes}}{60}$ = 8.9 hours per day × 250 days per year = 2,225 hours per year.

Saving per year: 2,225 hours × $1.10 (average earnings per hour) = $2,448.

‡ Does not include wait for elevator.

TABLE 3. SUMMARY OF SAVINGS REALIZED WITH REVISED METHOD *

	Annual Savings
Tangible Savings	
1. Material-handling costs reduced (Table 2)	$2,448
2. 502 square feet of floor space saved	251
3. One less hand lift truck required (depreciation and maintenance)	50
Total tangible savings	$2,749

Intangible Advantages

1. Less operator fatigue
2. Orders shipped faster, thus giving customers better service
3. Less confusion within departments
4. Overloaded elevator relieved
5. Fewer skids required

* *Flow*, March, 1948, p. 22.

TABLE 4. SUMMARY OF COST OF MATERIALS-HANDLING EQUIPMENT *

Equipment	Cost
Materials:	
9 10-foot lengths of 12-inch wheel conveyor ..	$270
3 90 turns for 12-inch wheel conveyor	90
17 conveyor stands	51
Maintenance-department labor and material costs:	
Cut hole in wall and floor	
Construct and install fire door	
Construct and install gravity chute	
Minor revisions in layout	300
Total	$711

* *Flow*, March, 1948, p. 22.

4. A tool for accurate allocation of man power

5. A constant control that enables supervision to apply remedial measures when necessary

6. A means of analyzing proposed revisions in order to predetermine if new expenditures will be justified on the basis of potential savings

The specific materials handled were (1) purchased automobile parts (fabricated, semifabricated, and rough); (2) raw materials for foundry and plating use; and (3) raw materials for expense fabricating, such as abrasives, paints, and others which are not directly car parts. Total tonnage amounted to about 200 truckloads and 15 rail-car loads per day. This was exclusive of the bulk raw materials for the foundry.

The first step in the program was to determine the most economical handling method. Layouts were made of the receiving room and of materials placement at various points of usage. By considering the way in which the material was received (loose, palletized, or cartonized), unit trailer loads were established. Methods were then determined for unloading receivables, placing them on the trailers, and unloading them at the point of usage.

After this step was completed, time studies were then taken on each part in order to establish basic standards on incoming materials. Handlings on the inter-plant tractor-trailer system were based on the manhours required for a given trip. By establishing routes and setting schedules, handling man-hours per engine or car could be determined.

The final step was the formation of standards and the preparation of a work routing sheet. This form includes standard time, method to be used for each material, and destination as to bay and department and receiving room to which the material is to be delivered.

2. Memomotion

This is a system devised and developed by Prof. Marvin E. Mundel of Purdue University to provide greater accuracy in time studies. A motion-picture camera is used for the observation of an operation. Instead of taking the picture at the conventional speed of 960 frames per minute or 1,000 frames per minute as commonly used for motion analysis, pictures are taken at 1-second intervals.

In addition to the economy of the method in using film (at a cost of $6.60 per roll, 1 minute costs 11 cents instead of $1.65), it permits greater accuracy in the taking of time studies. It also permits observation in greater detail, greater flexibility in studying the operation, and provides a positive record.

Memomotion study is designed for the following purposes:

1. Motion study of:
   a. Long cycles
   b. Irregular cycles
   c. Crew activities
   d. Work or material flow over large areas
2. Time study of:
   a. Any job normally studied by stop-watch methods
   b. Lengthy or complex cycles
   c. Crew jobs

In Fig. 29, the method has been used as the basis of the multi-man time chart illustrated. The study was made of a nine-man foundry crew. In taking the study, normal overhead lights were replaced with No. 2 photofloods.[3]

3. Gang Process Charts

This chart is a composite of individual member process charts arranged to permit thorough analysis. These operations which are performed simultaneously by gang members are indicated side by side. The basic purpose of the chart is to analyze the activities of the group and then compose the group so as to reduce to a minimum all waiting time and delays.[4]

The activities of each member of a gang are recorded in turn and the steps are arrayed side by side on the chart. The description of each element is written out at the side and the number of that element is put into a chart symbol to show the type of activity involved. A complete

[3] M. E. Mundel, Memomotion Study Technique Simplifies Work Analysis, *Factory Management and Maintenance*, June, 1949, p. 84.

[4] Ralph M. Barnes, "Motion and Time Study," 3d ed., p. 50, John Wiley & Sons, Inc., New York, 1949.

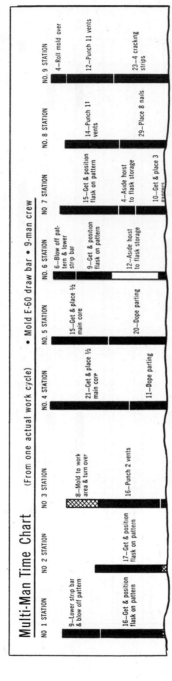

Fig. 29. Multi-man time chart showing the functioning of a nine-man foundry crew. (*Factory Management and Maintenance, June*, 1949, *p.* 84.)

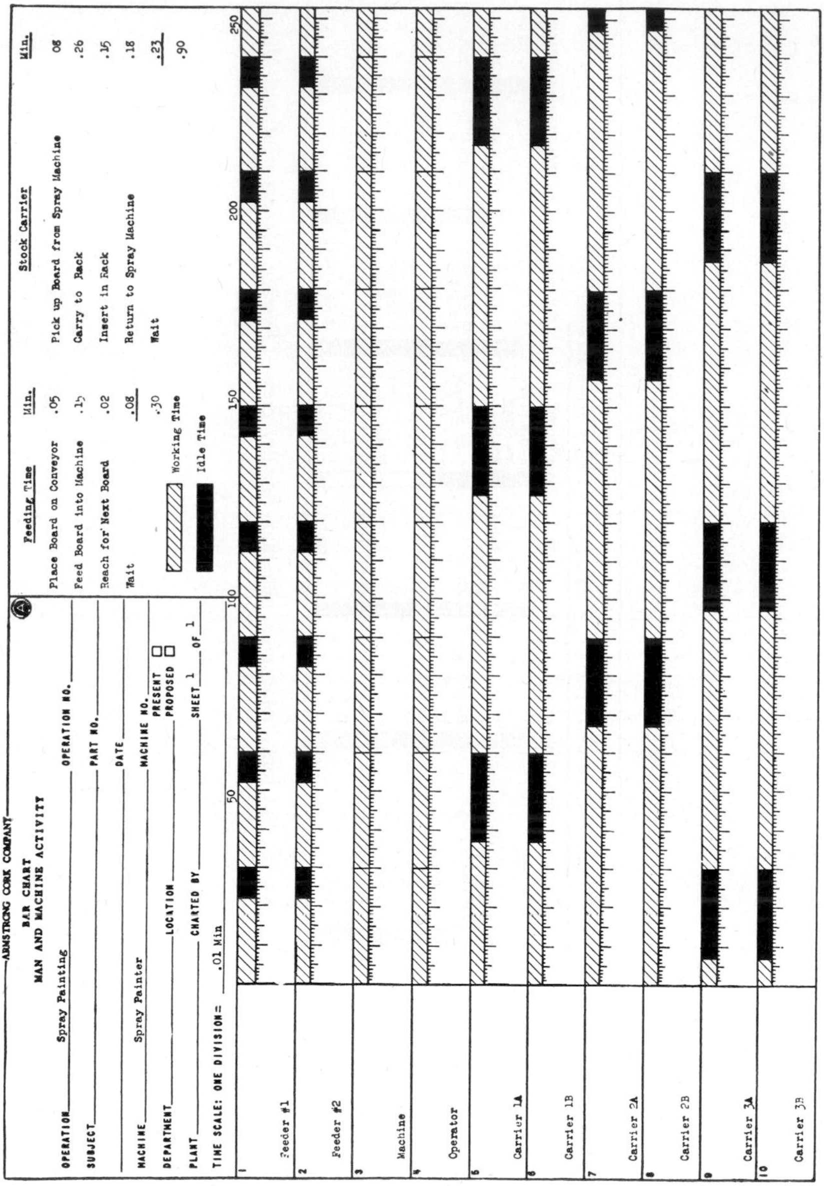

Fig. 30. Bar chart showing multi-man activity. (*Armstrong Cork Company.*)

cycle should be taken for the worker having the largest number of elements to perform. By balancing the activities of the group and paying particular attention to the waits and delays, handling operations can be speeded up and labor costs reduced.[5]

4. Multi-man Activity Chart

When a limited number of men are involved in an operation and the elements are of sufficient length, a running account may be made of the time for the completion of each element. These times may be reconstructed later on a chart side by side to show the relationship of the work performed by each of the members of the group.

When elements are too short for this method or more accuracy is desired, a time-study man may be assigned to each operator and the times recorded on a time-study sheet in the usual manner. These times are charted in the same way to show the relationships of the various activities of the group.

5. Ratio-delay Study

In the search for a better method of determination and evaluation of delays incidental to the performance of work, a number of methods, each involving the use of all-day studies (called production studies), were employed. To permit the time-study man to make studies of this type, a large number of observations are taken at random intervals. The method as applied to materials handling indicated the percentage of time spent by each of ten men on various handling operations. The study showed that it would be more economical to use a recommended system of pallets and fork lift trucks.[6]

A number of tests of the reliability of this method have been made by Robert Lee Morrow. Comparison with full-day production studies and down-time recorders showed a very high correlation to the ratio-delay studies. As a result of studies made in the J. E. Ogden Company, Bayonne, N.J., the following four major precautions were advised: [7]

1. A truly random time of observation must be used; otherwise a periodic stop synchronized with the clock, such as a rest period, might be recorded every day if the observer made his rounds at the time of the rest period.

2. A definite basis must be established on each job for a decision on what

---

[5] Also see John V. Valentine, Gang Process Charts in Work Simplification, *Factory Management and Maintenance*, November, 1946, p 125

[6] Edwin H. Schaeffer, Observation Ratios, *Factory Management and Maintenance*, July, 1941, p. 58.

[7] Robert Lee Morrow, "Time Study and Motion Economy," p. 175, The Ronald Press Company, New York, 1946.

MAN AND MACHINE CHART
ACTIVITY CHART

OPERATION __Adhesives__ OPERATION NO. _____
SUBJECT __Packing 5 Gallon Containers__
             DATE _____
MACHINE _____ MACH. NO. _____
DEPT. __Sundries__ LOCATION _____
PLANT _____ CHARTED BY _____
PRESENT ☐   SHEET _1_ OF _1_
PROPOSED ☒

SUMMARY

ACTIVITY	A WORK-ING TIME	% TIME	B IDLE TIME	% TIME	TOTAL CYCLE TIME
1. Operator	37.6	93	2.9	7	40.5
2. Mixer	23.9	59	16.6	41	40.5
3. Packer	40.5	100	–	–	40.5
4.					
5.					

LEGEND

Crosshatch — Working Time
Solid — Idle Time

TIME SCALE: ONE DIVISION = .20

1. ACTIVITY — Mixer Operator	2. ACTIVITY — Mixer 60 Gallon/Batch – 15 Min. Mix Time	3. ACTIVITY — Packaging Paste 5 Gallon Pails
Charge Alcohol (1 can -35 Min.) Charge Clay (5 Bags) — 2.45	Idle — 3.23	Fill 5 Gallon Pails (8 Pails) — 11.7
Charge Oil (175#) — .78		
Get and Weigh 20# Clay Get Asbestos — 1.64	Pre-mix — 1.64	
Charge Clay (2 Bags) — .95		
Charge Balance Oil (115#) — 1.02	Charge and Pre-mixing — 2.80	
Charge Asbestos and Clay — .83		
Fill Barrel with Oil for Next Batch from 2-450 lb. Drums (Incomplete) — 3.50	Pre-mix — 4.50	
Check Viscosity – Add Clay if Neces. (1.00)		Fill 1 Gallon Sample Can — 1.85
Fill Barrel with Oil for Next Batch — 5.60		Scrape Hoe, Door – Close Box — 2.17
(Complete)		Place Lids on 12 Pails — 1.70
		Cap Pails and Aside on Pallet — 4.25
Remove Empty Drum, Bags to Slab Get Drum Oil and Can Alcohol — 5.70	Mixing Time 15 Minutes (Spec.) — 15.0	Position Skid (.30 Min.) Get Pails — 1.39
		Prepare 13 Labels — 1.67
		Label 12-5 Gallon Pails — 3.10
Get Clay (7 Bags) Weigh Asbestos — 2.15	Mixing Time Extended Due Man Capacity — 3.30	Remove Lids and Stack Pails on Loading Platform — 2.18
Fill 1/2 Pt. Sample — .85		Straighten Tubs – 12 Lids — 1.90
Idle — 2.91	Mixing Time Extended Due Man Capacity — 2.91	Prepare Sample Can Open Chute Door (.57 Min.) — 1.57
Remove Platform Open Mixer Dump Adhesive in Chute — 3.01	Idle — 7.11	Fill 5 Gallon Pails (2 Pails) — 2.80
Scrape Adhesive from Mixer and Chute Level Mixer Replace Platform — 4.10		Scrape Chute Plunger — 1.24
		Fill 5 Gallon Pails (2 Pails) — 2.91

FIG. 31. Man and machine activity chart. (*Armstrong Cork Company.*)

is to be considered down or running, depending on the job conditions, and also which delays are allowable and which are unnecessary.

3. The operators must be persuaded that they must act as if the observer were not present; otherwise an operator, for example, ready to talk to his neighbor, might postpone his conversation upon seeing the observer coming until the observer had passed. This type of procedure will give incorrect results and must be avoided.

4. Long delays must be noted and recorded as but one delay.

As many materials-handling operations are irregular and occur at infrequent intervals, a sampling technique such as this is often the answer to the discovery of handling costs. Under the title of "Work Sampling" this technique has been revived to provide a valuable tool for the collecting of handling costs and data.

6. Methods-Time Measurement

This is a system developed by the Methods Engineering Council to provide operation times without the necessity of making stop-watch studies. In the words of the authors: [8]

Methods-time measurement is a procedure which analyzes any manual operation or method into the basic motions required to perform it and assigns to each motion a predetermined time standard which is determined by the nature of the motion and the conditions under which it is made.

The system is based on the development of time-data tables for elementary types of motions. These motions are primarily an extension of the therbligs developed by the Gilbreths in 1910, which have been added to several times since. Motions have been further revised and grouped on the basis of their characteristics.[9]

These basic time data have been developed for the following motions: *reach, move, turn* (including *apply pressure*), *grasp, position, disengage,* and *release*. These seven types of manual motions observed to date make possible a wide application of the system.

The time of each of these motions is measured in terms of decimal hours. In order to overcome the difficulty of a large number of decimal places needed for timing these elementary motions, an arbitrary unit of measure of 0.00001 hour was selected. This was called "time measurement unit" and abbreviated to TMU. Times expressed are leveled times, but include no allowance for fatigue, personal necessities, or unavoidable delays.[10]

[8] Harold B. Maynard, G. J. Stegemerten, and John L. Schwab, "Methods-time Measurement," p. 12, McGraw-Hill Book Company, Inc., New York, 1948.

[9] *Ibid.,* p. 175.

[10] *Ibid.,* p. 41.

FIG. 32. Two methods used to feed steel strips to punch press. (*a*) Two men lift a stack of four strips from hand truck to table. (*b*) Feeding table is adjustable to permit strips to be maintained at various heights. (*Rack Engineering Company.*)

METHODS ANALYSIS CHART

Part: *Strip steel*   Dept. *Press*   Dwg. _____   Item _____

Operation: *Lift strips to platform horses*   Date *10-17-50*

Description——Left Hand	No	L.H.	TMU	R.H.	Description——Right Hand
1. Move to supply truck					
			18.6	T B C 1	*Turn to truck*
			15.0	W 1 P	*Step to truck*
			29.0	B	*Bend to pick up material*
				W1R	*Step to stack*
Reach for stack		R-B		R-B	*Reach for stack*
			62.6		
2. Grasp stack					
Grasp		G 1 B	3.5	G 1 B	*Grasp*
Apply pressure		A P 1	16.2	A P 1	*Apply pressure to lift*
		M2B30*	4.8	M2B30*	*Lift off truck*
Regrasp stack		G 2	5.6	G 2	*Regrasp stack*
			30.1		
3. Wait for other man					
to grasp stack			30.1		
4. Move stack to					
platform horses			31.9	A B	*Arise from bend*
			68.2	2SS12C2	*Sidestep to horses*
Move onto horses		M22B38*	21.2	M22B30*	*Move onto horses*
Move fingers out of way		M2B	4.2	M2B	*Move fingers out of way*
Release		RL1		RL1	*Release*
Return hands to sides		R12E	11.8	R12E	*Return hands to sides*
			137.3		

Total time for one stack = 260 *TMU.*

*Time for 3 stacks - 3 x 2*60.1= 780.3 *TMU. or .0078 hours*

FIG. 33. Methods Analysis Chart used to develop time standards for the methods shown in Fig. 32. (*Methods Engineering Council.*)

One advantage of the system is that it permits the formulation of time standards before an operation is set up. Thus time standards can be set in advance of production activities. The fact that this system is faster than stop-watch time-study methods also extends the area in which it can be profitably applied. This is particularly true of materials-handling operations which may be of an intermittent nature.

Figure 32 shows the kind of handling problem that is frequently encountered in machine shops. Long steel strips are often used in punch-press operations. At the left (*a*) two men lift a small stack of four strips from a hand truck onto horses from which the operator moves each strip into the press. At the right (*b*) the operator moves the strips directly from a feeding table with an adjustable elevating mechanism.

The difference in operation time is the time it takes the two men to handle the strips from the trucks to the horses. The Methods Analysis Chart in Fig. 33 shows the time for this operation as developed by MTM. It covers the time for the operator only, though actually the total time will be twice this because two men are involved.

The operator moves to the supply truck, grasps one stack, and moves the stack to the horses. Each stack weighs 60 pounds. There are three stacks; therefore he must repeat the operation—three times in all. The total time then for one man is 260.1 TMU's for each stack. The time for the three stacks is $3 \times 260.1 = 780.3$ TMU's or 0.0078 hour.[11]

QUESTIONS

1. In what ways is time study used in the study of materials handling?
2. What steps were taken at Cadillac to determine time standards for handling operations?
3. What is memomotion? Where is it used?
4. Discuss the applications of the gang process chart and of the multi-man activity chart.
5. What precautions must be observed in making ratio-delay studies?
6. What is MTM? What is the purpose of MTM?

PROJECTS FOR FURTHER STUDY

1. Prepare a report on MTM applied to materials handling.
2. Observe a handling operation involving more than one person, and chart it on the appropriate type of form.
3. Prepare a time study of a truck-loading operation.
4. What are the difficulties encountered in preparing time standards for handling operations?

[11] This section reviewed by Harold B. Maynard, president, Methods Engineering Council.

Part III

MATERIALS-HANDLING EQUIPMENT

CHAPTER 7

FACTORS IN SELECTION OF EQUIPMENT

The result of an analysis of a materials-movement problem is usually the selection of some kind of equipment to be employed. This analysis should develop:

1. The path or area involved (flow lines, flow charts, layout).
2. The method to be employed in handling and preparation for handling.
3. The equipment (materials handling or fixed plant) to be used.

The following factors will determine the choice of specific types of materials-handling equipment to be used. They are listed in the order in which they should be considered. Thus the first item consists of the various characteristics of the product or materials to be moved. Final consideration is the cost comparison of the various methods and types of equipment which satisfy the other conditions.

1. Material to Be Moved

a. Characteristics. From a handling standpoint, materials are first divided into bulk materials and package items (see Appendix B). Bulk materials are further subdivided according to particle size and flowability. Package items are divided on the basis of weight or on the basis of shape.

b. Physical State. The fragility or durability of the items to be handled is next considered. With bulk materials, the shape of the particles, their hardness, possible damage to particle shapes, dust, temperature variations and moisture on the product, aftereffects, such as dripping from various processing operations, and need for product protection are involved.

c. Possible Chemical Action. This ranges from corrosion, which may make scrap out of expensive steel parts, fumes, and explosion, which may be damaging to the plant and to personnel, to the danger of fire in large stocks of coal when not leveled off properly. It includes the effects of temperature and moisture changes when these may cause or set up a chemical action.

2. Nature of Operation

a. Permanency of Operation. A temporary handling problem will justify only a limited amount of equipment expense unless the equipment is readily adaptable to other situations. Flexibility of the equipment and ease of setting it up (if conveyors) is important. A more permanent situation would justify a greater investment in fixed equipment of a less flexible nature.

b. Sequence of Operations. Again, a fixed sequence quantity may permit consideration of fixed-path types of equipment with a closer control over rate of movement. Its main effect, however, will be on layout of the area over which the materials have to be moved. Analysis of this sequence often shows that a changed layout is required to reduce the travel of materials through the plant.

Many companies have a rule that no major purchase of new equipment for movement of materials will be made unless preceded by a methods study and a thorough examination of the layout of the areas involved. Where excessive distances still remain, consideration will be given to those types of equipment which require no labor attention other than loading and unloading regardless of the distance involved (certain types of fixed-path equipment).

c. Volume of Production. The more expensive the handling equipment used, the more important it is to operate it at or near full capacity. Highly intermittent and varying production levels may demand a different type of equipment than is needed where levels are fairly constant.

The movement of a certain volume of materials depends upon the capacity (weight or size) of the carrying medium times the speed at which the equipment may be operated. Generally, this speed will vary inversely with the weight or size of the materials carried, *i.e.*, heavier loads will move at slower speeds. Other problems may be introduced by awkward shapes and extremely light items.

d. Continuous or Intermittent Flow. Although this flow is the result of the production rate and the sequence of operations, it should be considered separately. The continuous flow of material may utilize fixed-path equipment or non-fixed-path types if a schedule is set up to provide a constant flow or delivery of materials.

The operation of equipment may also be termed continuous or intermittent. Continuous types, such as belt conveyors, deliver a product in a steady stream but in smaller units. Intermittent types (fork trucks or cranes) handle one load at a time but in a larger sized unit. The former type affords more control over production schedules. The latter type provides more flexibility, and it is easier to insert additional units in case of breakdown.

e. Nature and Extent of Movement. How and in what direction is the material to be moved? Is the movement horizontal, vertical, or a combination of both? As vertical movement has a higher power-cost requirement and is generally an intermittent movement, it should be avoided where possible. Where combined movements are involved, a horizontal type of equipment may be used on an incline to eliminate the need for a separate elevating unit.

The distances involved will also affect equipment selection. Fork trucks have limits of economical operation on a horizontal plane. Beyond these limits, the tractor-trailer system is more efficient. Vertical distances also will demand different types of equipment.

3. Plant Facilities

The selection of equipment is often limited by physical aspects of the industrial plant, which the materials-handling engineer has to accept as part of the problem. In fact, much of the engineer's time is spent in thinking of ways to overcome the disadvantages of a heritage of bygone days: elevators that were inadequate some years ago, buildings constructed over a period of years with no thought of production relationships, floors that should have been replaced long ago, and in many cases a physical plant which hangs like a millstone around the neck of the present occupant.

a. Building Characteristics. The most common limitations encountered are inadequate floor-load capacities and insufficient clearance heights. This is overcome in new structures by the trend for high-ceiling single-story structures which permit high stacking, even of heavy commodities. The use of overhead handling systems is limited by low ceilings and weak overhead supports. Spacing of columns often complicates the situation further. The cutting of a door may often shorten a path of travel and ease a critical movement problem.

The use of industrial trucks may be restricted by different floor levels between departments. This is particularly true of plants which have grown by a series of additions. Ramps are only a partial solution for this condition, and often provision has to be made for hydraulic lifting platforms to link the various levels.

The condition of the floor is even more important to the use of industrial trucks. Rough floor surfaces may also seriously interfere with operation of trucks. At the same time, the small wheels used on hand-operated power trucks are very hard on ordinary floor materials and some sort of reinforcing is often necessary.

b. Existing Materials-handling Equipment. In multi-floor buildings, elevators must always be considered in plans for handling. Few of the older types are built to withstand the shock of an 8,000-pound fork truck entering with a full load. Many a multi-floor plant with an otherwise efficient fork-truck system has to load pallets and skids to the elevator with a hand truck and unload at the other floor with another hand truck. This is due to the inadequate capacity of the elevator and to the fact that it was not designed in the first place to take the off-center stresses of a heavy power truck with its load.

Where specific types of containers are already in use, the question is soon raised as to how these can be fitted into the new handling system. The cost of changing over from one type of container to another may prevent the installation of equipment which would otherwise provide the most logical solution to the problem.

4. Materials-handling Equipment

a. Safety. Mechanized handling is safer handling. Hand lifting and stacking always involves danger to personnel. Accidents are decreased as the degree of mechanization increases. At the same time, the decrease in number of accidents is offset to some extent by the increase in the severity of accidents when they do occur. In the selection of equipment, safety must be considered from the standpoint of the equipment itself, of the operators using it, and the contact of third parties in the normal course of their duties.

b. Noise and Fumes. In some areas noise is objectionable. Ball-bearing wheels mounted on rubber tires reduce the noise of hand trucks. Electric-powered units can be used instead of gasoline-powered units for the same purpose. In closed working areas, the fumes from gasoline trucks may form a dangerous concentration, or in any case be objectionable to workers.

c. Flexibility. In general, equipment should be selected to do not only its primary job but to perform miscellaneous handling tasks that may arise within its area. One explanation of the popularity of the fork truck is its extreme versatility. A wide variety of attachments made available within recent years has increased the range of this adaptability still further.

d. Reliability. Where paced production is involved, the dependability of the transporting medium is of the utmost importance. According to a survey of materials-handling equipment made in 1948 by the magazine *Industry and Power,* the reliability of equipment, which is dependent upon maintenance requirements and durability, governed the selection of equipment in 66 per cent of the plants contacted.[1]

5. Cost Balance

Consideration of all the above factors will in most instances narrow down considerably the types of equipment that may be utilized for the particular problem at hand. Even with these limitations it will invariably be found that there are several types which will do the job satisfactorily and will satisfy all the demands that will be made. As most equipment available on the market today may be safely termed more than adequate technically, the question remains: Is it the best equipment for this particular handling job? This question will be answered primarily by the cost balance sheet prepared and interpreted through the experiences of the company making the installation.

a. Initial Costs. Costs will include first of all the equipment itself and any expense of installation. Any building changes or any changes in layout made to permit its efficient use will also be included in initial costs. Some companies include an item for lost production time or down time for manufacturing facilities, where involved. In new installations of extensive scope, some allowance must also be made for less than standard performance until the workers get accustomed to the new methods.

b. Rates of Depreciation and Obsolescence. Although these rates will in many instances be limited by the legal rate of depreciation for the specific type of equipment involved, the usable life of the system must be considered along with the amount of the initial cost. For example, companies which have insisted on a six months' amortization of equipment have written off large sums each period for wood pallets when steel containers would have been more economical in the long run for that particular situation.

c. Operating Costs. The first item is the cost directly related to the amount of use of the equipment or to the amount of production in the area being served. This is primarily the cost of the necessary power consumption such as gasoline, diesel oil, electricity, or battery recharging. Labor cost of operating the unit is added next. All maintenance and repairs, including spare parts, replacements, and repair labor, are then considered. Cost of any breakage (or savings due to lack of breakage as compared to another system) is included.

[1] John R. Immer, "Layout Planning Techniques," p. 325, McGraw-Hill Book Company, Inc., New York, 1950.

d. Other Cost Considerations. Finally, taxes on the equipment and on the operating surplus of the company are considered. This subject is developed in more detail in Chaps. 18 and 19.

The final consideration is the financial position of the firm and the general competitive picture. The progressive company is constantly striving to improve its production methods and lower its production costs. Less progressive companies may be forced by competition to make drastic changes in their methods of handling.

The selection of materials-handling equipment and improved and more efficient methods of moving materials through the plant cannot be disregarded by any company today, regardless of its competitive position. Though the selection of specific methods and types of equipment is a technical matter, *the establishment of a firm policy of aggressive handling improvement is a responsibility of top management.*

QUESTIONS

1. What should be the result of a materials-handling analysis?
2. What is the final determinant in the selection of materials-handling equipment?
3. What factors determine the choice of materials-handling equipment to be used?
4. How do the materials to be moved affect equipment selection?
5. Discuss the effects of the various types of operation on equipment selection.
6. Do existing plant facilities tend to widen or contract the range of equipment which may be used? Explain your answer.
7. What special problems arise from the use of industrial trucks?
8. What special problems are involved in the use of overhead handling equipment?
9. What characteristics of the equipment must be considered?
10. What cost considerations are involved in equipment selection?

PROJECTS FOR FURTHER STUDY

1. Prepare a report on the article Survey Reveals Status of Materials Handling in Industry, *Industry and Power,* January, 1948, p. 80.
2. Compare the above report with other reports on the selection and use of materials-handling equipment.
3. What cost elements are involved in the comparison of movement between two points by trolley conveyor and by fork truck?

CHAPTER 8

HORIZONTAL FIXED ROUTES

The student and the materials-handling engineer alike are interested primarily in the capacity of materials-handling equipment to move materials. It is important for both to know the different types and capacities of the equipment available which will accomplish the particular movement desired.

Fig. 34. In the final assembly of small aircraft, the airplane is mounted on a wheeled jig. Notice monorail overhead. (*Cessna Aircraft Company.*)

In any problem of production it is desirable to ascertain at an early stage the most efficient method of performing each job. Instruction sheets are usually prepared carefully in detail to guide the operator and thus ensure maximum production and minimum wasted effort. The movement of materials between operations, treated in like manner, may often be accomplished most efficiently by fixed paths or routes.

1. Materials Moved or Carried on Wheels or Bogies Drawn by Cable or Chain along a Fixed Route

a. Wheeled Products. In one of the early efforts to obtain progressive assembly in the manufacture of motorcars, the wheeled chassis was pushed by hand from one work station to the next. The next step was to connect each vehicle to a chain or cable and have the whole line drawn along.

FIG. 35. Assembly of diesel engines for tractors and general power purposes is simplified by chain conveyor which moves the units along. (*Link-Belt Company.*)

In the mass production of airplanes in the Second World War, special wheeled jigs were drawn along in similar manner. Later in the process after wheels were affixed to the fuselage, the plane itself was drawn along, and assemblies were added. In some instances, a slow continuous movement moved the planes from one assembly station to the next. In other instances, the cycle system was employed, in which all units were moved forward to the next station at the same time. Theoretically, the work of each assembly station was completed within the scheduled period. In any case, the line was moved forward on the appointed time, and special teams of trouble shooters roved the line finishing up any uncompleted

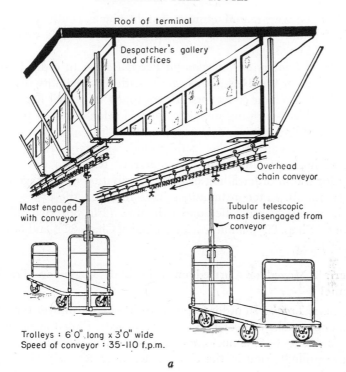

Roof of terminal

Despatcher's gallery and offices

Overhead chain conveyor

Mast engaged with conveyor

Tubular telescopic mast disengaged from conveyor

Trolleys : 6'0" long x 3'0" wide
Speed of conveyor : 35-110 f.p.m.

a

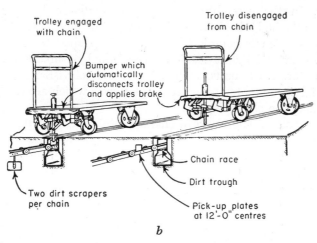

Trolley engaged with chain

Trolley disengaged from chain

Bumper which automatically disconnects trolley and applies brake

Chain race

Dirt trough

Two dirt scrapers per chain

Pick-up plates at 12'-0" centres

b

FIG. 36. The tow-type conveyor has changed warehousing methods within recent years. The overhead type (*a*) is used where an existing structure or floor surface must be utilized. The floor-type conveyor (*b*), developed later, eliminated all overhead equipment. (*"Freight Handling," Anglo-American Council on Productivity, London,* 1951, *pp.* 18, 19.)

work. After the war, manufacturers of light planes continued to use this method of pulling the fuselages along by a cable while assembly was completed (Fig. 34).

b. Carts or Trailers Pulled along a Fixed Route. In order to combine the advantages of the fixed-path systems with the flexibility of non-fixed-path equipment, chain conveyors are equipped to propel hand trucks or trailers. The basic carrying unit is a four-wheeled castered trailer. With a special coupling device it is easy to attach this unit to an overhead conveyor which will pull the load around an established circuit. This method of horizontal movement of materials has been developed particularly for use in order filling or for redistribution of packaged items in freight terminals. Later installations have replaced the overhead trolley with a chain conveyor installed under the floor (Fig. 36). See rail terminal operations (Chap. 32), union truck terminals (Chap. 32), and order filling (Chap. 29).

2. Materials Moved or Carried on Wheels or Bogies on Track or in Channel

a. Channel Tracks. In order to provide closer control over the assembly line, channel tracks are set in the floor. In extending the same idea to smaller components, it is necessary to mount them on wheeled platforms which are pulled along in the channel track or set on various types of raised tracks.

b. Rails. In the assembly and working of large heavy pieces of machinery, attached wheels move the unit on rails laid in the floor. As an assembly operation is completed, the unit is pushed to the next work station. Smaller and lighter sections are worked on at the waist height of the operator. These units, such as radio and television sets, are often set in special jigs mounted on wheeled platforms which are easily pushed by hand along the channel track.

c. Motive Power. The use of a chain, cable, rope, or linkage between units, the whole line being moved by a single motive power, eliminates hand movement of the units and provides a control over the speed of movement. This control element is very important to high production methods as it reveals immediately any failure to meet the set schedule.

In many of the airplane plants referred to above, channel tracks were set in the floor to guide the airplane along a designated route. Movement was generally accomplished by means of one or more chain conveyors set in the floor. Chain connections permitted the planes to be affixed or taken off easily without delay to the line. The same method or modifications thereof are now used for the assembly of motorboats, machine tools, tractors, etc.

d. Platforms. Platforms for the assembly of smaller components and items are often drawn along a track at a steady speed by some kind of chain or connecting unit. In many cases the operation is performed while the part is being drawn along without removing it from its platform on the line. One company in order to perform an operation removes the wheeled platform holding the small radio assembly. It is returned to the line where an engaging cog of the chain moves it to the next work station.

FIG. 37. Pouring operations in foundry are speeded up with carrousel conveyors consisting of four-wheel cars pulled by chain. (*Mechanical Handling Systems, Inc.*)

The wheels of these platforms may roll on a flat surface or may be guided between angle irons (or side walls) or may run on tracks. In most instances they are propelled by a chain conveyor underneath, which may connect with the undercarriage. In some carrousel types, the chain drive may be mounted on the inner side of the circle and attached to the platform or undercarriage from the side. The roundabout or carrousel type of platform conveyor is used in foundries and where jigs must be returned to a starting point.

e. Wheeled Jigs. Jigs and special holding devices for large assemblies are often mounted on rails or between guides in the floor and pulled along by various arrangements of chain or cable conveyors. Larger units such as airplanes may be guided forward by two or three chain conveyors set in the floor. It is quite common in the assembly of airplane and automobile engines to have a turnover device on the jig to provide access to all sides.

3. Materials Carried on Conveying Mechanisms

Many materials are not suited for movement without a solid sustaining surface. Bulk materials and small or delicate items require a continuous bearing surface. Certain types of conveying devices with this characteristic also provide unusual flexibility and have other desirable features in their operation.

BELT CONVEYOR

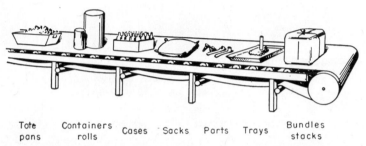

Tote pans   Containers rolls   Cases   Sacks   Parts   Trays   Bundles stacks

Fig. 38. Handles most items that will travel on roller conveyor. Effective for many articles not suited to direct contact with conveyor rolls, such as sacks, flexible or uneven bottom items, and small parts. Not adaptable to certain kinds of extra-heavy handling or where there is appreciable loading shock. (*Logan Company.*)

a. Belt Conveyor. A solid sustaining surface is provided for a wide variety of materials, both bulk and packaged items, by various types of belt conveyors. The most common type of belting used is made up of various plies of cotton duck bonded together or vulcanized with rubber. The bottom and top are also protected with a rubber covering. Synthetic rubber (neoprene, etc.) may be used where chemical reaction, such as that produced by oil and coal, affects natural rubber. Cord reinforcing construction has been developed by one company to provide greater resistance to impact shocks. For ability to stand even greater tension, important in increasing the length of belt conveyors, steel wire cables are embedded in the carcass of the belt.

The rubber belting described above is used as a flat belt for packages and small items and the troughed belt is used for bulk and loose flowing materials. The belt will be supported at regular intervals by idlers, either flat or trough-shaped. The spacing, size, and surface material of these idlers will strongly influence the lift of the belting used on them. For extremely light requirements, belting may be slid over a smooth surface made of hardwood or steel.

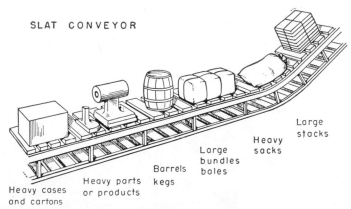

SLAT CONVEYOR

Large stacks

Heavy sacks

Large bundles bales

Barrels kegs

Heavy parts or products

Heavy cases and cartons

FIG. 39. Will handle virtually anything, but use is indicated where there is definite loading shock, or where weight is too great for efficient handling by belt conveyor. Advantageous for operating on inclines and frequently used to lift or lower between floors. Provides a strong, rigid carrying surface. (*Logan Company.*)

FIG. 40. Modern hog-cutting methods use conveyorized tables. Capacities up to 600 hogs per hour can be accommodated. (*Link-Belt Company.*)

With all these surfaces, employed in the form of a continuously moving belt, movement is caused by power applied to one of the ends of the loop. Take-up devices are used to maintain constant tension of the belt. A supporting surface is necessary. This may be a solid surface or it may consist of idler rollers at intervals for support of the belt and its load. The latter type is used exclusively for bulk materials.

Fig. 41. Crescent-shaped segments provide a continuous bearing surface and permit sharp right-angle returns which modern packaging methods often require. (*Link-Belt Company.*)

Although special types of rubber belts will stand temperatures of 250 to 300°F., woven-wire belts are better adapted to higher temperature requirements and special duty. Heavier materials may be carried on chain conveyors with integrated links to provide a uniform carrying surface. Flat steel belts are used where the surface must be constantly cleaned or where sanitation of carrying surface is important. These may be floated on water to provide a rapid cooling of the product being carried.

b. Slat Conveyor. This conveyor consists of slats of wood or metal connecting two strands of chain conveyor and is used for heavy loads deposited with considerable impact. It is often used to provide a flush surface for assembly operations. The product being assembled may be deposited directly upon the conveyor surface (as in the case of tractor assembly) or may be elevated on stands (automobile-engine assembly) to provide a convenient working height for the assemblers (Fig. 39).

c. Apron Conveyor. The apron conveyor is similar to the slat conveyor except that the segments abut or overlap each other to provide a continuous surface. When used for bulk handling, the conveyor will have side aprons for holding larger quantities of materials. This type is sometimes called a "pan" conveyor. With metal segments they can handle abrasive or hot materials and stand extremely hard usage.

A single chain may have rounded segmented plates to permit 90-degree turns. This type is widely used in the bottling industry. Larger types are sometimes set in the floor to provide a continuous surface where a turn or bend is required in the installation (Fig. 41).

d. Wire Conveyor. Multiple strands of wire or cable provide a continuous bearing surface of parts through heat-treating and sintering operations. They are adapted to the movement of lightweight, flat objects.

4. Material Rides Directly on Fixed-position Wheels or Rollers

Materials with a reasonably flat bottom surface can be moved directly on rollers or wheels. These are supported by side frames which may extend above the rollers as guides or remain below this level to permit movement of wider materials. The width of the conveyor and the spacing, diameter, and internal construction of the rollers will depend upon the size and weights of the materials to be carried. If heavy materials are to be dropped with considerable impact, the rollers may be mounted on springs to absorb the shock.

a. Gravity Roller Conveyor. This type of equipment will move materials a considerable horizontal distance with no power application or other attention. This distance is limited only by the fall required to utilize the force of gravity, and this limitation can be overcome with booster units set in the line. These are short sections of powered belt conveyors provided to raise the materials to a higher level again.

The gravity roller conveyor is used for the horizontal movement of materials, to provide live storage and live banks of materials between operations. Between machine operations, for example, a number of items may be stored at working height. Often the conveyor sections will run from one machine to the other so that the worker has only to push the machined part onto the conveyor when his operation is completed.

b. Powered Roller Conveyor. For a controlled movement of materials or where level operation is desired, power may be applied to the rollers by means of a belt on the underside of the rollers or by a chain moving over sprockets on the end of the rollers. The belt type provides enough slippage to prevent damage to the product when the line "builds up."

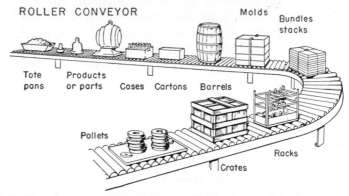

Fig. 42. Roller conveyors will handle virtually any type of package, container, or article which has a reasonably firm and straight surface to contact the roll. Irregular articles and flexible items such as sacks are not practical unless placed on pallets or in containers. Sacks are sometimes handled with steep pitch and close spacing. (*Logan Company.*)

c. Wheel Conveyor. Wheels mounted on ball bearings replace the rollers where the broad supporting surface is not needed. They are used for movement of boxes and other broad-bearing surfaced items. Wheels

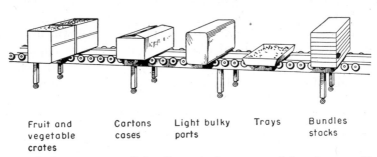

Fig. 43. Wheel conveyors will handle items having a solid and reasonably firm bottom. They have a limited use for certain light- and medium-duty handling jobs and find extensive favor in canning and fruit-packing industries. They are also used to handle bundles, like shingles, and certain irregular shapes. Will operate on slightly less grade than roller conveyors. (*Logan Company.*)

may be arranged on the side supporting bars or with several to a supporting axle. They will operate with a slighter incline than the roller conveyors and are used more for light and medium handling.

5. Materials Carried in Containers Pulled by Continuous Chain on Track

Bulk or loose flowing materials will be transported on a fixed route in small containers or buckets. The close position of the buckets permits them to be loaded from overhead chutes while in motion. They are unloaded by means of a trip device which may be remote-controlled.

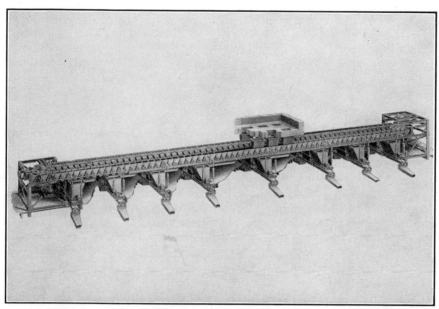

FIG. 44. Diagrammatic view of "Sidekar-Karrier," showing multiple-bin openings and spring-suspended hoppers. (*Link-Belt Company.*)

a. V-type Bucket Conveyor. The Peck carrier has become the standard carrier of this type. It provides vertical as well as horizontal movement for materials too fragile to be dragged along by flights or scrapers. Overlapping buckets are carried between two chains supported on guiding rails. Materials are fed to it from overhead chutes and removed by a tripping device at the desired point. Buckets remain in a horizontal position regardless of the movement of the conveyor.

b. Sidecar Carrier. This type of equipment was invented to provide a closed conveyance for materials too fragile for other means of horizontal movement. It consists of a series of buckets mounted on rollers which are guided along tracks, and it is powered by a chain attached to the inner side of the buckets. It is fed from an overhead chute and dumped at the discharge point by one of the methods shown in Fig. 44. Automatic discharge to a number of points may be obtained. Surplus material is recirculated until a new discharge point is found. Since it is completely enclosed, there is no dust leakage.

6. Material Dragged or Propelled along a Fixed Channel

When fragility of the materials is not a consideration, it has been found more efficient to move them horizontally by various means of dragging

Fig. 45. A malleable iron conveyor and steel chain with bar flights is used for receiving pulpwood from railroad cars. (*Link-Belt Company.*)

devices. Although used more for the movement of bulk materials, it is also adapted to the movement of items such as logs, boxes, crates, etc.

a. Drag Chain Conveyor. This conveyor consists of one or more strands of chain with links adapted to drag the specific materials along a trough. Links are often designed with special lugs for the movement of large objects and of bulk materials (Fig. 45).

One or two chains built with flat links are often used for movement of boxes where a circuitous path and sharp curves must be followed. Side rails guide the boxes or cases. This type is often used in bottling operations (Fig. 46). Other types with lugs are used in the sorting of lumber. One installation of this type has roller units mounted on each link of the chain to facilitate removal of boards.

b. Flight Conveyors. This is a type of drag conveyor with flights which push the material along a trough. It is suitable for the movement of lumpy or small materials of a nonabrasive nature. The following four types are used:

1. *Scraper flight conveyor.* This consists of a single strand which pulls the flights along the troughed bottom. Cable or rope is often used in

Fig. 46. Freshly bottled milk is moved to waiting delivery trucks by chain conveyor which carries it easily around sharp curves. (*Link-Belt Company.*)

place of a chain and may be used in an open trough to move bulk materials or logs depending on the spacing of the flights. This type is often completely enclosed when used for bulk materials only.

2. *Suspended flight conveyor.* This is also a single-strand conveyor with wearing shoes attached to the flights which suspend them on the edge of the trough to clear them on the bottom. The wearing shoes also support it on the return run.

3. *Roller flight conveyor.* In this type of conveyor the flights are kept clear of the bottom of the trough by rollers running on the edge of the trough.

4. *Roller chain conveyor.* This is a double chain conveyor with the chain and the flights supported on rollers running on the edge of the trough. It is recommended for greater capacities and heavier service.

c. Vibrating Conveyor. The movement of hot abrasive materials is often accomplished on long metal troughs which advance the materials by means of a reciprocating or vibrating action. It is ideal for movement of hot sand and castings, clinker and chips, and turnings, as well as fine, lumpy, or stringy materials.

Gentle electromagnetic action is also used to feed small parts into machines in a specifically oriented position without hand sorting or po-

Fig. 47. A 36-inch-wide oscillating conveyor with torsion-bar mounting handles sand and castings from foundry floor to shakeout screen. (*Link-Belt Company.*)

sitioning. This has been applied successfully to the feeding of zippers in a specified oriented position, nuts to a tapping machine at the rate of 290 per minute, and to checkers fed into boxes, all face up.

d. Sluice. Where water is plentiful, it makes an efficient carrying agent for logs over a considerable distance. Since a sluice needs only a trough and a constant water source, it is quickly set up and may be used even for temporary handling of this type. It is also used in handling of sand or ashes. One contractor recently removed a sand dune in California to make way for a sewage-disposal plant. Sand was deposited to form a sandy beach along the ocean front.

7. Material Moved through a Closed Channel

Materials which need to be kept free from contamination or from contact with lubricants are moved through enclosed channels. Other materials of medium and small particle size, especially where vertical movement is also involved, are efficiently moved by this type of equipment.

a. Screw Conveyors. Materials of this type may be moved efficiently for short distances by screw conveyors. These conveyors provide dust-tight fully protected transport for materials from food products to hot tar, ash, and slack coal.

b. Pneumatic Tube. Although this type is used more generally for vertical movement, it is sometimes employed for the horizontal movement

Fig. 48. Central desk of pneumatic-tube system in department store for dispatching cash to and from substations located in various departments. (*Standard Conveyor Company.*)

of small-particled materials, such as grain, soybeans, flour, and flaxseed. The Pfister Hybrid Corn Company uses two pneumatic systems for conveying hybrid seed corn over distances ranging from 50 to 500 feet.

Similar types of equipment are used for the rapid transmission of papers, letters, blueprints, and other documents within a factory and from other buildings. Such a system is used in Paris to provide rapid delivery of letters to other substations in the city.

The Burroughs Adding Machine Company of Detroit, Mich., recently installed a pneumatic-tube conveyor to deliver small parts from its main stock room to two light-assembly departments. This system has cut the delivery time on these small parts from an hour or more to less than five minutes.

c. En Masse Type. The en masse type is an enclosed conveyor with an internal skeleton consisting of a chain or coiled wire. Materials, of small-lump particle size or smaller, can be moved economically within this closed column by the principle of the coherence of the mass. This is a movement of the whole mass induced by the skeletonized or framed

FIG. 49. Portable sections of wheel conveyor are quickly set up for unloading of semitruck to receiving room. (*Minnesota Mining and Manufacturing Company.*)

FIG. 50. Portable belt conveyor is used for high stacking of boxes. Note its use with flexible roller conveyor in foreground. (*Food Machinery Corporation.*)

flights. It provides dustless movement horizontally at any angle or turning and may also be used where vertical movement is required (see page 508).

8. Material Moved by Temporary Fixed Routes

The economy of movement of materials by fixed routes is often limited by the temporary nature of the handling problem. Where the permanent

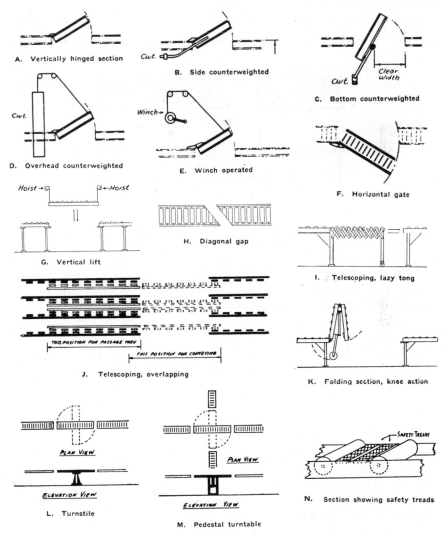

A. Vertically hinged section

B. Side counterweighted

C. Bottom counterweighted

D. Overhead counterweighted

E. Winch operated

F. Horizontal gate

G. Vertical lift

H. Diagonal gap

I. Telescoping, lazy tong

J. Telescoping, overlapping

K. Folding section, knee action

L. Turnstile

M. Pedestal turntable

N. Section showing safety treads

Fig. 51. Types of gates for roller conveyors. (*Modern Materials Handling, April, 1951, p. 51.*)

installations are thus not justified by cost savings or required by the nature of the handling problem, temporary routes may be set up with portable handling devices.

These devices consist of a conveyor and a carriage or support by which it is moved around. Power for the operation of the conveyor and the moving of the unit from place to place will be mounted on this carriage. This may consist of an electric motor to be plugged into electrical outlets or of a separate power plant.

a. Roller Conveyor. Portable sections are mounted on temporary adjustable supports and are easily set up for an unloading operation. They

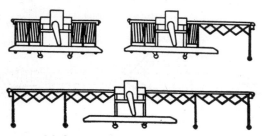

Fig. 52. Portable powered belt conveyor contracts to 10-foot length or extends to 46-foot length. (*Standard Conveyor Company.*)

were used in the Second World War in the field to speed up the loading of trucks with groceries and cases of ammunition. One company has an accordion type for greater flexibility. Short sections are often installed on the floor of trucks to aid in loading of palletized materials. They have also been put on the platform of a lift truck to aid in the loading of heavy materials. For ease in handling, new types of 10-foot sections in aluminum and magnesium have been developed.

b. Portable Wheel Conveyor. This type of conveyor is also made in 10-foot lengths and mounted on light adjustable tripod stands. A telescopic unit consists of a supporting wheel unit on casters and two to four 10-foot sections which slide out to provide the desired length up to 40 feet. Its lightness and portability make it ideal for portable conveyance of packages of small and medium weight.

c. Portable Belt Conveyor. This is a powered unit and may be used for the loading and unloading of both bulk and single-item materials. For the latter a flat belt is used, sometimes with cleats when a steep incline is involved. Bulk materials are also moved on a flat belt (with or without cleats) or a troughed belt. One unit, the Extendo-veyor, will extend to a length of 46 feet and is easily moved from one loading location to another.

FIG. 53. This portable power conveyor can move up to thirty 100-pound sacks a minute. (*Mechanical Handling Systems, Inc.*)

FIG. 54. Bags may be elevated at inclines of 70 to 90 per cent and can be handled at up to 75 tons per hour. (*Mechanical Handling Systems, Inc.*)

d. Twin-spiral Conveyor. This portable unit consists of 8-foot segments upon which are mounted two coarse screwed spirals rotating counterwise to each other. Segments are easily assembled to provide a flexible conveying system. It is used primarily for movement of bags and small bales.

e. Portable V-belt Conveyor. The trade name for this type is Ropeveyor. It consists of a drive unit and standard 8-foot sections of nondrive, each mounted on casters for greater movability. It supports bags and crates on four V-type belts, spaced on regular grooves in the end of each unit. Although limited in the items with which it may be used, it has considerable flexibility.

QUESTIONS

1. Describe the various methods by which materials are moved or carried along a fixed path by or on wheeled carriers.

2. What conveyors provide a solid sustaining surface for materials being transported?

3. What is the distinction between a slat and an apron conveyor?

4. What materials can be moved on roller conveyors?

5. How will the size and weight of materials being moved affect the construction of roller conveyors?

6. Where are powered roller conveyors used?

7. Compare the directional limitations of the V-type bucket carrier and the sidecar carrier type of conveyor.

8. What types of conveyors drag the materials along a trough or flat surface?

9. What types of equipment move materials through closed channels?

10. What advantages do temporary fixed routes offer?

11. What conditions limit their use?

12. What types of equipment can be used for temporary fixed routes?

PROJECTS FOR FURTHER STUDY

1. Prepare a chart showing how different types of materials can be moved along a fixed route.

2. Locate in current issues of industrial-management and materials-handling magazines examples of each of the major types of equipment used for fixed routes.

3. Discuss the use of various types of equipment for handling specific materials, such as coal, gravel, flour, or steel castings.

CHAPTER 9

OVERHEAD MOVEMENT OF MATERIALS

The utilization of the third dimension for handling as well as for storage has long been a dream of the industrial engineer. The pressure for greater production within the same amount of floor space and the expense of providing additional space have added an extra premium to the utilization of air rights.

In addition, the overhead movement of materials has a number of intrinsic advantages. Aisles do not have to be wide enough for the movement of products being handled. Floors do not have to be able to carry these loads. The handling system is made independent of factory floor surfaces and levels. Materials movement is kept away from the working areas of the factory.

1. Materials to Be Moved Over Limited Area

There are few types of lifting devices which do not require some degree of horizontal movement for their operations. A number of them provide for a limited movement along with the lifting function. These are adapted to special handling requirements on and around machines and special assembly areas.

a. Jib Cranes. Where the function of the handling equipment is to move materials only within the restricted confines of a specific working area, jib cranes have special advantages. The area serviced by these cranes is generally an arc described by the range of the swinging jib. In the instance of a column jib crane, the area will be a circle whose radius will be the swinging jib. By overlapping the arcs, it is possible to provide for movement over an extensive working area. An interlocking jib crane is often used to extend the travel of a monorail hoist by providing a stationary extension of trackage. When not in use, the jib is swung out of the way to permit passage of rail cars, ship and barge superstructures, etc.

Jib cranes are also mounted on heavy undercarriages which move back and forth on rails set at floor level. These walking jib cranes are generally used for heavy lifting under bridge cranes. Another type consists of a rigid jib or arm extending out from the wall at a right angle. It is moved

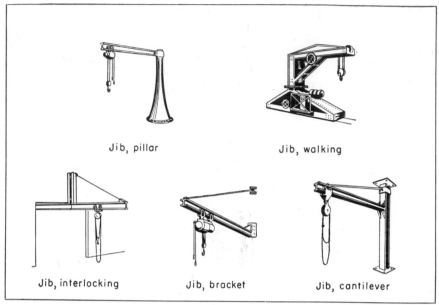

Jib, pillar   Jib, walking

Jib, interlocking   Jib, bracket   Jib, cantilever

FIG. 55. Types of jib cranes. (*"Flow Directory."*)

FIG. 56. Monorail and hand-operated hoist used in maintenance shop of the Central Greyhound Lines, Inc., of New York. (*Cleveland Tramrail.*)

along the wall on rails similar in construction to the runway of a traveling bridge crane.

b. Monorails. For the movement of materials along a single plane, a monorail section will provide a smooth runway for the hoist. This is particularly effective when pickup and deposit areas for the beginning and end of machine operations are clearly marked and infrequently changed. Monorail sections are often used in the assembly of tractors and automobiles as short transfer sections from one area to another. An added advantage of the use of monorails is the holding of a small bank of heavy assemblies such as engines or car bodies.

c. Derricks. Various types of derricks and free-swinging booms are available for the overhead movement of materials within a limited area for outside handling. These devices service an area limited by the swing or extent of the boom. They are easily installed and put into operation. Their mobility makes them valuable for construction work and other duties of a temporary nature.

2. Materials Moved Longer Distances at Irregular Intervals

a. Monorail Conveyors. For the intermittent overhead movement of materials where greater distances within the plant are involved, the monorail conveyor with the numerous attachments and controls available for it provides a system of handling adapted to a wide variety of uses. For the small shop with limited weights to be lifted, a 3-inch I-beam rail is often adequate for the horizontal movement of the hoist whether operated by hand or by electricity. In larger installations, heavier hoists and electrically powered drives will handle greater loads at considerably more speed and for longer distances. Where a more extensive system is required, automatic controls may be set on each drive unit to take its load to any one of a number of different stations and discharge or carry it through a variety of processes. For closer operator control, telpher systems with the operator riding in a cab suspended from the overhead monorail permit the movement of one or a dozen individual carriers along the overhead monorail system.

The system recently installed at the Wire Rope Division, Jones & Laughlin Steel Corporation, Muncy, Pa., consists of a cab-operated monorail crane operating on a system of 18 monorails. This provides for complete off-the-floor movement of the 50 tons of wire received daily. This wire is received in coils averaging 150 pounds in weight. The coils are loaded into "boats" or frames with a 30-cubic-foot capacity which hold over 4,000 pounds of wire. The crane operator picks up these boats of wire and stores them in the warehouse under one of the 18 rails extending the length of the warehouse.

With this system, one man, the crane operator, takes care of the handling and movement of coils from the loading dock, through the warehouse, to the winding machines. The design of the new warehouse

FIG. 57. At the Grand Rapids, Mich., plant of the Nash-Kelvinator Corporation, 5-ton packages of sheet steel are carried to the warehouse with this telpher monorail system. (*Cleveland Tramrail.*)

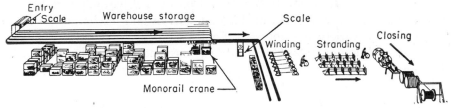

FIG. 58. Diagram of wire-handling system at Wire Rope Division of Jones & Laughlin Steel Corporation. (*American Monorail Company.*)

area has made available for production over 20,000 square feet of space formerly used for stock piling wire. The discontinuance of manual lifting of coils has also improved the plant's safety record.[1]

[1] Novel Wire Handling, *Modern Materials Handling*, May, 1948, p. 32.

A simpler system was used to solve the problem of moving bananas from rail cars to curing rooms at Badalement, Inc., of Detroit, Mich. A monorail system with individually controlled battery-powered carriers

FIG. 59. "Boatload" of wire coils is carried to assigned storage place in the warehouse by operator in overhead carrier. (*American Monorail Company.*)

moves the bananas in long trains, each of which is operated separately. This power system has the advantage of greater safety for the operators standing on the wet floors. An antenna safety arm at the front of the train automatically stops it if it overtakes a slower train.[2]

b. Overhead Skid Plant. Another example of overhead handling in one plane is provided by the overhead log skidding plant. This consists of

[2] *Ibid.*

head and tail supports with a track rope and a carrying line. Logs may be skidded on the ground or suspended in the air. Bunching lines permit a number of logs to be carried along at one time.

3. Continuous Overhead Movement of Materials for Longer Distances

a. Trolley Conveyors. Where large quantities of materials must be moved at a regular rate, a fixed path is often the most economical. Trolley conveyors provide such a path along with wide flexibility both of vertical and horizontal movement. The placing of trolley hangers on the chain makes it possible to provide a nearly continuous movement regardless of the size, shape, or nature of the product being moved. Materials can also be run through various processes without any extra handling. Even dipping operations such as bonderizing, degreasing, plating, or dip painting can be performed with this system. The same items can then be carried through paint spray and drying ovens as required.

In addition to the movement of materials, the trolley conveyor also permits the use of overhead space for storage of materials in process. At the Mengel plant in Louisville, Ky., large stocks of furniture in process are kept on the 8,000 feet of trolley conveyor which serves as the moving and storage system of the plant.

This continuous movement is of special value where objectionable processes are involved. Degreasing operations, either dip or vapor processes, benefit greatly from this characteristic of the system. Sandblast or automatic spray painting of parts difficult to handle may be accomplished with trolley conveyors. Often, free-swiveling carriers are used which constantly rotate the parts to ensure a more uniform treatment. By lowering the conveyor tracks, materials may be dipped without any manual handling. This system also provides rigid control over the duration of dipping, draining, drying, and subsequent operations.

This continuous movement of materials by an overhead system has made it possible for many a company to overcome the disadvantages of poor or inefficient layout. One large automobile plant consists of a number of factory buildings built at various times in its development. The engine plant is separated from the final assembly plant by a main highway and the body plant is separated from the other plants by a four-track railroad. Despite these disadvantages, continuous and uninterrupted flow of materials is obtained with an extensive system of trolley conveyors.

b. Belt Conveyors. Another system for the overhead movement of materials is where regular fixed-path devices are mounted overhead. Belt conveyors and roller conveyors are used separately or with each other. Belt conveyors are often used for the movement of bulk materials, and are located above the ordinary working height to form an overhead handling system.

4. Combination of Continuous and Irregular Overhead Movement of Materials

a. Power-and-free Conveyor System. Sometimes it is necessary to remove loads from the continuously moving trolleys of the trolley conveyor.

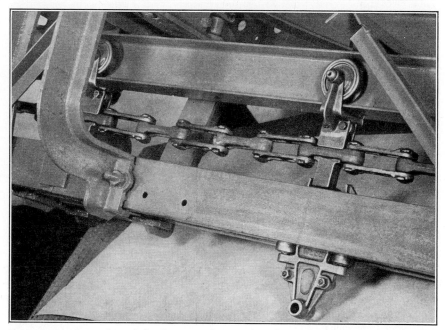

FIG. 60. Load is released for free travel as pusher dogs of trolley chain are raised. (*Jervis B. Webb Company.*)

In order to accomplish this without taking the item off the conveyor, a power-and-free system has been devised. In this system, the load trolleys run on a special monorail track. Pusher dogs extending down from the power trolley engage the arms of the load carriers and pull them along with the system. Switch track connections or vertical bends in the trolley system releases the load trolleys for free monorail movement.

5. Overhead Movement of Materials in Two Planes

The monorail and trolley systems just described provide for a continuous or intermittent overhead movement of materials in a single plane only. This movement of materials along a single line has many advantages, but it is not sufficient where it is necessary to provide lifting service and horizontal movement over a complete working area. This complete coverage requires a sidewise movement as well as the forward movement already described.

a. Traveling Bridge Cranes. Two-plane overhead movement within factory areas means essentially the use of traveling bridge cranes. In fact, in many monorail systems the necessity for sidewise movement has

Fig. 61. This traveling bridge crane is floor controlled, electrically driven, and has a special low-headroom construction for operating under low ceilings. (*The Louden Machinery Company.*)

led to the use of transfer bridges to provide a more complete overhead coverage. Sometimes it is difficult to say whether a specific system is a monorail system with transfer bridges or a small capacity system of overhead traveling bridge cranes with monorail attachments.

The simplest bridge crane may consist of a single underslung I beam upon which a hoist (hand, air, or electrically operated) may be moved back and forth. The crane may be pushed by hand or propelled by an electric tractive unit. Heavier duty bridge cranes are divided into classes according to the type of service demand to be made on them. These service duty classifications are: [3]

[3] R. J. Wadd and F. M. Blum, "Selecting Electric Traveling Crane Equipment for Service Performance," paper presented to Materials Handling Conference at Westinghouse Electric Corporation.

Class I. Stand-by duty (powerhouse, motor room, etc.). Slow speeds and occasional use characterizes this type. The maximum demand for full-load lifts per hour equals 2 to 5.

Class II. Light duty (machine shops, etc.). Moderate speeds and infrequent lifts. Maximum demand for full loads per hour equals 5 to 10.

Class III. Moderate duty (light foundry, etc.). Average speeds and intermediate lifts. Maximum demand for full-load lifts per hour equals 10 to 20.

FIG. 62. Gantry crane in which hoist, trolley, and crane controls are integral and pendant from hoist. (*The Louden Machinery Company.*)

Class IV. Constant duty (heavy foundry, production lines, etc.). Fast constant operation with sustained service requirements. Maximum demand for full-load lifts per hour equals 20 to 40.

Class V. Severe duty (magnet, grab bucket, stock yard, etc.). Fast or extra speeds with steady use include rugged construction for maximum operating conditions. Maximum demand for full-load lifts per hour equals 40 to 80.

b. Gantry Cranes. For outdoor overhead movement of materials the gantry crane performs the same function as the traveling bridge crane where elevated runways are available. The gantry legs rest on wheels which run on steel tracks. For use alongside buildings such as on docks

FIG. 63. Single-leg gantry crane used to load fabricated steel sections from temporary storage. (*The Louden Machinery Company.*)

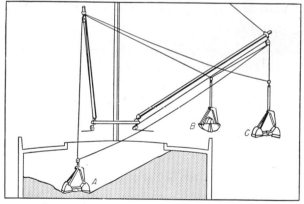

FIG. 64. "Burtoning." Position *A*—empty bucket ready to close on cargo material. Position *B*—loaded bucket being swung from hatch to hopper. Position *C*—bucket being dumped automatically, by man on hopper platform, or by trip line to signal man on deck. (*Blaw-Knox Company.*)

and wharves, a semigantry is often used. This type has a single gantry leg with the other end of the bridge resting on an elevated runway alongside the building. The semigantry is also used inside factory buildings to provide an auxiliary service for a larger traveling bridge crane. The revolving gantry, described more completely in Chap. 9, also provides for overhead

Fig. 65. Types of trestles used to support ropeways over long distances. (*British Ropeway Engineering Company, Ltd.*)

handling of a wide variety of materials. It is used particularly in shipbuilding and around dock and wharf areas.

c. Burtoning. The control of a bucket or sling supported at the end of a cable suspended from two points provides for more rigid control over its path. This is accomplished by the ship's gear with two swinging booms. The same system is used with one cable suspended from the end of the ship's boom and the other suspended from a pulley on the side of a building on the dock or from some other elevated point on shore. By the two winches simultaneously reeling out and taking in, the cargo is unloaded from ship to shore.

d. Drag Scrapers. Complete coverage of an outside area for the movement of bulk materials is often accomplished by means of traveling slings and drag scrapers. Powered from a fixed-base winch, the drag scraper is an inexpensive device, easy and quick to set up, and will move large quantities economically. These characteristics make it particularly useful for temporary locations or where considerable flexibility is required.

FIG. 66. Cableway serving mine tip. (*British Ropeway Engineering Company, Ltd.*)

6. Inter-plant Movement of Materials by Overhead Transport

The movement of materials from one plant or from one working site to another is often accomplished with overhead handling equipment. Where surface irregularity or uneven terrain is to be covered, this may be the only practicable means of transport. In southern India, a ropeway 9 miles in length replaced a 20-mile mountain road which was often impassable. In Sweden, a ropeway has been built over 60 miles in length. Other installations have provided capacities of 500 tons per hour by a single plant.

a. Cableways. These systems cover a site in one span and are provided with means for hoisting and lowering the load as well as transporting it. They have been built to carry unit loads up to 30 tons. Hoisting speeds are provided of 100 to 400 feet per minute with running speeds on the cable of 400 to 2,000 feet per minute. By mounting the tail tower on a radial track a wide area can be covered.

b. Drag Scrapers. These units are similar in construction to cableways. Power and movement of the scraper units are derived from a fixed-position winch or hoist and are delivered through a head mast. The tail tower may be fixed but is more often mounted on either a straight or a

Fig. 67. Ropeway handles timber for paper mill. (*British Ropeway Engineering Company, Ltd.*)

circular track for greater area coverage. They are commonly used for large coal-storage dumps.

c. Ropeways. This equipment is used for overhead transport of materials where greater distances are involved. Ropeways consist primarily of cars, platforms, grabs or cages operating on cables supported at regular intervals by sheaves mounted on towers or pylons. Loading and unloading may be manual or automatic and will vary according to the materials being transported and the type of operations involved. The general types of ropeways are:

Monocable systems. These systems have one rope which sustains the load and propels it. Because of this double duty the system is suitable only for light loads and small hourly capacities. They are also limited in gradient unless special gripping carriages are provided (Fig. 68).

Bicable systems. In these systems one cable is used for propelling the load and another cable is used as a rail upon which the cars travel. They

Fig. 68. Monocable type of ropeway. (*British Ropeway Engineering Company, Ltd.*)

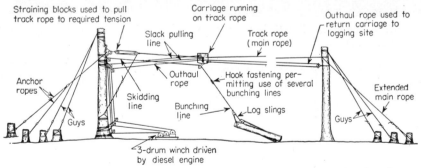

Fig. 69. Diagrammatic arrangement of overhead skidding plant employed in logging operations. (*British Ropeway Engineering Company, Ltd.*)

are used for heavy-capacity long-length installations and may be operated at steep inclines (Fig. 69).

Double-track systems. The double-track system uses four-wheel carriers running on a pair of supporting cables for tracks. Another cable tows the carriers along. Carrying and return runs are located above each other or side by side.

Shuttle system. This system carries buckets or cars to a discharge point and returns, operating in the manner of a balanced skip hoist.

Jigback systems. This type of system provides for the automatic discharge of the contents of the bucket when the direction of travel is reversed. Jigback systems are generally used to cover only short distances.

QUESTIONS

1. What are the advantages of moving materials overhead?
2. What equipment is used for movement within a limited area?
3. How are materials moved at irregular distances for longer distances?
4. What equipment is used for the continuous movement of materials overhead?
5. Where materials must be moved sidewise as well as in a straight line, what types of overhead handling equipment are used?
6. What is the power-and-free conveyor?
7. How are overhead bridge cranes classified?
8. What are the general types of ropeways?
9. Explain what is meant by the term "burtoning."

PROJECTS FOR FURTHER STUDY

1. What considerations determine the selection of specific types of overhead handling equipment selected for a specific installation?
2. What are the main parts and equipment involved in an installation of monorail conveyors? Of trolley conveyors? Of bridge cranes? (Refer to catalogues of manufacturers of each type.)
3. Build a working model to demonstrate the operation of burtoning.

CHAPTER 10

VERTICAL MOVEMENT OF MATERIALS

In considering the types of equipment to be employed for the vertical movement of materials, the nature of the movement involved is of prime importance. The situation may require straight vertical movement or vertical movement associated with some degree of horizontal movement.

1. Irregular Movement of Materials for Vertical Lift Only

This movement involves fixed or portable equipment in which there is either no horizontal movement associated as in elevators or in which such movement is of secondary importance as in stackers or tier machines.

a. Freight Elevators. The most common piece of equipment used for the vertical movement of materials, especially where a number of floors are involved, is the conventional freight elevator. It has the advantage of being able to serve a wide vertical range as well as providing quick service between floors spaced widely apart.

b. Dumb-waiters. Where lesser heights are involved and loads are limited and less frequent, a dumb-waiter may be more economical, at least in installation cost. This type of equipment may also be used to advantage where the basic plant movement system consists of various types of conveyors in which materials are moved a piece at a time.

c. Hydraulic Platforms. Where elevation of only a few feet is needed, various types of hydraulic platforms are used. In one instance, the movement of trucks to another part of the plant where the floor level was 2 feet higher was accomplished in this way. Difficulties in loading caused by variations in the height of truck beds may be overcome by adjustable ramps which may raise the truck to the dock level or may adjust the dock level to the truck-bed height. Hydraulic sections may be used to raise a part to an overhead fixture or suspended assembly without manual lifting being required. They are often used to provide an adjustable surface for feeding sheets to a press.

d. Skip Hoists. In the movement of bulk materials, especially where considerable vertical distance is involved, various types of skip hoists are used. These are found in plants where loose-flowing materials must be raised to bins or cupolas. These consist of a bucket or car moving on

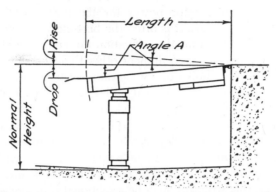

FIG. 70. Hydraulic loading platform adjusts to the height of the truck bed. The maximum angle permissible for the dock is determined by the clearance of the equipment. Dock must be long enough to get angle *A* as flat as required for clearance. (*Modern Materials Handling.*)

FIG. 71. Types of portable elevators. (*a*) Four-post stacker may be used as a portable elevator or a between-floor lift. (*b*) Lightweight hand-operated unit. (*Lewis-Shepard Products, Inc.*)

steeply inclined rails. A rope or chain attached to a sprocket or drum at the head end provides motor power for the unit. For high lifts and lumpy or abrasive materials, it is often the best elevating medium.

e. Fixed-base Hoists. For the elevation to considerable heights of various types of materials in equipment other than the skip buckets mentioned above, fixed-base hoists of a wide range of types and capacities are available. The cable runs over a head pulley at the top of the supporting structure. This may consist of a derrick or boom which is movable, in which case horizontal movement within the arc of the swinging member is provided. From the head pulley on a fixed support the cable is generally attached to a platform or cage upon which or within which the load, material, or personnel is carried. For construction jobs and other temporary installations, this structure may be a sectional frame easily assembled to the desired height.

f. Mobile Elevators. For very limited elevation of materials, mobile elevators are used. These may be hand operated or powered with gasoline or electric motors. They come in a wide variety of platform sizes and of adjustable heights, including telescoping and nontelescoping types. Powered units often have dual controls to permit their operation from the base of the machine or from the elevated platform. Operating units used for higher elevations often have a guard rail for the safety of the operator.

2. Regular Movement of Materials for Vertical Lift Only

In a plant having a conveyor system which serves as the central device for the continuous movement of materials, a special type of elevating mechanism is needed. If it is desirable to preserve this motion of the materials in process, some type of continuous vertical conveyance is necessary. The different types of equipment available for this purpose are differentiated primarily by the container or holding device on the elevating unit which consists of a belt or chain (one or more).

a. Package Lift. Barrels, large boxes, and other regularly shaped materials are generally moved vertically by various types of arm or tray lifts. The arm type is used for raising barrels, boxes, etc., from one floor to another or higher. Loading and unloading are generally automatic. The suspended tray type has a tray mounted between two chains in such a way as to retain a horizontal position. It may be loaded by hand or automatically. Irregularly shaped objects like bananas are transported vertically in slings suspended from bars between the two chains.

b. Bucket Elevators. Bulk materials are elevated by means of a series of small buckets or containers kept in constant motion by chains, belts, or cables. They are classified by the way in which the material is discharged.

The containing units are mounted on a belt or a single chain. More often they are suspended from two chains.

c. Enclosed Types. Bucket elevators are often completely enclosed in order to get a dustless operation or for other reasons. Other types depend for their action on an enclosed tube or area through which a skeletonized chain is drawn. In some instances a rope or cable with various types of

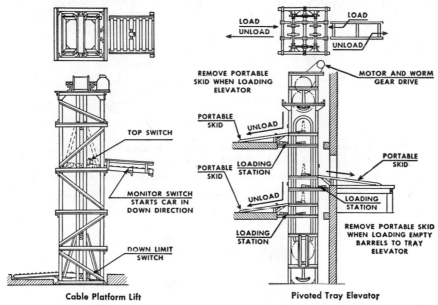

Cable Platform Lift   **Pivoted Tray Elevator**

FIG. 72. Two types of elevating units. (*a*) Cable platform lift; (*b*) pivoted tray elevator. (*Samuel Olsen Manufacturing Company, Inc.*)

buttons or flights or a spiral cable may be employed; the purpose of all these devices is to achieve vertical movement through induced flow of the materials.

3. Irregular Vertical Movement of Materials with Associated Horizontal Movement

Most vertical movement is associated with some type of horizontal movement. This combination in a large number of types of equipment often causes difficulty when one tries to classify them by purpose. It is necessary, then, to consider the predominant function performed by each individual type and classify it on that basis.

a. Hoists. Vertical movement of materials within this range is accomplished by means of hoists. The selection of the particular type for each installation will depend upon the weight to be lifted, the frequency

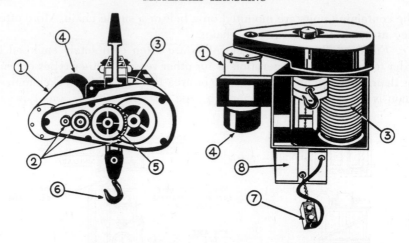

1. Electric Motor   2. Gear Train   3. Drum & Cable   4. Motor Brake   5. Load Brake   6. Hook   7. Control   8. Control Panel

FIG. 73. Main components of electric hoist. (*Modern Materials Handling.*)

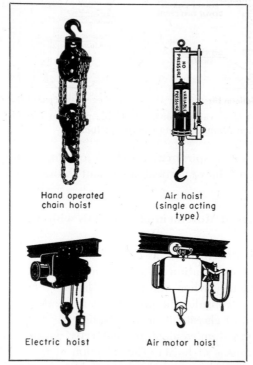

FIG. 74. Types of hoists. (*Modern Materials Handling.*)

of the lift, and special requirements for care and ease in handling. Attention will also be given to special operating conditions, such as close headroom, explosive atmospheric conditions, and the type of horizontal movement involved.

Where limited weights are to be moved vertically, a number of types of hand chain hoist may be used. These are used primarily for infrequent

a   b

Fig. 75. Types of derricks. (a) Stiff leg; (b) guy. (*American Hoist & Derrick Company.*)

lifts where the volume of work does not warrant the larger investment of a power hoist. They are also used where slow lifting or careful positioning is required.

Electrically operated hoists may be used for the fast vertical movement of light materials or for the lifting of large and extremely heavy components or assemblies. These hoists may be operated at close hand or from a remote control point. These control points may be located integrally with the hoisting unit or in a central control point such as the cab of a telpher monorail system or a cab-controlled traveling bridge crane.

Where potential explosive conditions exist, air-operated hoists are often used for this vertical movement. The ability of this type of equipment to take heavy overloads without injury or to permit delicate hoisting control makes it adaptable to many uses, particularly in foundries or hotdip processing operations.

b. Equipment for Horizontal Movement. Hoists will generally be used with some other type of equipment to provide horizontal movement. As the purpose is to raise an item or materials to an easier handling height, this other equipment will usually be in the nature of overhead handling

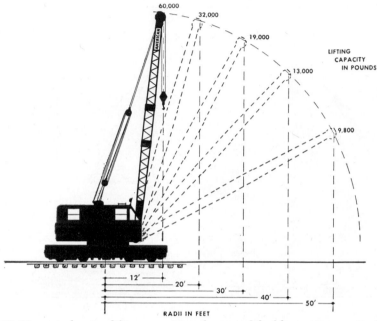

Fig. 76. Diagram showing lifting capacities of one model of locomotive crane. Actual work being performed must be taken into consideration when computing stability ratings. (*American Hoist & Derrick Company.*)

(see Chap. 8). Movement along a single line will be provided by a monorail, while a broader area will be served by a traveling bridge crane. Jib cranes will provide this movement for a restricted area.

c. Derricks and Booms. The area covered by the arc or traverse of a boom adds considerable horizontal movement to the lifting function and in addition both functions can be performed at the same time. The amount which may be lifted and transported over this distance is limited by the strength of the boom and cable and the reinforcement of the unit against tipping. This latter characteristic also limits the distance from the base of the boom at which weights can be lifted.

Stiff-leg derricks are supported by structural members extending from and supporting the mast. They can cover an arc of 270 degrees. Guy derricks are supported by guy wires in the same way, but do not have such a wide arc. Free-swinging booms of the same type are a common fixture on ships for unloading of materials in slings. Closer control over swing of materials while lifting is achieved with the system called "burtoning" which suspends the load between two points. Alternate slackening and

a   b

c   d

FIG. 77. Supporting structures for revolving cranes. (a) Elevated fixed base; (b) barge-mounted unit with a capacity of 75 tons at 70 feet; (c) gantry-mounted unit outfitting a Liberty ship at a Gulf Coast shipyard; (d) locomotive-type revolver uses special grapple to handle pulp logs. (*American Hoist & Derrick Company.*)

tightening of the lines provides wide horizontal movement from ship to shore. Another type, the column derrick, supports the weight from the end of the boom by the strength of a revolving column. This gives it a 360-degree traverse.

d. Revolving Cranes. The complete traverse offered by revolving units makes them an efficient mechanism for the rapid horizontal and vertical movement of materials, both in large units and of bulk materials. The fixed-column revolver, for example, is often used for unloading of ships and barges at a fixed station. Revolving cranes may be mounted on barges for added flexibility in dock operations. They are also mounted on a traveling gantry frame to extend the scope of its operations. For even greater flexibility, if for a smaller capacity, they may be mounted on a rubber-tired truck frame.

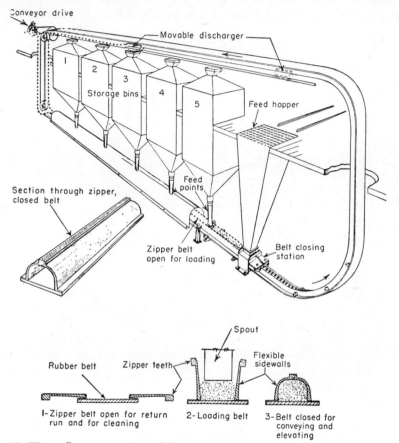

Fig. 78. "Zipper" conveyor is used for movement of fragile materials. (*Stephens-Adamson Manufacturing Company.*)

4. Continuous Vertical Movement with Associated Horizontal Movement

In many modern mass-production plants a conveyor system will be the chief means of movement of materials. Any changes in elevation, whether raising or lowering, is accomplished by the equipment providing for vertical or inclined movement. With the exception of gravity units and powered roller conveyors, the equipment described in Chap. 8 can provide this elevation.

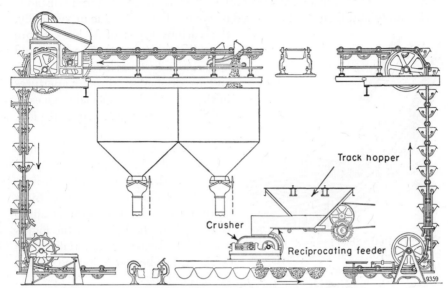

Fig. 79. Diagram showing typical Peck Carrier installation and general arrangement of mechanism. Any combination of horizontal, vertical, or angular runs in a single vertical plane can be used. (*Link-Belt Company.*)

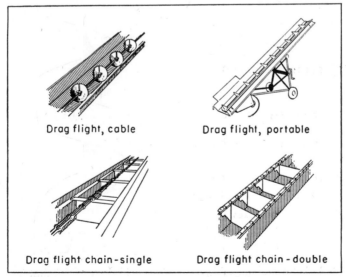

Fig. 80. Drag-flight scraper conveyor used for elevating bulk materials. (*"Flow Directory."*)

a. V-bucket Conveyors. Where bulk materials are carried some distance horizontally and then must be raised or lowered at an incline or vertically,

the various types of V buckets are commonly employed. These are fed automatically from overhead chutes and are discharged through apertures in the trough or by special devices to tip the buckets where required (Fig. 79).

b. Flight Conveyors. Bulk materials may also be moved up steep inclines by dragging along a trough with transverse flights pulled by a chain or a cable. The angle of climb is limited by the height of the flights and the tendency of materials to fall backward when the incline is too steep (Fig. 80).

Fig. 81. Reversible inclined pusher-bar conveyor. (*Modern Materials Handling, September,* 1948, *p.* 22.)

c. Push-bar Conveyors. For other materials of larger size, similar dragging action is accomplished by transverse bars to drag the materials up an incline. The carrying surface must be smooth (metal or hardwood)

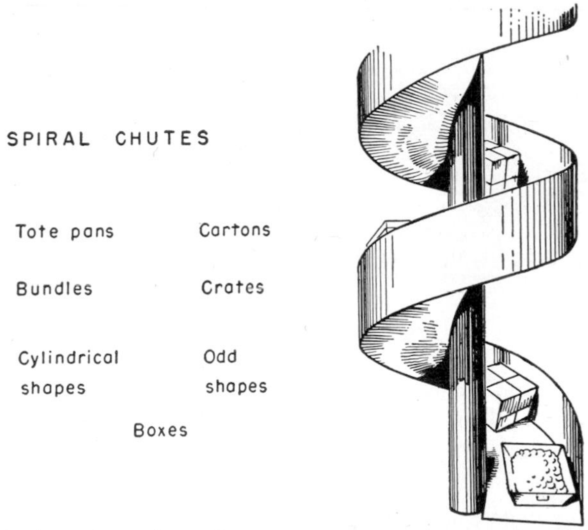

SPIRAL CHUTES

Tote pans　　　Cartons

Bundles　　　Crates

Cylindrical　　Odd
shapes　　　　shapes

Boxes

Fig. 82. Spiral chutes are adaptable to use in a wide range of industries. Because of pitch required there is more chance of breakage and spillage from open-top containers. (*Logan Company.*)

and the objects so moved must be of regular shape and free of projections and rough surfaces at least on the underside. These bars are generally carried along by two chains powered from sprockets on a common head-drive pulley (Fig. 81).

d. *Solid-surface Lowering Devices.* The utilization of gravity makes the lowering of materials easier and more economical than raising them. The chute, both straight and spiral, has many adaptations in this respect both for free-flowing bulk materials and for packaged items. Where more control is desired for the lowering of packages, belt conveyors are used.

FIG. 83. Spiral roller conveyor used with switches to provide distributing line for cartons. (*Standard Conveyor Company.*)

By means of the Spiramatic classifier, distribution may be made from the lowering device to a number of alternate conveyor routes (Fig. 255).

e. *Roller and Wheel Lowering Devices.* For the lowering of heavier boxes and regular-shaped units, roller and wheel conveyors are used. Straight runs are employed for limited heights; spiral systems are used for greater heights such as several stories. These units will also be used for the transfer of heavy metal rolls or coils. The rate of incline will be limited by the weight of the materials being lowered.

5. Combined Horizontal and Vertical Movement with Mobile Units

Increased emphasis upon utilization of the cube space available for storage of materials has widened the application of the many mobile units available for the elevating of packages, bags, bales, and bulk materials. The provision of fixed overhead handling facilities is fairly expensive and requires a large initial capital outlay which is justified only for a rapid turnover of materials within limited areas. The alternative is a mobile lifting unit of the capacity and type desired.

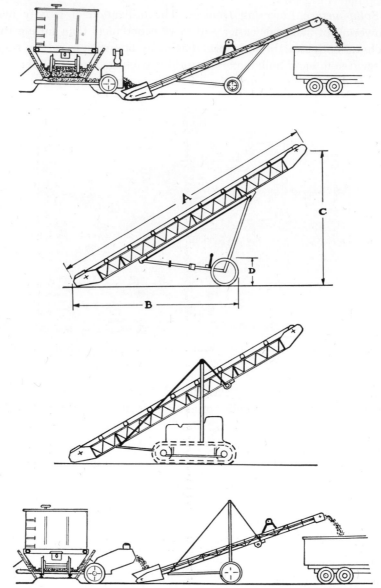

FIG. 84. Types of portable belt-conveyor units. (*George Haiss Manufacturing Company.*)

a. Portable Belt Conveyors. Various types of portable belt conveyors, used for elevating of packages and bulk materials alike, have found wide use in the loading of transport equipment and for the high stacking of bags, cartons, etc. For steeper inclines, the belt may be equipped with cleats. It is often used as a booster unit to regain elevation on a system of gravity wheel or roller conveyors (Fig. 84).

b. Portable Flight Conveyors. This type of equipment is used for the loading of coal and similar materials on trucks and rail cars. The portable car unloader consists of a flight conveyor for elevating combined with a belt conveyor which pulls the material from under the car being unloaded (Fig. 85).

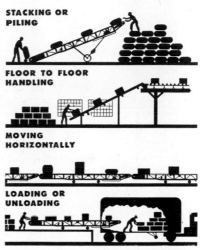

c. Portable Bucket Conveyors. These conveyors, used primarily for loading of bulk materials into trucks and rail cars, elevate at a much steeper angle and have a higher capacity than flight conveyors. This type of conveyor is wheel-mounted and is pushed by hand (for the smaller units) or moved by its own power (for the larger units).

d. Portable Elevating Tables. The positioning of heavy materials to a machine is often solved by means of elevating tables, most of which are

Fig. 85. Uses of portable belt conveyors. (*A. B. Farquhar Company.*)

raised and lowered hydraulically. In the feeding of sheet steel to a press, for example, the table may be raised to maintain constant level of the feeding stock (Fig. 86).

e. Fork Lift and Skid Lift Trucks. Although these trucks are generally considered as equipment for horizontal movement primarily, their main use is to provide an elevating device for materials. This equipment is an effective lifting unit for the high stacking of pallets and skids. At the warehouse of the Lazarus Company in Columbus, Ohio, elevators have been replaced by lift trucks for moving goods from the receiving (ground) to the storage (mezzanine) floor.

f. Mobile Cranes. This is the chief industrial equipment used for the combined vertical and horizontal movement of materials over nonfixed paths. From the industrial-handling standpoint, there are three main types of equipment.

Where crane service is infrequently used, a special crane arm or attachment is added to the elevating mechanism of a fork truck. A similar

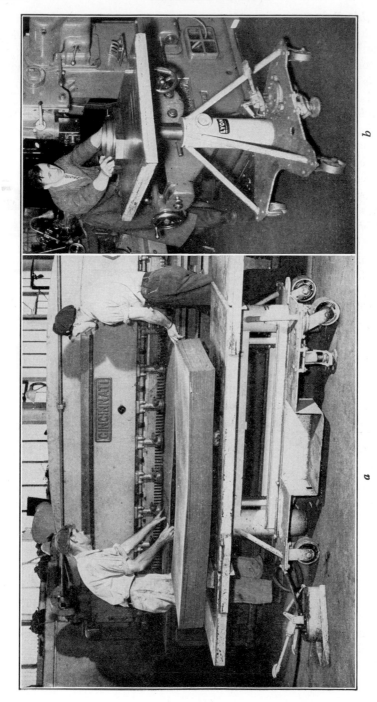

Fig. 86. Portable hydraulic elevating tables. (*a*) Transferring dies to machine tools; (*b*) feeding tables for steel sheets keeps stock at correct height for feeding to brake press. (*Lyon-Raymond Corporation.*)

FIG. 87. Industrial crane trucks. (*a*) Hand slewing-crane attachment handles 2,000 pounds at 42-inch outreach; (*b*) motorized slewing-crane truck. (*Automatic Transportation Company.*)

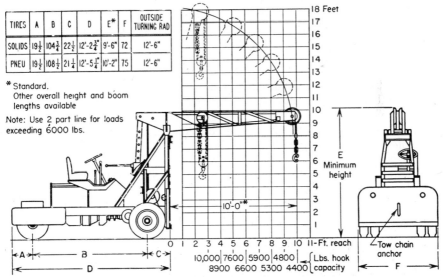

TIRES	A	B	C	D	E*	F	OUTSIDE TURNING RAD
SOLIDS	$19\frac{1}{2}$	$104\frac{1}{4}$	$22\frac{1}{2}$	$12'-2\frac{3}{4}''$	9'-6"	72	12'-6"
PNEU	$19\frac{1}{2}$	$108\frac{1}{2}$	$21\frac{1}{4}$	$12'-5\frac{1}{4}''$	10'-2"	75	12'-6"

* Standard.
Other overall height and boom lengths available

Note: Use 2 part line for loads exceeding 6000 lbs.

FIG. 88. Equipment and operating dimensions of new type of front-boom industrial crane. (*Silent Hoist & Crane Company.*)

device may be added to a portable elevator where even less horizontal movement is required.

Industrial trucks may also be built with a rigid boom for lifting or with a revolving boom on an industrial-truck frame with or without a platform.

Crane booms are also mounted on an industrial-truck chassis. The boom is fixed in some types and swinging in other types, either with hand or power slewing. The latter may also have a platform for self-loading of heavy materials.

Over-the-road truck-type cranes may have a swinging boom from a fixed mount on a truck frame or a revolving hoist and boom unit which provides a 360-degree coverage of the unit. They are commonly used in yard operations where steel or other heavy materials must be handled. Where conditions warrant, the same type of revolving unit may be mounted on caterpillar treads, in which case it is referred to as a "crawler" type.

QUESTIONS

1. Where a straight vertical lift is required for the irregular movement of materials, what type of equipment may be used?

2. What are some of the uses for hydraulic platforms?

3. What type of equipment may be used where a straight vertical lift is needed for the continuous movement of materials?

4. Discuss the various types of equipment which may be used in the irregular and the continuous vertical movement when horizontal movement is also required.

5. How can continuous movement of materials be obtained when both horizontal and vertical movement is required?

6. What mobile units can be used for both vertical and horizontal movement of materials?

7. Discuss the use of mobile units in obtaining both vertical and horizontal movement of free-flowing bulk materials.

PROJECTS FOR FURTHER STUDY

1. Write a report on hoists (see *Modern Materials Handling*, March, 1949).

2. Discuss the vertical movement of bulk materials.

3. Prepare a report on the combined vertical and horizontal movement of materials over nonfixed paths. Illustrate each use with an example taken from current literature. (If current technical magazines are not available, examples may be selected from other sections of this text.)

CHAPTER 11

HORIZONTAL MOVEMENT—
NONFIXED PATH

The movement of materials by a nonfixed path not only antedates fixed-path methods but also has a wider application. It is only within comparatively recent time that fixed-path equipment has been available or that there has been any need for it on a large scale. Fixed-path movement is a characteristic of a highly organized and standardized procedure. A substantial part of industrial, distributive, and other commercial activity requires more flexibility and movability of equipment for the movement of materials.

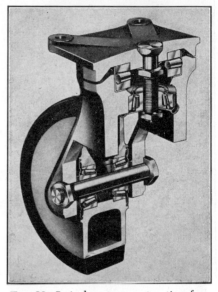

FIG. 89. Swivel caster construction features. (*Aerol Company, Inc.*)

1. Use of Wheels or Rollers

a. Wheels and Casters. Wheels for industrial hand trucks are made from 4 to 10 inches in diameter and from 1 to 3½ inches in width. Wheel size is determined by the maximum load to be carried and the condition of the floor surface. The larger wheel carries a greater weight and rolls over rough surfaces more easily. Wheels and their treads are made of wood, metal, fabric, plastic, and rubber. Selection is determined by the presence of chemicals or acids, danger of electrical sparks, noise of operation, ease of starting, and costs.

Casters increase the maneuverability of wheels. They consist of a caster frame attached to the truck by its top plate; the lower part or yoke supports the wheel and axle. The rigid caster permits movement only forward and backward; the swivel type permits movement in any direction. Casters are made of metal, wood, plastic, rubber, or fabric. Although casters are

Fig. 90. Some common types of wheels. (*a*) Semi-steel with roller bearing; (*b*) hard rubber tread composition resilient to water, oil, and acid; (*c*) macerated canvas phenolic resin impregnated composition; (*d*) soft rubber tread vulcanized on iron core; (*e*) natural rubber tread vulcanized on aluminum core; (*f*) floating hub reduces noise and vibration. (*The Bassick Company.*)

generally designed for use where complete flexibility of movement is desired, castered platforms or trailers are often run between tracks. One type, consisting of a grooved wheel, may be operated on an inverted angle-iron track.

FIG. 91. Long unwieldy boxes are rolled around easily with a Roll-a-lift under each end. Built-in hydraulic unit raises item off floor for necessary clearance. (*Skarnes Engineering & Supply, Inc.*)

b. Rollers. Although known more for their application in a fixed position on frames (roller conveyor), rollers are used in a number of other ways in the industrial movement of materials. A few lengths of gas pipe, for example, are often very handy in moving heavy pieces of machinery a short distance. Rollers may be mounted on platforms for ease in loading and unloading. In a Swedish foundry the platforms of a carrousel conveyor are so equipped for quick removal of molds after pouring. Trucks for handling of heavy dies may have rollers on the supporting bed. Motor trucks often have rollers set into the bed of the truck to expedite handling of pallet loads.

c. Crate-lifting Devices. One difficulty encountered with rollers and dollies is that of raising the object so they may be put underneath. This difficult has been overcome by the recent development of the Rol-a-lift. This device is designed to be used in pairs. Each unit consists of an in-built hydraulic jack to lift the box or machine off the floor. Full-swiveling casters then make it easy to push or manipulate the load to the desired position. Recently a 6,000-pound press was moved across the floor to a new location with an elapsed moving time of 10 minutes. This was the time from disconnecting the power source at the old location to the connection to another outlet at the new location.

2. One-, Two-, and Three-wheeled Devices

These devices are generally used to supplement the work of other equipment, although in a few instances they may be used as a prime transporting medium.

a. One-wheeled Devices. Where bulk materials have to be transported a short distance to constantly varying points of discharge, the wheelbarrow is still commonly used. Its principal use is in the construction industry where the site of application is frequently changed. It has become mechanized and is described as a powered wheelbarrow under three-wheeled devices.

b. Two-wheeled Hand Truck. This versatile handling device is light in weight, inexpensive, adapted to use within restricted or cramped areas, and is particularly useful where packaged units must be moved a short distance in small quantities at a variety of points. Its main advantage is its flexibility coupled with low initial investment and maintenance cost which make it valuable to the small business or installation.

There are two basic designs: in the Western pattern, the wheels are arranged on the inside of a straight frame; in the Eastern pattern, the wheels are placed outside the frame which is tapered to the bottom. Leg supports are usually provided on the side frames below the handles to permit resting the load. This type of truck (which carries its load at an angle) is also provided with one or two additional wheels to support heavy loads and one model is powered by a small gasoline motor.

c. Other Two-wheeled Devices. Hand carts are available in a wide variety of shapes and sizes for the carrying of special objects. The two-wheeled carboy truck has two prongs extending forward which support the arms or frame of a carboy, boxes, or special containers or tote pans

(Fig. 93). A two-wheeled pry truck has a steel nose which slides under a heavy box. It may be used in pairs to move heavy crates, etc., or may

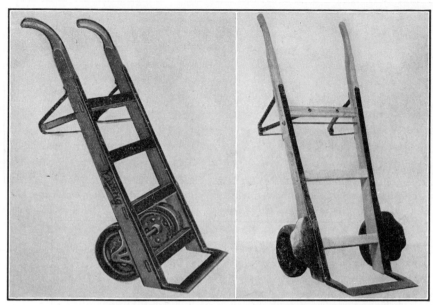

Fig. 92. Two-wheeled hand trucks. (*a*) Hardwood bag truck, Western style; (*b*) hardwood frame, general type, Eastern style. (*Nutting Truck and Caster Company.*)

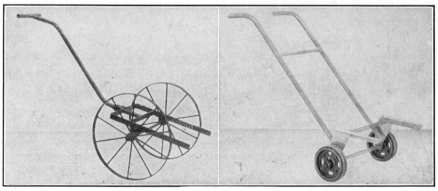

Fig. 93. Two common types of carboy truck. (*Nutting Truck and Caster Company.*)

be used to raise the load to permit other rollers or dollies to be put underneath. Hopper types are generally of a forward dumping variety.

Of a special type is the two-wheeled maneuvering unit or lift jack used in connection with semilive skids. These skids are supported by wheels or

casters at one end and metal legs at the other. The lift-jack unit slips
under the dead end of the skid and the leverage attained raises the load

Fig. 94. End-dumping hopper trucks. (*Nutting Truck and Caster Company.*)

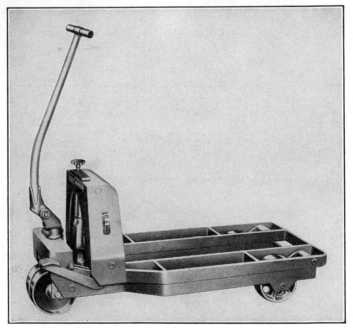

Fig. 95. Jack lift is used to move semilive skids. (*Lewis-Shepard Products, Inc.*)

off the floor when the handle is moved from a vertical to a near-horizontal
or pulling position.

d. Three-wheeled Devices. The mechanized wheelbarrow, powered
with a gasoline engine, has up to four times the capacity of the ordinary

FIG. 96. Mechanized wheelbarrow provides adaptable prime mover. (*Bell Aircraft Corporation.*)

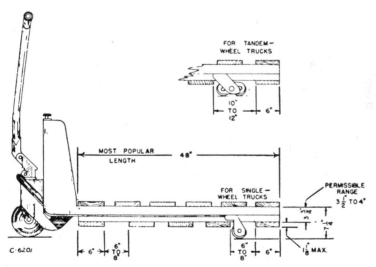

FIG. 97. Hand-operated fork truck for use with pallets. Bottom face of pallets must have boards spaced to take wheels of truck. (*Lewis-Shepard Products, Inc.*)

wheelbarrow. One such unit has been adapted to use with a platform as a half-ton platform truck and with a scraper on the front as a "baby" bulldozer.

There are many types of industrial powered and hand trucks with three wheels as well as the more common four-wheeled models. These include tractors, hand-operated hydraulic and lever-type hand lift trucks, powered hand trucks, and even the riding-type fork lift and platform lift truck. The main advantage is the increased maneuverability of the three-wheeled model. Usually the third wheel, located on the opposite end of the lifting or load-supporting end, is the steering wheel only. In some models, however, the third wheel is also a drive wheel, in which case the wheel is wider or may consist of two wheels on either side of the supporting column which, nevertheless, turn as one. This characteristic is carried over into one type of commercial vehicle, manufactured in England, which is used for over-the-road transportation and delivery in congested areas.

3. Four- and Five-wheeled Nonpowered Devices

a. Hand Truck. The standard unit in the group used for the movement of materials is the four-wheeled cart or hand truck. These are intended to be pulled or pushed by hand where relatively light loads are handled and where the distance is fairly restricted. Variations within the group are mainly by type of superstructure, the arrangement of wheels, use of swivel or fixed wheels, and the method employed for steering.

b. Trailers. The adaptation of the four-wheeled cart to use as an industrial trailer involves primarily the method of steering and guiding. Also, where power devices are to be used for forward motion, heavier loads may be carried and, thus, a heavier trailer will be needed. Variations will be the same as in the regular four-wheeled truck. The development of tractor-trailer trains for movement of materials over greater distances has given impetus to the further development of trailers of various types.

c. Wheeled Racks and Containers. Special handling problems involving the movement of various types of materials and component parts over nonfixed routes has led to the development of a wide variety of other four-wheeled equipment. Racks on wheels are used to provide a large number of small or irregular parts within easy reaching distance of the assembler or the machinist performing the next operation on them. One type provides a movable tier for tote pans containing small parts. Another type supports gears on small pegs as they are moved to succeeding operations.

Wheeled containers will vary from canvas bags supported on a metal frame for the handling of rags and clothing to wood or metal bodies for the movement of everything from bread dough to rough castings. They may be of a fixed type or arranged for forward or sidewise dumping of their contents.

d. Low-lift Trucks. This group of trucks is used for the horizontal movement of pallets and skids. It is characterized by the placing of the load-bearing wheels under the load to be carried. Skid and platform types,

FIG. 98. Tractor tows a trailer-train load of rolls of newsprint from ship wharf to warehouse at the Commercial Marine Terminal, Detroit. (*Clark Equipment Company.*)

then, are limited in wheel size by the height of the skid. The pallet type is limited in wheel size by the 3½-inch space between the top and bottom of the pallet. Proper spacing of the bottom boards of the pallet is also necessary (Fig. 99).

The load is lifted up to 3 inches from the floor to provide clearance while in transit. This lift is accomplished by mechanical action in some models and by hydraulic action in others. The latter is activated by action of the guiding arm or by a conveniently located foot pedal. The load is lowered by a foot release or a handle release (Fig. 100).

e. High-lift Trucks. This group also is characterized by the placing of the load-bearing wheels under the load to be carried and was developed in response to the demand for simple hand-operated units to provide a higher lift. For that reason their primary function is to elevate materials

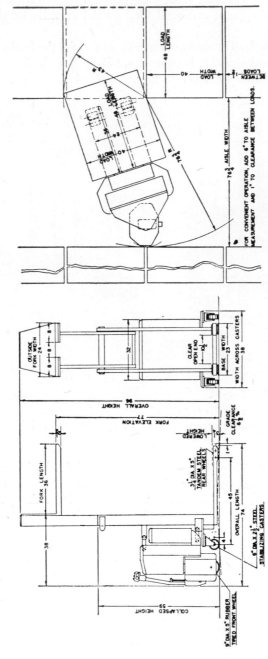

Fig. 99. Operating measurements of hand power-operated fork lift truck shows its flexibility of movement in restricted areas. (*Lewis-Shepard Products, Inc.*)

rather than any horizontal movement that may be involved. They, therefore, serve as portable elevators. They are raised hydraulically or by cable or chain winch. (See also high-lift power trucks.)

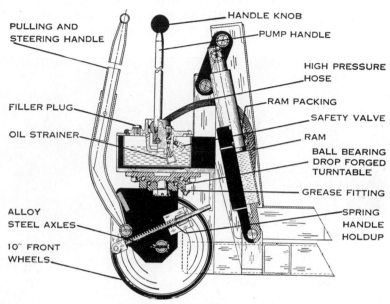

FIG. 100. Diagram showing operation of hydraulic lift mechanism of nonpowered hand platform truck. (*Service Caster & Truck Corporation.*)

4. Four-wheeled Powered Devices, Nonlift

This group is designed primarily for the powered movement of materials where some other means of loading or unloading is employed. This means, generally, the loading by hand of each item to be transported. Its main economy is in the speed with which the materials may be moved to a distant destination. In point of development this is the oldest type of powered industrial-handling equipment for non-fixed-path movement.

a. Baggage Trucks. The development of baggage trucks at the turn of the twentieth century revolutionized the handling of baggage and opened up a new industry. They are still being used advantageously where limited amounts of materials are to be transported a considerable distance and where loads are delivered to a number of different points.

This type of truck is electric powered with frames at each end. It is built with a high platform with the motor mounted underneath or with a drop-center platform with the motor under the end.

b. Burden-carrying Trucks. These are fixed-platform electric- or gasoline-powered trucks. They are loaded by hand, by cranes, or by other lifting equipment. They are of the walkie type, in which case the operator walks ahead of the unit, or of the driver-ride type. They are also commonly called "load carriers" (Fig. 101).

c. *Industrial Tractors.* Another unit is used primarily for the pulling of loads on trailers. Where considerable time may be lost by the loading of parts to the transporting vehicle, it is inadvisable to load directly to

FIG. 101. Powered load carrier where self-loading is not required. (*Lewis-Shepard Products, Inc.*)

the power unit. This is a violation of the principle of the prime unit (see page 28). It is more economical to tie up the time of the inexpensive trailers than to delay the movement of a much more expensive prime mover. Furthermore, movement of materials by fork lift truck is more expensive when the distance is more than approximately two hundred feet. In these places the rapid movement of loaded trailers within the industrial plant provides the most economical means of handling.

5. Four-wheeled Powered Devices, Limited-lift or Self-load Types

The main feature of this group of equipment is its ability to pick up or deposit a load without the need of other means of handling or additional equipment.

a. Fork Lift and Skid Lift Trucks. In both types of trucks the load-bearing wheels are generally under the load to be carried, although cantilever design hand trucks are available. These units are designed to be guided by an operator walking in front of the load and controlling its movement by the controls located in the handle. They are also referred

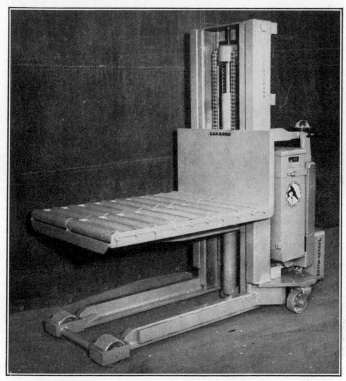

Fig. 102. Special form of platform truck has rollers to facilitate the loading of heavy dies. (*Lewis-Shepard Products, Inc.*)

to as "powerized walkie" or walking type. The extent of the lifting ability of the group is simply to permit automatic loading of the unit. These units will be powered by gasoline, electric, or gasoline-electric motors. Lifting will be by hydraulic pressure (hand pump or powered) or by take-off from the drive mechanism.

b. Side-loading Truck. A recent addition to the family of self-loading equipment is the Traveloader, which permits the handling of materials of long length by loading them from the side instead of from the front as in ordinary fork trucks. In addition to having this ability of picking up a load from the side, it is able to move the load back over the bed of the unit and rest it there while being moved to a new location (Fig. 104).

Fig. 103. Electric-powered hand truck easily moves large Dravo shipping unit from truck dock to warehouse area. (*Dravo Corporation.*)

Fig. 104. Side-loading unit loads long lengths with either fork-lift mechanism or crane attachment and rests burden on deck for long hauls. (*Lull Manufacturing Company.*)

c. Straddle Truck. Another self-loading device also used primarily for the handling of long lengths is the straddle truck. As the name implies, it is designed in such a way as to be able to straddle the load, grip it, raise it off the ground, and move it to a new location where it is lowered to the ground and the prime unit is thus moved away leaving the load

Fig. 105. Straddle truck handles long side members for automobile frames at the plant of A. O. Smith Corporation, Milwaukee. (*The Ross Carrier Company.*)

behind. Its main limitation of use is in the height to which the materials may be stacked. However, this objection may be overcome by the use of heavy-duty fork trucks along with the straddle trucks (Fig. 105).

This truck was developed primarily in the lumber industry. It has since been adapted to the handling of pipe, large crates, structural steel, and steel sheets. It is used also to handle unit loads of automobile frames at the A. O. Smith Corporation plant in Milwaukee and at the Lincoln Division of the Ford Motor Company. In the Second World War it became part of the standard equipment of the military services for the loading of ships. At one port the supporting arms were lengthened to permit one unit to pick up five or six loaded pallets at a time. In the pineapple industry, these trucks are used to remove the complete load of a semi-truck trailer in one handling operation. In the lumber industry, they are used in dry-kiln operations handling nearly 5,000 board feet per load.

d. *Container Dump Trucks.* Various types of bins and hoppers have been devised for the handling of bulk materials. One truck, the Dumpster,

FIG. 106. This self-loading and self-dumping unit can handle from 1½- to 10-ton loads of materials ranging from rock, coal, and garbage to chemicals loaded at 1500°F. (*Dempster Brothers, Inc.*)

uses a system of hydraulic arms to pick up a variety of specially designed containers. Release mechanisms permit the containers to be held aloft and the bottom opened for quick discharge of its contents. The ease with which the various types of containers may be picked up by the prime mover, emptied or deposited, has presented new lines of thinking for the executive in the moving of bulk material. In one rock quarry, for example, 27 container bodies are kept in constant motion with only 3 trucks in around-the-clock operations.

e. *Crane Trucks.* Crane trucks are used primarily in industrial handling as a portable elevating mechanism. They are discussed more fully in that connection in Chap. 9. As a self-loader, the crane truck provides a method of moving materials over a nonfixed path without the aid of other equipment, even when the materials being handled are of considerable size and weight. In this connection two distinct types of cranes should be noted. The first is a specially designed nonelevating platform truck with the crane elevating arm fixed at one end. It is thus able to load and unload heavy weights and carry them a considerable distance. This type is generally electrically powered. The second type is an ordinary mobile crane pulling behind it one or more trailers. The latter type is more commonly used for outdoor operations where weights up to 15 tons must be moved. In steel-supply houses particularly, it provides an expeditious means of assembling orders of a variety of heavy metal shapes.

6. Powered High-lift Units

This group has the ability not only to load and unload itself but to elevate its load and discharge or pick up at a high level. With the increased emphasis on high stacking of materials and the utilization of the cubic content or air rights of the warehouse or the factory, this has become one of the most important groups for the economical movement of materials on a non-fixed-path basis.

a. Source of Power. Fork lift trucks and platform or skid trucks are powered by gasoline engines or by electric motors. The latter derive their current from storage batteries which are carried with the unit. For continuous operation, spent batteries may be replaced with freshly charged units, and the machine immediately returned to use. Otherwise, the battery may be left in the machine while its vitality is being restored by a charging unit. As the electricity so consumed is taken in off-peak hours, the cost to the company of this energy source is very small.

Another type, the gasoline-electric truck, uses a gasoline engine to generate electricity for the battery from which the electric motor derives its power. This type is favored for continuous operation. Some types of portable elevators also use an electric motor which is plugged into a conventional power source.

Although the characteristics of gasoline-powered trucks and of electric-powered trucks make them applicable to many installations in common, the experience of the last few years has gradually evolved a list of certain conditions under which the use of one type has certain advantages over the use of the other.

The use of the gasoline-motor truck is advantageous under the following conditions:

1. Long hauls of over 300 feet. This involves sustained operation.
2. Intermittent operations where unit is operated only at intervals.
3. On rough surfaces because of larger wheels and soft rubber tires.

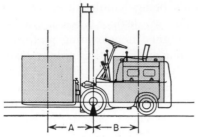

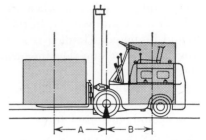

a. A load with its center of gravity *A* distance forward of the center line of the drive wheels, which is the fulcrum of a fork lift truck, must be counterbalanced with more than an equal weight with its center of gravity at the same distance, *B*, to the rear of the fulcrum point.

b. If the outward length of the load is increased without decreasing its weight, the now greater distance, *A*, requires additional counterbalancing weight in basic design in order to retain the maneuverability inherent in a short wheelbase; or, at the cost of increased turning radius and decreased maneuverability, the *B* distance must be extended in ratio to the increase in the *A* distance.

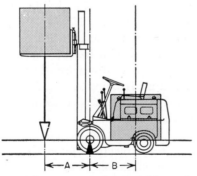

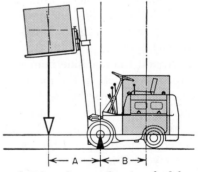

c. The capacity of a fork lift truck remains constant regardless of the raised height of the load as long as the uprights of the truck remain vertical and as long as the truck is not subjected to sudden starts and stops. Here again the counterbalancing load is more than equal in weight to the raised load and the distances *A* and *B* are the same.

d. When the uprights are tilted forward in positioning and depositing a raised load, the center of gravity is extended, the *A* distance increases and additional counterbalancing weight must be provided as in (*b*). In order to incorporate maximum margins of safety, designs should concentrate heaviest counterweighting at the rear of the truck with maximum *B* distances consistent with favorable turning radii.

Fig. 107. How fork truck capacity is rated. (*Clark Equipment Company.*)

4. Lower first cost.

5. High stacking operations involving sustained lifting operation.

6. Long steep inclines.

7. Plants at a distance from available electric service facilities.

8. Where fixed overhead costs are most important.

9. Outside operations subjected to weather of all kinds.

The use of electric-powered trucks is advantageous under the following conditions:

1. Short hauls with frequent stops.

2. Closed areas where fumes or noise are objectionable.

3. Where continuity of operation is extremely important.

4. Lower operating and maintenance cost.

5. Continuous use over long period of time.

6. Short stacking operations.

7. Ideal floor conditions free from long inclines.

8. Where variable costs are more important than fixed cost.

9. Maximum power application desired at beginning of operation.

b. Fork Lift and Skid Lift Trucks. The high-lift truck designed for use with skids and platforms generally has the load-bearing wheels under the load to be carried. The high-lift truck equipped with forks for the handling of pallets is built on the cantilever principle, in which the weight of the truck must overbalance the weight being lifted (Fig. 107). The lifting capacity of the truck is rated at a given number of pounds at a given number of inches from the fulcrum or balance point which is the center line of the front wheels. The height of the load does not affect this balance unless there are sudden stops or a change of direction is made with the load elevated.

c. Attachments. Although special purposes will often justify special types of fork trucks, in the main, these requirements will often be satisfied

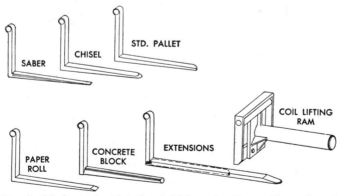

FIG. 108. Types of forks used with industrial lift trucks. (*Lewis-Shepard Products, Inc.*)

by means of standard units of the desired capacity and size and the later addition of special attachments. Attachments are very important in extending the use of the truck and making it more valuable to the user. In the handling of coils of wire or wide metal coils, the ram attachment is

PAPER SCOOP   RAM   CRANE

CLAMP-LIFT   SHOVEL   BRICK FORKS

ROTATING FORKS   PUSHER   PUL-PAC.

Fig. 109. Attachments and devices to expand the uses of industrial lift trucks. (*Clark Equipment Company.*)

most important. It is also used to move large unwieldy fabricated units. A hydraulic push frame enables the operator to push the pallet load off the tines of the fork. Another attachment, designed for use with a carrier sheet of corrugated cardboard in place of the pallet, grips the edge of the sheet to draw the load onto the tines of the truck. For handling long or outsize crates, extensions may be added to the conventional forks. A revolving head attachment permits the operator to pick up a pallet container of waste material, rotate it through a complete circle to dump it, and then return the empty container. In handling large paper rolls, a special scoop is provided to pick them up and place them on end or on their side as desired. Various types of clamps aid in the handling of a large number of crates or boxes.

For use as a crane, a large variety of standard attachments include fixed and swinging booms and lifting action from an overhead cable or by elevating the boom itself. In addition, various clamps may be combined with the crane attachment for lifting difficult objects. Scoops are used for the handling of bulk materials.

d. *Pallet Omission.* Although the pallet speeds up handling of material and permits higher stacking, it serves no purpose in itself. Therefore, considerable attention has been given to ways of retaining the benefits of palletizing while eliminating the pallets themselves.

For the handling of certain types of packaged items, wide sharp-tapered tines have had success in some instances. In the handling of brick and concrete blocks, three or four rows will support the rest of the load. By means of hydraulic side plates to each of the tines, the load is picked up and transported as a unit (see page 348).

QUESTIONS

1. Discuss the use of two-wheeled devices.
2. Explain the carrying characteristics of the various three-wheeled devices.
3. What types of four-wheeled nonpowered devices include a lifting action?
4. Outline the purposes for which nonlift four-wheeled powered devices are used.
5. What types of powered equipment are self-loaders?
6. What types of powered equipment are best suited to the movement of long lengths such as pipe, bar stock, or lumber?
7. Discuss the relative advantages of each type of power for high-lift trucks.
8. Discuss the differences in the various types of high-lift trucks.
9. How do attachments extend the usefulness of industrial lift trucks?

PROJECTS FOR FURTHER STUDY

1. Using the formula given in Fig. 107, check the rated capacities on various models of high-lift fork trucks. Use data from manufacturers' catalogues.
2. Prepare a report on wheels for industrial hand trucks.
3. Investigate the uses to which the "mechanized wheelbarrow" have been put.
4. Compare the classification of equipment (see 13.00 Industrial trucks) in the Appendix with the organization of this chapter.

CHAPTER 12

INDUSTRIAL STORAGE FACILITIES

A wide variety of auxiliary devices are provided for the handling and storage of industrial materials. The main function of these devices is to permit the higher stacking of materials, regardless of the shape, size,

Fig. 110. Storage shelves and bins mounted on wheels permit several rows to be installed in front of fixed units. Front rows are easily rolled aside for access to rear shelves. (*Acrow Engineers, Ltd.*)

weight, or fragility of the unit. Another purpose is to permit the handling of a large number of units together as a single load. This principle, commonly referred to as unit-load handling, is one of the most important developments in the reduction of handling costs within recent years. Still another purpose is to provide product protection while in storage or in transit.

1. Shelf, Bin, and Rack Devices

The multi-tier storage of small parts requires special shelving and racks for the economical utilization of storage space. Shelves and bins are commonly made of wood or of steel. In the latter case, they will generally be composed of standardized sections which may be easily dis-

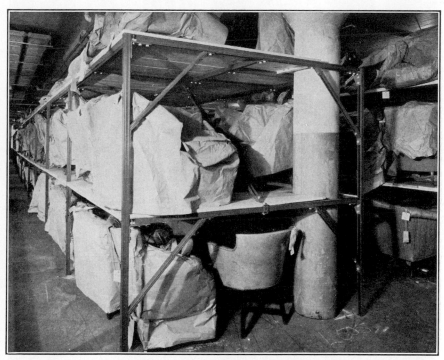

FIG. 111. Multi-tier storage of chairs made possible with racks made of standard sections at Marshall Field & Company, Chicago. (*Unistrut Products Company.*)

asscmbled and recombined for new storage requirements. One recent innovation for shelving has been the Flowstore which consists of shelves or bins mounted on rails laid in the floor. The units are mounted on ball-bearing wheels and may be moved aside easily to provide access to similar units located behind (Fig. 110).

Where multi-tier storage or handling of irregular-shaped objects is desired, some type of auxiliary support must often be provided. There are a number of metal systems available for the construction of these racks. Although details will differ from one company to another, in most instances these rack systems are composed of standardized units and assemblies which facilitate their installation for a specific purpose or

Fig. 112. Prefabricated pallet racks are designed for any length, height, aisle space, and load requirement. (*Equipment Manufacturing Company, Inc.*)

Fig. 113. A wide variety of shapes and sizes of materials are handled on pallets in the Philadelphia warehouse of Sears, Roebuck & Company. (*Unistrut Products Company.*)

their dismantling where changes in layout are later required. The small size of the supporting and separating sections reduces to a minimum the loss of space.

Where these racks are used for the storage of objects that are of less than pallet size, continuous surfaces or shelving are provided. Where pallets, skids, or standard-sized platforms are used, they may consist

Fig. 114. Small boxes are neatly stacked on shelves made of standard parts. Numbers refer to types of standard sections. (*Unistrut Products Company.*)

simply of tubular frames within which the palletized loads are stored (Fig. 114). Warehouses specializing in the long-term storage of household furniture often have a system of special racks for the storage of overstuffed furniture and divans which are packed first in a standard container for protection against deterioration while in storage.

2. Skid Handling Systems

The earliest container system devised for the unitized handling of materials is that which utilizes a wooden or metal support for a platform which is thus elevated slightly to provide floor clearance while in transit. The height of the skid provides ample clearance for a lifting platform with wheels of sufficient size for satisfactory use with available floor surfaces and floor materials.

The use of wood skids is most commonly associated with large crates and heavy wooden boxes to be handled by fork trucks and cranes. Various types of wood platforms are used, most of which have some type of iron band reinforcing around the edges. These are supported by metal legs at all four corners to provide a dead skid. Other types, called live skids, have wheels, castered or fixed bearing, under the two corners of

Fig. 115. Metal skid containers filled with small parts are stacked on top of each other with a hand-controlled electrically operated hoist and crane. (*The Louden Machinery Company.*)

one end. This is to enable an operator to lift the dead end on a small mobile jack and move the skid easily to another location. The same unit may also be moved by hand- or power-operated platform trucks. The platform, providing a load-bearing surface, may have mounted on it a wide variety of frames, boxes, or containers for handling of small parts.

The metal skid is used for the handling of heavier materials, such as castings and forgings, and where service demands are strenuous. It, too, consists of a single platform upon which individual parts may be placed. Smaller parts are carried in a container fixed to this base. For the handling of longer length materials, the container body may be replaced by upright supports on the sides or on the ends. These metal skid containers often have special reinforcing around the top to provide for the tiering and nesting of units on top of each other.

Fig. 116. Long lengths of pressed-steel shapes are stored five high in special containers at the Birmingham works of Fisher & Ludlow, Ltd. [*Mechanical Handling* (*London*).]

3. Pallet Handling Systems

a. Purpose. Pallets are used for a purpose. Although much has been written about the use of pallets, it is seldom that they can be considered by themselves as a method of handling. Their most effective use is as a part of a system which primarily involves the characteristics of unitized handling. If pallets are desired for use within the confines of a factory, the other types of handling systems of the plant must be considered. If they are needed for shipments to a distant customer, the economics of the customer's unloading costs as well as the handling equipment of the shipping agency must be brought into the picture. The purposes of a palletizing program are:

1. *To lower the cost of moving materials.* This is accomplished by moving a number of items at a time.

2. *To increase storage space.* If materials formerly stacked to a height of 3 feet can now be stacked 6 feet high, the cubic storage space has been doubled.

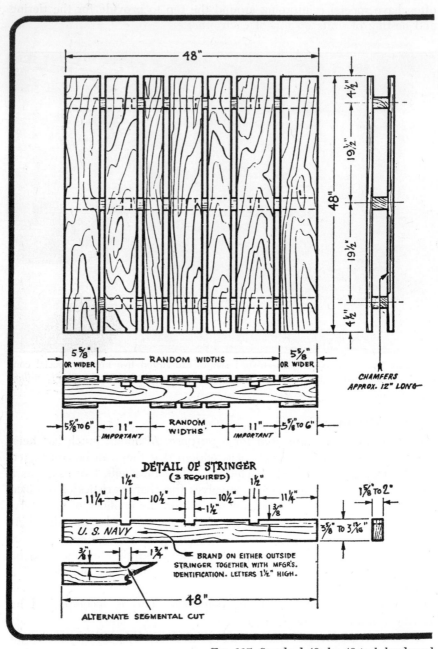

Fig. 117. Standard 48- by 48-inch hardwood

48" x 48" NAVY STANDARD HARDWOOD PALLET

NAILING

a. Use #6 screw gauge x $2\frac{1}{2}$" cement coated or chemically etched drive screw nails or #10 wire gauge x $2\frac{1}{2}$" cement coated or chemically etched annular ring (fetter ring) nails.

b. Boards 3-5/8" to $4\frac{1}{2}$" require 2 nails at each bearing point.
   4-3/4" to 6-3/4" " 3 " " " " " " .
   7" to 9" " 4 " " " " " " .
   9-1/8" to 11" " 5 " " " " " " .
   11-1/8" to 12" " 6 " " " " " " .

c. Drill deck boards if necessary to prevent splitting.

d. Stagger nails to prevent splitting.

e. Nailing thru notches not acceptable.

f. When a board exceeding 5" nominal width covers a notch, one less nail can be used.

LUMBER

a. Use sound square edge lumber free of decay and free of knots with an average diameter greater than 1/3 of the width of the board. No piece shall contain any defect which would materially weaken the strength of the piece.

b. Use the following woods: white ash, beech, birch, rock elm, hackberry, hickory, hard maple, oak, pecan.

c. Use random width boards 3-5/8" or wider, surfaced one side 7/8", hit or miss. Surfaced faces to be exposed faces. All boards on any one face to be of uniform thickness.

d. Space between top deck boards to be 1" min. and $1\frac{1}{2}$" max. Space between bottom deck boards not to exceed $1\frac{1}{2}$" except 11" spaces as noted.

e. Boards must be placed so that each notch is completely covered by a single board of not less than 4" nominal width.

f. Length tolerance plus or minus $\frac{1}{4}$".

g. Minimum moisture content shall be not less than 12% and the maximum moisture content not to exceed 25% at time of shipment.

DEPARTMENT OF THE NAVY
Bureau of Supplies and Accounts

SW RELEASE NO. 52C (Superseding RSX Release No. 52B)
31 October 1948

pallet. (*Official U.S. Navy photograph.*)

3. *To increase production.* A large number of parts can be stored on pallets adjacent to an assembly line to reduce handling time of assemblers.

4. *To reduce terminal time of prime movers.* Time for loading a rail car can be reduced from 50 to 8 man-hours; for loading a truck, from 54 to 8 man-hours.

5. *Product protection.* Palletized shipments properly secured offer greater protection to the product while in transit. Damage from handling at each transfer point is materially reduced.

b. Planning a Palletizing Program. Like the planning of any other type of materials-handling system, this task involves the assembling of a large mass of information. One of the first steps for the materials-handling engineer, then, is to devise a form which will best serve his particular problem. The form used for this purpose by the International Harvester Company includes additional columns for the computation of various cost elements (Fig. 166).[1]

In preparing a proposal for a pallet system, the following items should be considered:

1. What is to be handled?
   a. Size, weight, shape, and quantity of materials to be palletized
   b. Number of pieces per pallet
   c. Production per day
2. Purpose in handling?
   a. Intra-plant:
      (1) Raw materials or finished process storage
      (2) Storage of materials in process; temporary banks
      (3) Movement of materials from one operation to next
   b. Inter-plant:
      (1) Return of pallets (collapsible, demountable, etc.)
      (2) Use as storage aid or stores containers
   c. To consumer:
      (1) Return of pallets (weight, nesting to save space)
      (2) Method of shipping (sling-type for dock loading)
      (3) As sales aid (use of "expendable" pallets)
3. Consideration of physical plant and equipment?
   a. Physical:
      (1) Stacking height available
      (2) Condition of floor favorable to trucks

---

[1] Another analysis form developed by the Westinghouse Electric Corporation was illustrated in *Factory Management and Maintenance,* January, 1948, p. 90.

Also see John R. Immer, "Layout Planning Techniques," McGraw-Hill Book Company, Inc., New York, 1950.

(3) Floor-load and spacing of columns

(4) Doorway and aisle space

b. Equipment:

(1) Fork truck (hand truck requires open space pallet)

(2) Elevator capacity (may limit pallet weights)

(3) Crane handling with slings uses dock-type pallets

c. Securing load:

(1) Wire and steel strapping

(2) Gummed tape and adhesive tape

(3) Glued loads

4. Types of Pallets

One difficulty that arose early in the development of the pallet industry was that of the standardization of size, materials, design, and construction.

a. *Pallet Size.* At the present time considerable progress has been made in the standardization of pallet sizes both in the United States and in other countries. The size to be selected by an industry should take into consideration the economic loading of rail cars and trucks. The dimensions of both of these common carriers strongly influence the pallet size.

In the United States, the 40- by 48-inch pallet is best adapted to the width of these carriers and to the efficient stacking thereon of a wide variety of products. In the wholesale grocery industry, this size has become accepted as standard in the Simplified Practice Recommendation R-228-47.

In Great Britain, the problem of adjusting the pallet size to truck and rail-car dimensions is more difficult. Many British rail cars are only 15 feet 6 inches long and for these a pallet size of 42 by 36 inches is the most economical. Fortunately, the width of both rail cars and trucks is approximately 7 feet 3 inches. Door widths of wagons and trucks vary from 55 to 60 inches, so that the maximum size for loading is about 54 inches. By 1948, the following standard sizes had become accepted for common usage:

36 × 36 in.	48 × 36 in.	54 × 42 in.	60 × 60 in.
40 × 32 in.	48 × 40 in.	56 × 48 in.	72 × 36 in.
42 × 36 in.	48 × 48 in.	60 × 40 in.	72 × 48 in.
48 × 30 in.	50 × 44 in.	60 × 48 in.	72 × 54 in.

The Admiralty has also done considerable research on the problem of standardized pallets and packaged units. They have devised a series of package sizes which will fit into successively larger sizes ranging up to the dimensions of a standard pallet. In Australia, also, much work has been done by the Division of Industrial Development of the Department of Post-War Reconstruction to standardize pallet sizes to fit the rail cars and trucks of that country.

In Sweden, there is a Committee on Pallet Standardization of the Swedish State Railways. This committee has made contacts with Denmark, Finland, and Norway in an effort to establish a pallet standard

STANDARD NAVY PALLET PATTERNS

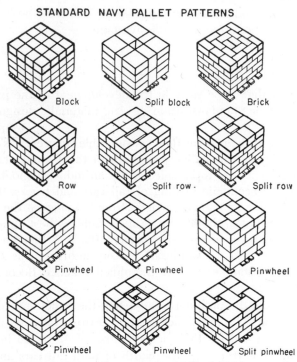

FIG. 118. Standard Navy pallet patterns. (*Official U.S. Navy photograph.*)

which would be accepted by all the other Scandinavian countries. A meeting was held in Krylbo, Sweden, Sept. 30, 1947, by representatives of the railroads of these countries. American recommendations were strongly considered at this meeting. To date, two alternative proposals for pallet standards have been made. The pallet size 48 by 32 inches is based on the committee's own investigations in Sweden. The alternative proposal suggests two pallets 48 by 40 inches and 40 by 32 inches. These sizes correspond to the standard sizes recommended by the National Bureau of Standards of the United States.

b. Shape and Type of Pallets. The shape of pallets has become fairly well standardized and, in most cases, is dependent upon the particular use and operating requirements of the pallet. Where little stacking is involved or materials will easily support a concentrated weight, a single-faced pallet may be used. This consists simply of a top platform surface supported by two or three transverse 2- by 4-inch members on edge. For multi-tiering, a two-faced type with a corresponding support on the bottom is used. This type is also called a two-way pallet, because the tines of the fork may be inserted from two directions. To provide more flexibility, short upright supports replace the solid members to provide entry of the tines from four directions. The placing of these supports may

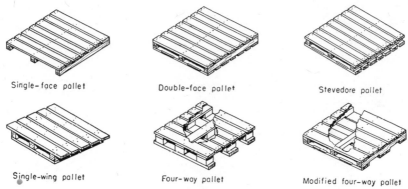

Single-face pallet Double-face pallet Stevedore pallet

Single-wing pallet Four-way pallet Modified four-way pallet

FIG. 119. Major types of pallets. (*Pallet Sales Corporation.*)

also be arranged in order to provide approach at a 45-degree angle, resulting in an eight-way pallet. The outside stringers of the two-way pallet may also be set in a short distance from the edge to enable the placing of a supporting arm or sling of a dock crane for the loading of ships and barges.

c. Materials. A number of materials are used in the construction of pallets; the material most used is wood. The type of wood to be used will depend upon the strength desired, the weight, durability, capacity, and length of service, and cost considerations. The rough handling of heavy commodities such as castings requires the use of heavy oak pallets with twisted nails or bolts and metal reinforcing may also be used. Where intra-plant transportation is involved, the weight of the pallet may become important, in which case hickory may be used. For the lighter handling requirements of rail and truck movements, particularly when the pallet is not to be returned, inexpensive woods, simple construction, and lighter members are used.

These special requirements for pallets lead to the use of other materials. Plywood pallets are easily made, with supporting blocks to separate the panels. The rising cost of plywood has retarded the development of these types, however. For heavier requirements, pressed-steel pallets and skids are used. The weight and cost of these units have been reduced by lighter metal members and improved design. Pallets made of cold-rolled wire or wire mesh are more durable and lighter than many wood pallets. One make, in the 42- by 48-inch size, weighs only 80 pounds. In the search for lightness, aluminum has also been used.

STANDARD ALL PURPOSE PALLET PANELS

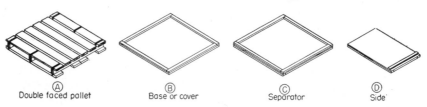

Ⓐ Double faced pallet   Ⓑ Base or cover   Ⓒ Separator   Ⓓ Side

TYPICAL ASSEMBLIES OF STANDARD ALL PURPOSE PALLET PANELS

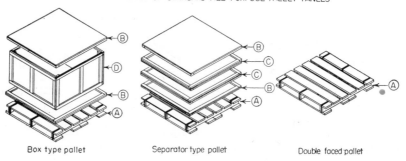

Box type pallet   Separator type pallet   Double faced pallet

Fig. 120. Use of standard pallet sections. (*International Harvester Company.*)

d. Superstructure. In addition to the variety of shapes and materials used for pallets, a number of types of superstructure, either fixed or de-mountable, have been erected on them. For the handling of smaller items as a single unit, a container may be constructed with a pallet base. For the handling of electric motors, International Harvester Company uses a series of platforms. A top platform is used to hold all the other parts in place. Wire strapping holds the parts together as a unit (Fig. 120).

The pallet container or box may be built with demountable sides so that the whole unit when empty can be returned in a knocked-down state. Often special panels may be removed from the front to permit easy removal of parts. One company eliminated the need for storage bins by using this type of pallet container. Wire pallet containers are used in the same way. The fact that the empty container may be folded together to form a compact package makes them more valuable for inter-plant shipments. One of the most far-reaching innovations in the handling of bulk materials has been the use of these wire containers with special paper liners (see Fig. 321).

Merchandising firms and warehouses handle products of a wide variety of shapes and sizes, not all of them regular or of such nature as to support other products on top. Brooms, tires, air cylinders, and carboys are only a few items of a very long list of such products. In some places crates with one side open or removable are used to permit multi-tier stacking. Other pallets may then be supported on top of the frame or the units may be supported in pallet racks. Various types of metal pallets also have provisions for the insertion of corner posts and a superstructure to permit stacking of irregularly shaped materials. One army instruction on the use of pallets recommends temporary upright supports of wood for extra support of wooden box pallets.

5. Live Storage

Ordinary methods of storage involve a considerable amount of handling, both in the introduction of materials to this state and in their removal. In the early days of automobile production, several companies developed at about the same time the concept of keeping materials continuously on the move. C. W. Nash, for example, in 1918 stressed this idea in his motto, "Don't let the material touch the floor." The River Rouge plant of the Ford Motor Company, shortly after this, boasted that all materials in process were kept in constant motion. A number of methods have been devised since then to provide for the live storage of materials.

a. Overhead Handling Systems. The overhead trolley-conveyor system was first used to eliminate handling in the storage processes. Within recent years a number of notable installations in practically every major industry has sharply reduced handling costs where storage has been involved. The Mengel Furniture Company of Louisville, Ky., uses such a system to provide for a bank of materials between operations and processes. Much of this storage is accomplished in overhead areas where it does not interfere with actual production processes. In the treating of metal parts, materials in process may have a number of operations performed on them and may be taken in and out of temporary storage with no handling involved.

b. Roller-conveyor Systems. Live-storage systems similar in plan to those above have also been constructed with roller conveyors. Where only a small bank of materials is needed between operations, short sections of gravity roller conveyors provide for live storage. On longer runs, gravity roller systems are often combined with powered roller sections or belt conveyors. In some instances additional overhead handling space is obtained by elevating these conveyor sections to the ceiling areas above ordinary working height.

In the curing and pickling of metal coils, large numbers of rolls must be stored at various steps due to the different time elements of the operations. In order to use the oldest rolls first constantly and to minimize ac-

FIG. 121. Rollers set in floor provide a continuous roller-bearing surface for stacks of corrugated cardboards at the Seaboard Container Corporation. (*The E. W. Busch-man Company, Inc.*)

tual handling, heavy roller conveyors are used. Deflecting curves permit the transfer of rolls onto any one of a number of conveyor sections. At the other end of the storage area, similar curves permit their assembly on another line.

c. Roller Floor Systems. Rollers may also be constructed so as to cover the major portion of the storage area. In the handling of large-sized cardboard stock, this method has reduced handling cost, speeded up production, and eliminated a former bottleneck (Fig. 121). In this particular installation, a transfer table is used to move the materials into and out of storage.

Another system provides for the storage of pallets on similar roller sections set in the floor. This "car-aisle" system is adapted to the carlot handling of fast-moving grocery items. As carload lots of merchandise are received, they are put on pallets and deposited at one end of the conveyor. The slight incline feeds pallet loads toward the other side of the storage area from which the oldest items are also removed by other fork trucks.[2]

6. Other Unit-load Handling

Although the term unit load has become very closely associated with the palletization of materials, there are other means of accomplishing this objective. The importance of the unit load has already been emphasized. The many ways of unitizing materials should constitute a very important part of the repertoire of the materials-handling engineer on the most effective specific ways of accomplishing the economical movement of materials.

a. The Unitizing Agent. The unitizing agent is the means by which a number of materials are held together for unit-load handling. In addition to various types of pallets another technique termed "pallet omission" may be used. This is simply an arrangement of the materials being handled to permit some handling device to pick up a large number of pieces as a single unit. In the handling of brick and tile, the bottom layer may be arranged to permit the entry of the tines of a special fork truck. Hydraulic units in the tines clamp in a sidewise direction on this layer and provide a rigid support by which the entire stack of materials may be moved. Other attempts to obtain this benefit of pallets without the expense and bother of their use include the use of flat cardboard platforms which are gripped by a special attachment on the fork truck and pulled onto the tines (Fig. 122).

Another group of unitizing agents consists of various binding and tieing devices to hold the load together. Steel strapping or steel wire may be used to bind materials together on a pallet or skid as well as to provide stability of the load while in transit. Tests recently made by the Navy have shown the advantage of unitizing materials in cardboard containers by the application of a small amount of glue on the bottom of each carton which binds them all together. Carloads of materials so prepared showed a much smaller amount of damage than any other type of loading.[3] Another binding agent has recently been developed which consists of an adhesive tape with a strength of 500 pounds to the square inch.

[2] "Streamlined Wholesale Grocery Warehouses," Industrial Series 18, U.S. Department of Commerce.

[3] "Carloading Impact Tests Data, Report 1, 26 March 1946," U.S. Naval Supply Operational Training Center, Naval Supply Depot, Bayonne, N.J.

b. The Handling Unit. The handling unit for unit loads is customarily the fork truck or the platform truck. This may be a simple hand-operated type or a unit powered with an electric or gasoline motor and may be equipped to raise loads to an effective stacking height of 15 to 20 feet. Because of the advantages which have been obtained by using the largest sized unit which may be handled, special types of handling de-

FIG. 122. Single carrying sheet used in place of pallet. Hydraulic gripper grasps carrying sheet for pickup. Hydraulic frame pushes load off wide forks. (*Clark Equipment Company.*)

vices have been developed. Fork trucks of up to 30 tons capacity are now in use. In addition, the straddle truck, though used primarily for the handling of long lengths, is also adapted to other types of unit-load handling. For example, it may be used to remove the entire load of a semitrailer in one handling operation (Fig. 124).

Overhead handling of large units is often done by traveling bridge cranes and monorail systems. In the storage of 5,000-pound rolls of paper at the Waldorf Paper Products Company in St. Paul, Minn., an overhead traveling crane with a special tong permits storage of rolls on end to a height of 42 feet (Fig. 123). No aisle space is required, and workers do not have to come in contact with the rolls while located in the storage area. In another installation, kegs of nails on pallets are stacked by means of a special hook suspended from an overhead traveling crane.

The General Electric Company uses a similar system in the stacking of crated refrigerators as well as palletized parts.

Various types of mobile cranes are also used for unitized handling. Unitized skids have become an accepted part of the amphibious landing

FIG. 123. Rolls of paper stacked on end to maximum height of 42 feet. A turnover mechanism on the grab makes it possible to set rolls down in any position. (*Cleveland Tramrail.*)

of military supplies. These loads, carefully planned, are mounted on skids and hoisted over the side of carrying ships or landing craft. They are then pulled onto the beach by caterpillar tractors and prime movers.

Unit-load handling is changing the economics of the movement of materials in practically every industry. Benefits of this type of handling have resulted in decreased truck rates in various instances. In at least one barge terminal, the handling charges have been cut in half for pal-

FIG. 124. Straddle truck unloads trailer load of pineapples in one operation. (*The Ross Carrier Company.*)

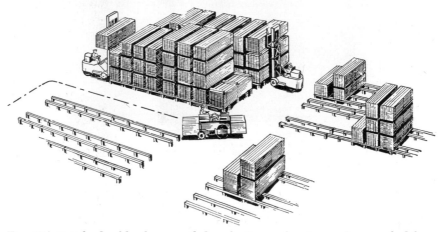

FIG. 125. Unit loads of lumber are piled on footings or bearings and are worked from center to runway when placed in storage. The procedure is reversed when the units are removed. (*The Ross Carrier Company.*)

letized shipments. In every industry in which the movement of materials still involves a large amount of handling, the opportunities for the unitizing of shipments remains unlimited.

QUESTIONS

1. Explain the advantages of unit-load handling.
2. What equipment may be used to unitize materials?
3. Describe the equipment used in connection with a skid-handling system.
4. What results should be expected from a palletizing program?
5. What considerations are involved in the planning of a palletizing program?
6. Discuss the various types of pallets used in industry.
7. Discuss the problem of standardization of pallets in foreign countries.
8. What materials are used for the construction of pallets? Explain the uses and limitations of each material.
9. Can materials of irregular shape be palletized? How?
10. Explain how bulk materials can be moved on pallets.
11. What types of equipment may be used to provide live storage?
12. Unit loads are handled by what types of equipment?

PROJECTS FOR FURTHER STUDY

1. Show how specific companies have used unit-load handling successfully. (Examples may be taken from current magazine literature, sales materials of the equipment manufacturers, or from other sections of this text.)
2. Show how specific companies have used live storage in their operations.
3. Prepare a list of the different ways in which pallets can be used. Provide the name of the company for each example used.

PART IV

PACKAGING SECTION

CHAPTER 13

SHIPPING CONTAINERS FOR PRODUCT PROTECTION

1. Designing the Container

a. Laboratory Design of Cardboard Containers. The selection of the proper weight and type of cardboard to be used in a container and the best way of designing it to take care of the strains of the item contained is a job for packaging engineers. These men know the strength of various types of cardboard materials and their resiliency. From their past experience they know how to reinforce and bulwark cardboard containers in order to provide complete protection to the product with a minimum of packaging expense.

One laboratory follows these steps in the design of cartons. In Fig. 126*a*, a manufacturer has called a conference of his staff to consider the effectiveness of the present container. The head of the shipping department, the sales manager, the purchasing agent, and the advertising manager each contribute in planning cost, protection, packing, and sales objectives for the new box. General objectives are decided upon, and the packaging laboratory is called in.

First, a careful study of the external features of the product is made (Fig. 126*b*). The exterior is photographed, unpacking operations are timed and analyzed, and accurate measurements are taken (Fig. 126*c*). The packing procedure of the manufacturer, methods of shipping, distribution channels, display potentialities, and possible use by the ultimate consumer must be considered. Following the collective analysis of all the data, a box is engineered on paper (Fig. 126*d*). In the design of the new carton, careful attention is given to the practical aspects of production, shipment, identification, and display in terms of color, layout, typography, and copy units (Fig. 126*e*).

While this is being done, a custom-built sample is constructed of corrugated cardboard. Working from the designer's blueprint, a sample box is cut out (Fig. 126*f*). This box is tested in a revolving wheel which duplicates the roughest treatment to which the box might be subjected in shipping and handling (Fig. 126*g*). The box is then removed, opened, unpacked, and carefully examined for any evidence of a weakness. The

a. The Problem

b. Photograph Container

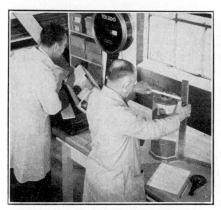

c. Basic Measurements

d. Created on Paper

e. Plan Art Design

f. Custom-built Sample

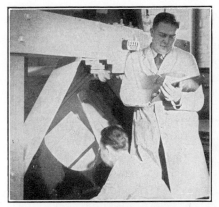

g. Torture-chamber Testing

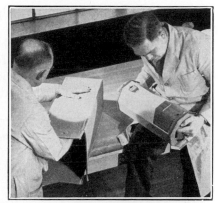

h. Reexamination

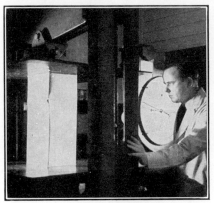

i. Compression Test

j. Presentation

Fig. 126. How a carton is designed. (*Hinde & Dautch Paper Company.*)

product is also checked for any damage as a result of the above treat
ment (Fig. 126*h*). A compression test is also used which establishes the
ability of the carton to meet maximum stacking and loading requirements (Fig. 126*i*). Presentation to management (Fig. 126*j*) is the final
step. The new improved carton is lower in cost, can be packed more
quickly, and its 50 per cent lighter weight saves in shipping costs. It provides greater protection in shipping and storage and does an advertising
and selling job at the same time.

b. User Development of Shipping Containers. The electrical industry
provides a good example of the development of packing techniques and
methods. As equipment design becomes more sensitive, more resilient
packaging materials and methods are necessary. One very good example

of this is in the preparation for shipping of vacuum tubes at the General Electric Company.

A few years ago the largest of these tubes had a shop value of considerably more than $1,000. It was formerly crated in a wood crate with a tube suspended on wood springboards (Fig. 127). The new package consists of a corrugated paperboard container with the tube suspended

FIG. 127. Former method of packing 100-kilowatt electronic tube. (*General Electric Company.*)

in the same material. This new method reduced the size of the package considerably and cut the railway shipping weight from 210 pounds to 95 pounds (Fig. 128).

2. Layout of Packing and Crating Section

As in other industrial operations, efficiency requires advance planning of the work area, proper positioning of materials and tools, and adequate handling facilities. This means that attention will have to be given to packing the product long before the end of the production line is reached. For example, many products such as washing machines, refrigerators, and hot-water tanks are assembled on a wooden platform designed to serve as the base of the crate which will later encase the product. A machine is often designed with lugs and other devices by which it can be later bolted to a frame for security in transit.

a. Planned Layout. Packing and crating should normally take place at the end of the assembly line. The product should move through the section in a straight line (with no backtracking or recrossing) and emerge

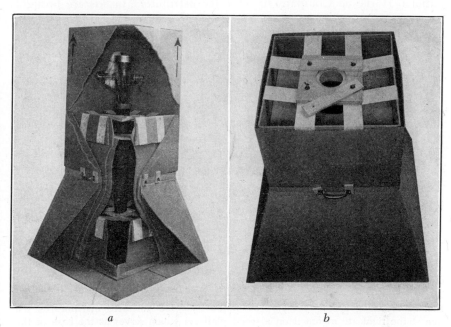

a   *b*

FIG. 128. New method of packing 100-kilowatt electronic tube. (*a*) Tube packed in corrugated-board carton with parts cut away to show construction; (*b*) sling for supporting tube in new shipping carton. (*General Electric Company.*)

at or near the shipping area or final stores area. One company saved a 400-foot haul for each assembled item by doubling the final assembly line back so that the other end of the U-shaped production line adjoined the crating line.

The packing and crating operations should be included in the operations list of the product. In one refrigerator plant, after final inspection a protective paper covering is slipped over the unit. At the next work station a preassembled wood-reinforced cardboard carton (minus bottom) is slipped over this and fastened to the base upon which the refrigerator was assembled. The boxed item is then ready for shipping or for finished stores.

In the Ashtabula plant of the Reliance Electric and Engineering Company, electric motors are spray-painted with a quick-drying synthetic gray enamel before packaging. Each motor is then mounted on a wooden base and placed on a roller conveyor. While still on this conveyor, the container is dropped over the motor. Corrugated boxes are used for motors of from 1 to 3 horsepower and wire-bound crates for larger motors.

In the new single-story parts depots being constructed by the International Harvester Company to serve its distributors, orders are brought

Fig. 129. Crating line for washing machines. Note that uncrated machines on the line at the right are mounted on a wood platform which serves as the base of the crate. (*Wirebound Box Manufacturers Association.*)

to the packing area in order carts. These are pulled through the order-assembly area by an overhead tow chain and are released adjacent to the packing and wrapping tables. Here, specially designed packing areas provide corrugated cartons of a variety of sizes (in flat shape), shredded paper, and other materials the packer will need. A belt-driven roller conveyor moves these cartons to the loading area. While still on the conveyor, they are steel-strapped. Here they become the responsibility of the traffic and shipping supervisor. He is in charge of the weighing, loading, and routing of all packed merchandise.[1]

b. Workplace Layout. In the above installation, all materials and tools were located within easy reach of the packer. Other functions of the

[1] For diagram of a parts depot packing system, see John R. Immer, "Layout Planning Techniques," p. 300, McGraw-Hill Book Company, Inc., New York, 1950.

packing section must be considered and their requirements incorporated into the workplace design. These functions are: [2]

1. Inclusion of instruction slips or booklets. If in a depot, order is checked for completeness; desk for all paper work required.
2. Packing of items; supplies, tools, and materials accessible.
3. Package sealing; gummed tape, stitching, wire, or strapping.

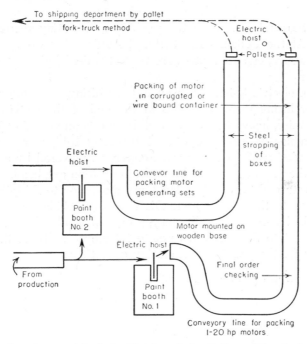

FIG. 130. Packing line at Ashtabula Division of the Reliance Electric & Engineering Company. (*Flow.*)

4. Package protection; corrosion-preventive measures.
5. Weighing; scales and means of recording weight.
6. Marking and addressing; stencils and documentation.
7. Delivery; loading or shipping area and facilities.

These functions require not only proper facilities for the movement of materials but also well-designed working tables and packing areas. All materials needed should be within easy reaching distance of the packer. Bulk corrugated paper should be placed on rolls at the side of the packing area from which the material may be easily unreeled as needed.

[2] Adapted from "Packing Room Layout," in "Storage in the Zone of the Interior," War Department Technical Manual TM38-402, March, 1946, p. 95.

Gummed tape and other fastening devices should be accessible but out of the way when not in use. Wire strapping can be applied from fixtures which swing out of the way. Scales and other weighing devices should be incorporated within the handling medium so that no lifting is required for this operation.

c. Equipment. Packing and crating, as a progressive operation, is best performed on some type of conveyor which positions the product within convenient working height of the packer. Larger items such as refrigerators may be carried through the packing and crating section on slat conveyors. At the Reliance Electric and Engineering Company's plant referred to above, electric motors are kept at waist height for the ease of the operator.

Here, too, electric hoists are provided for lifting the motors onto the line and for lifting them to pallets at the end of the packing line. In other companies, heavy items are lifted by hoists on swinging jib cranes, overhead monorails, or by overhead traveling bridge cranes. In one company a section of the roller-track conveyor, powered by a hydraulic lift, inserts the product into the box held in position overhead. The boxed product is returned to conveyor level and moved on to shipping.

In addition to the special materials used in packing operations (described in the balance of the chapter), provision should be made for their incorporation into the line so as not to interrupt or distort the straight line of flow for the packing and crating operations.

3. Metal Shipping Containers

a. Drums and Barrels. These items comprise most of the metal containers used for shipping industrial materials. Steel containers range in size from 10 to 110 gallons capacity and are made of 12- to 18-gauge black steel. The 55-gallon size is generally considered standard for liquids. A straight-sided drum with rolling hoops to facilitate handling is shaped to allow complete drainage. This is widely used in the chemical industry.

The major types of construction are:

1. The full open head. This type is used for packing dry materials and semiliquids. The cover is held in place by metal rings or lever locks.

2. The tight head. This type is used where a spigot is to be inserted. The 55-gallon gasoline barrel is the most representative of this type.

3. The bilge barrel. This barrel is used for the same purpose, but is made by cold-drawing the metal or by butt welding the joints.

4. The straight-sided drum. This drum is also used for liquids and is welded together at its body seams.

The stainless-steel drum is used to ship food products, soft-drink sirups, acid drugs, chemicals, cosmetics, etc. Ranging in size from 1 to 50 gallons, they use either the tight head or the full-removable head-type-shaped barrel. Aluminum drums are also increasing in popularity.

Various types of lining are used with steel containers (as well as fiber drums) to protect the contents from the container walls. Rubber is used to protect products affected by air, moisture, or odors. Other liners commonly used are (1) phenolic-base resin with filler and top coat used for corrosive products; (2) phenolic type, insoluble in most organic solvents, is used for alcohol, strong solvents, acetone, lacquers, and thinners; (3) synthetic oleoresinous type is sprayed on and used mostly for oils, greases, shortenings, etc.; (4) white Vichrome liner is used for food products or acids.

Covers for metal drums include the following types: (1) the friction lid, ranging from 4 to 15 inches in diameter, is the most popular type. (2) The bolted cover, fastened to the drum with bolts, is used mostly for pastes and powders. (3) The full open-head cover is held in place by metal closing rings which are secured tightly with levers or bolts. (4) The lug cover is secured by lugs which fasten on the drum and fold over the cover to hold it in place. It is used on grease drums.[3]

b. Metal Boxes. Steel boxes are sometimes used for shipping small heavy products such as spare parts for machinery. Extensive use is also made of large metal containers. These are used for unit load handling of materials and are readily moved around by a powerized hand truck (Fig. 103) or swung aboard a cargo ship (Fig. 314). They have the added advantage of security for the contents. The containers can be loaded with valuable merchandise and locked by the consignor and will remain secure until unlocked at the destination by the consignee in his plant or store.

4. Wood Shipping Containers

a. Barrels, Drums, and Pails. Wood barrels or drums are used for a wide variety of solid, semisolid, or liquid products. The "tight" type is used for solid products and holds from 1 to 60 gallons. It is usually custom-made for the user's purpose. The "slack" type, used for semisolids, is of less rigid construction and is represented by the nail keg and the nail barrel. Both of these types are usually made of pine or fir. The "liquid" type is composed largely of beer barrels and kegs which are generally made of oak. Pails are smaller in size and have sloped sides.

b. Nailed Wooden Boxes. Wooden boxes have the ability to withstand a large amount of punishment and are used where protection is desired

[3] This section adapted from "Modern Packaging Encyclopedia," Packaging Catalogue Corporation, New York, 1950.

against rough handling or where heavy weights are involved. The strength of the box and its ability to withstand strain is dependent upon lumber (type of wood, the way it is cut, edge grain, and moisture content), size of members, style of box, nails (size, spacing, and type); and reinforcing (metal bands or wood cleats).

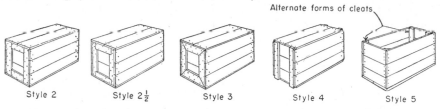

Alternate forms of cleats

Style 2   Style 2½   Style 3   Style 4   Style 5

FIG. 131. Styles of nailed wood boxes. (*Storage of Quartermaster Supplies, War Department Technical Manual* TM-10-250, *p.* 100.)

The styles of nailed wooden boxes are shown in Fig. 131. Style 1 is an uncleated box suitable for light loads of less than 60 pounds. Styles 4 and 5 have cleats running in a vertical direction, either inside or outside, and are suitable for loads up to 200 pounds. Style 6 is an uncleated box with locked corners where a tight rigid package is required. It is suitable for packages up to 150 pounds. For gross weights of over 200

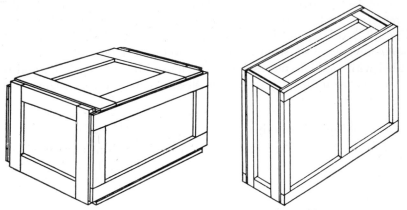

FIG. 132. Two styles of cleated plywood boxes. (*International Harvester Company.*)

pounds and for large-sized containers, styles 2, 2½, and 3 are used. They have fully cleated ends. The cleats prevent the ends from splitting and give the nails greater holding power.[4]

---

[4] "Bonnell's Directory of Packing and Shipping," Bonnell Publications, Inc., Plainfield, N.J., 1950. C. A. Plaskett, Principles of Box and Crate Construction, U.S. Department of Agriculture *Bulletin* 171.

c. Plywood. Where considerable protection is required for a valuable product, plywood is often used for box materials. For greater strength and rigidity, it is generally used with cleats: [5]

The chief characteristics of cleated plywood boxes are light weight, high resistance to diagonal distortion, resistance to mashing at the corners, and capacity to withstand severe tumbling and dropping. Cleated plywood boxes are neat in appearance, easy to handle, almost dustproof, and are difficult to

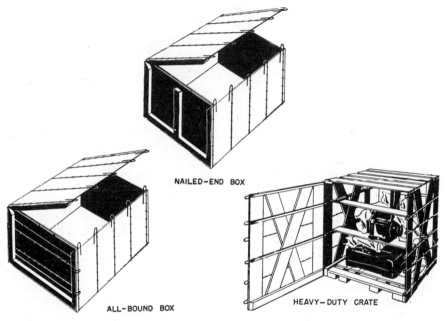

NAILED-END BOX

ALL-BOUND BOX

HEAVY-DUTY CRATE

Fig. 133. Types of wire-bound boxes. (*Wirebound Box Manufacturers Association.*)

pilfer. The thin plywood springs easily and thus absorbs many of the shocks which would otherwise cause damage to the contents.

d. Wire-bound Boxes and Crates. "The wirebound box is a lightweight shipping container that utilizes rotary cut lumber, spliced lumber, or thin-sawed lumber, in combination with cleats, wires and staples. . . . The springing action (of the thin material) enables the wirebound box to withstand severe handling. The wires and staples hold the parts together and make pilfering of the contents difficult." [6]

These boxes and crates are usually delivered to the user in flat form, bundled together for compactness, and are frequently palletized. In this

[5] Plaskett, *op. cit.,* p. 20.
[6] Plaskett, *op. cit.,* p. 22.

form they are easily handled and occupy little storage space. Some of the major types are shown in Fig. 133. This also shows the shape in which it is received by the user, *i.e.*, knocked down or flat. Other features in its construction are shown in Fig. 134.

e. Crates. This is a wood framework constructed around an object to be transported. It is easily constructed to provide strength and rigidity

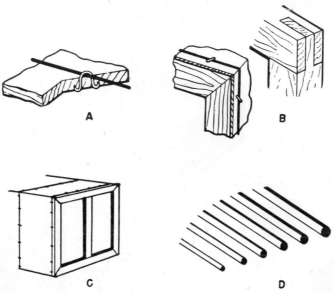

Fig. 134. Characteristic details of wire-bound boxes. (*a*) Wire staples are driven in with flared points to hold in place the binding wires. (*b*) Mitered cleats produce a tight joint. Tongue-and-groove cleats are also used. (*c*) Battens are used to structural supporting members used on outside end, top, or base of a crate. (*d*) Weight of wire depends upon the weight of product carried, shipping conditions, and container design. (*Wirebound Box Manufacturers Association.*)

and withstands a large amount of heavy punishment. It may be of an open framework type or sheathed for added product protection. It is easily adapted to a wide variety of heavy products. Sheathing may consist of solid wood boarding, plywood, or paperboard. The design of the corners and of the reinforcing members is particularly important in its construction.

5. Fiberboard Containers

Fiberboard is less expensive than other container materials. The variety of types and kinds of materials available make these containers useful for a number of purposes, especially where handling hazards are not too great. Even in this case, the use of fiberboard is constantly being extended into areas formerly reserved for more expensive container mediums. Fiberboard has a wide range of strength and physical properties. It may be waterproof and grease-resistant.

a. Corrugated Paperboard. This material consists of a sheet of corrugated paperboard that is glued between two outer flat sheets of paper-

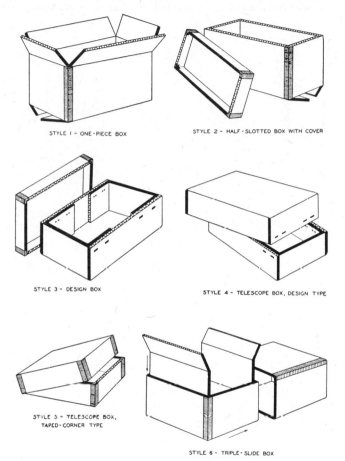

FIG. 135. Styles of corrugated-fiber boxes. (*U.S. Forest Service, Forest Products Laboratory.*)

board called "test liners." The resulting material is light in weight, has considerable strength, and provides a high degree of resilience for the container. Its low cost and adaptability to various container requirements also increase its popularity.

The material for the container is slotted in manufacture and scored to facilitate bending. The single vertical joint (see Fig. 135, style 1) is made at the factory with gummed tape of paper or cambric. It is delivered to the user in the knock-down flat shape. The ease of printing on the material increases the use of container advertising. The loaded container can be sealed with gummed tape or by wire staples.

b. Solid Fiber Boxes. "Solid fiberboard is formed by pasting one or more sheets of chip board (fiberboard prepared from waste papers of

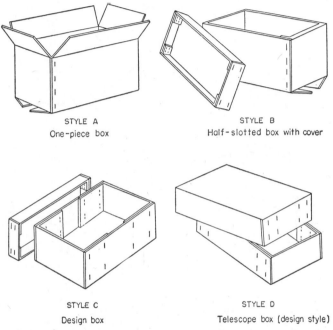

STYLE A
One-piece box

STYLE B
Half-slotted box with cover

STYLE C
Design box

STYLE D
Telescope box (design style)

FIG. 136. Styles of solid-fiber boxes. (*U.S. Forest Service, Forest Products Laboratory.*)

the lowest grade) between two test liners." [7] Solid fiber boxes are used for heavier products which need greater protection than that afforded by the corrugated box. It is more adaptable for use in overseas shipments. Styles of solid fiber boxes are shown in Fig. 136.

c. Fiber Drums and Pails. These drums and pails are used for solids and semisolids. The light weight of fiber and its adaptability to various size requirements has led to a steady increase in its use. Most of the drums consist of paperboard wound convolutely into the shape of a cylinder. Taper-sided pails range in size from ¾ to 75 gallons. The taper permits empties to be stored or shipped in a small space. Both drums and pails can be protected on the inside with paraffin and on the outside with lacquer or paint.

[7] Plaskett, *op. cit.*, p. 28.

6. Corrosion Prevention

The scientific study of corrosion prevention was largely a development of the Second World War. The need for getting metal products in dependable working condition to the troops in arctic or tropical conditions led to the extensive development of measures for prevention of rust and corrosion.

The methods of packaging recommended to preserve metal surfaces were: [8]

Designation	Methods of Packaging	Use
Method 0	Mechanical and physical protection. No added preservative or water-resistant wrap. Protected from breakage only.	Items requiring no protection from moisture, *e.g.*, painted or plated surface. Parts not susceptible to damage by atmospheric condition.
Method I	Part cleaned. Preservative oil or grease plus unsealed wrap.	Noncritical items not damaged by application and removal of preservative, *e.g.*, screw drivers, heavy springs.
Method IA	Part cleaned. Preservative where necessary, plus water-resistant sealed wrap.	Precision parts that could be cleaned and preserved, or noncritical parts that could not be adequately treated with a preservative, *e.g.*, bearings.
Method II	Part cleaned. Sealed in water-vapor-resistant wrap with desiccant inside to maintain low humidity.	Precision parts and assemblies that could not be adequately treated with a preservative, *e.g.*, electrical instruments, delicate mechanisms.

a. Causes. Corrosion is basically an electrochemical reaction which affects all ferrous and some nonferrous metals. Iron, for example, when exposed to moisture and oxygen begins to corrode. Some of the iron goes into solution and releases hydrogen. This breakdown of the molecular structure generates electrical currents which in turn speeds up the reaction. This action generates a polar field. Different metals have different degrees of "polarity."

One way to prevent corrosion is to slow down this reaction. This may be done by wrapping the product in a material which will corrode instead of the product when any moisture forms or enters the package. In iron and steel products, this is accomplished by aluminum foil, which should be wrapped tightly around the steel surfaces to be protected.[9]

Preventives are classed as organic or inorganic and are further divided into groups of permanent or temporary types. Permanent types such as

---

[8] Packaging and Packing for Overseas Shipment, JAN-P-116, Office of the Chief of Ordnance, Department of the Army.

[9] C. M. Rhodes and G. F. Chuse, Corrosion Control, *Modern Packaging*, March, 1945.

electroplating processes apply a permanent inorganic coating to the metal. Temporary protection of the metal is obtained by the following: [10]

1. Use of a protective coating to shield the metal from moisture.

2. Neutralization of the corrosive tendency of the air, as by the use of newly developed chemical papers.

3. Removing the moisture from the air with the package (as with silica gel).

b. Cleaning. The best preservative is practically worthless when applied on a dirty surface. All contaminating and corrosive materials must be removed and the surface must be dry and uncontaminated by handling at the time protective coating is applied.

Selection of the cleaning method is influenced by shape and design of the part; materials used in its construction, such as attached leather and rubber; type of residue on the parts; the cost, advantages, and disadvantages of various cleaners.[11]

One difficulty is the removal of various contaminating substances found on metal particles used in machining and processing operations. These may be divided into (1) animal and vegetable oils and fats and (2) minerals and mineral fats and greases.

The most common detergents and solvents used in cleaning are:

1. Petroleum-base solvents. These are less toxic than coal-tar solvents.

2. Coal-tar solvents. These have a greater degree of solvency than petroleum-base solvents.

3. Chlorinated solvents. These are most effective when used in a vapor degreasing process where the solvent is kept free of impurities.

4. Hot alkali solutions.

5. Hot alkali solutions containing soap. Both alkali cleaners have the advantage of low cost and noninflammability.

c. Pliable Protective Coverings. Harmful elements are excluded from metal by use of chemically treated paper wrappings and by pliable materials which take the shape of the article being protected. Petroleum derivatives were formerly the only type available for this latter purpose, but recent years have seen the development of a wide variety of other materials.

In order to stand conditions of severe exposure, chemical additives were developed. These should contain "polar" compounds opposed to

[10] Adapted from Robert G. Clendenin, A Review of Cleaning and Rust Prevention, *University of Illinois Experiment Station, Circular Series* 56, 1949, p. 56 (Proceedings of First Annual Conference and Short Course of the Society of Industrial Packaging and Materials Handling Engineers).

[11] *Ibid.*, p. 57.

that of the metal in which the oxidation is to be prevented. This forms a tight adhesion which bars all moisture and oxygen from the surface to be protected. The nature of the additive determines the effectiveness of the preventive, while the nature of the vehicle determines its physical characteristics. Their correct combination is a question for laboratory analysis.[12]

The main types of these preventives used today are: [13]

1. Grease or petroleum type. May be heated and applied by brush or spray, though dipping operations are most common. Low melting temperature.

2. Solvent type. These compounds are usually low-viscosity liquids at room temperature and may be applied by dipping, spraying, or brushing. Although waxlike coatings are most commonly used, they may be oily or varnishlike or used in combinations.

3. Oil type. These are used for short periods of storage particularly to protect the interior of internal-combustion engines. As they blend with other lubricants, they do not have to be removed before the product is used.

4. Plastic type. These are applied in a hot dipping operation and provide a tough protecting sheath for the product. They are limited in use by their cost. Used generally for high quality cutting tools.

d. Other Preventive Means. Wrapping papers used for product protection should be nonhygroscopic. They must be waterproof and vaporproof. They generally consist of two sheets of kraft paper with a waterproof material (most commonly asphaltum) in between. Other materials are wax, cellophane, metal foils, latex, and chlorinated rubber.

Silica gel or another desiccant should be included in the package to absorb the moisture packed with the product and which may later form due to difference in temperature, etc.

By means of a new skin-type film, a cocoonlike covering is provided for a complicated shaped product which may be completely assembled with operating lubricants in place. The covering can be easily peeled off in a few minutes. It has been used for the "moth-balling" of airplanes, vital parts of ships, and other military equipment.

This equipment has also been preserved in large metal binlike structures with desiccants provided to absorb moisture. Both of these covering systems have windows by which the state of the contents may be examined periodically.

QUESTIONS

1. How are cardboard containers designed?
2. What considerations affect the layout of a packing and crating area?

[12] Helen Sellei, Rust Preventatives, *Chemical Industries,* January, 1948, p. 62.
[13] Clendenin, *op. cit.,* p. 60.

3. What are the functions of a packing section?

4. What equipment should be provided for a packing section?

5. Discuss the various types of metal shipping containers.

6. Discuss the characteristics of each type of wood shipping container.

7. What are the types of fiberboard containers commonly used?

8. What are the causes of corrosion?

9. In order to prevent corrosion, what preparation of the surface is necessary before covering or treatment is added?

10. What is corrosion?

11. Discuss the types of pliable protective coverings used for corrosion prevention.

PROJECTS FOR FURTHER STUDY

1. Prepare a paper on corrosion. Outline a corrosion-prevention program.

2. Investigate the adaptability of various kinds of wood for use in containers and crates.

3. Prepare a paper on the use of corrugated paperboard.

CHAPTER 14

PACKAGING METHODS AND MATERIALS

Packing and packaging are "big business." On V-J day, 50 per cent of all the trees harvested in the United States and its possessions found their way into our homes as containers or packages of one type or another.[1] During 1948, 44 per cent of all paper and paperboard produced was used for packaging and 7 per cent of all finished steel that year was used for containers and other packaging needs.[2]

The importance to industry is exemplified by the following figures on packaging from the General Electric Company. In one year, the company purchased lumber and wooden boxes worth $8 million, corrugated containers and filler pieces worth $10 million, and paper products worth $2 million. These products would fill a freight train over 75 miles long. With purchases of this size, even small improvements in packaging methods may produce impressive savings figures. For example, specifications on a certain type of board were changed from $1\frac{3}{16}$ inch to $1\frac{1}{16}$ inch, and spruce was substituted for yellow pine. New supply sources eliminated former long hauls from the South. Yearly savings achieved by this change were $500,000 for reduction in board thickness and transport costs of $200,000 for the reduction of weight.[3]

1. Layout for Packaging

High-production packaging machinery demands the most efficient layout obtainable. It means handling equipment that will provide a continuous flow of packages if bottlenecks are to be avoided.

One example of the close coordination of packaging units needed is the high-speed packaging line in the New Orleans plant of the United Rice Milling Products, Inc. On this line it takes only $1\frac{1}{2}$ minutes to form, fill, glue, and seal a carton. The sequence of these operations is shown in Fig. 137. The 12-ounce cartons are filled with rice, weighed, and vibrated to settle the contents in the cartons. The tops are glued

[1] What the Armed Forces Want, *Modern Packaging*, November, 1948, p. 93.

[2] H. T. Holbrook, Papers for Packaging, "Modern Packaging Encyclopedia," p. 148, The Packaging Catalogue Corporation, New York, 1950.

[3] G. F. Simmons, Purchasing Low-cost Packaging Materials, American Management Association, Packaging Series 33, p. 6, 1950.

in the sealer and held in place while they pass through the compression machine. At the loading table, 30 cartons are packed to a corrugated paper carton, the bottom flaps of which have been sealed with gum tape and the top flaps glued. The case is then put upside down (to retain pressure on the glued surface) on a belt conveyor which takes it to the warehouse. The entire operation from carton preparation to delivery to the warehouse is done by four men.[4]

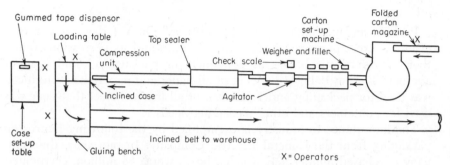

FIG. 137. Layout diagram of layout for packaging of rice in 12-ounce containers. (*Flow, December,* 1948, *p.* 50.)

The same close coordination is shown in the packaging of Phillips Milk of Magnesia. This new packaging line (Fig. 138) was installed at the Chas. H. Phillips Company Division of Sterling Drugs, Inc., in Gulfport, Miss. With 12 operators it packages a complex article at the rate of 125 per minute. Some of the major operations performed on the line are shown in Fig. 139.[5]

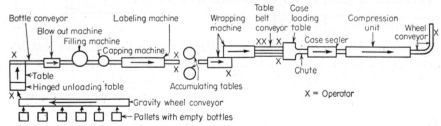

FIG. 138. Layout of packaging line for milk of magnesia. (*Flow, August,* 1948, *p.* 50.)

2. Packaging Machinery

The limitation of output, the tediousness of the work, and the high labor cost of hand packaging has led to the development of a machine for almost every packaging operation. The complexity of the operations

[4] Packaging Efficiency for Cartons, *Flow,* December, 1948, p. 50.
[5] Complex Package—High Volume Production, *Flow,* August, 1948, p. 50.

has resulted in expensive and complicated machines, with a strong tendency toward special designs for each application. There is a need for

a

b

FIG. 139. Views of packaging line for milk of magnesia. (*a*) Automatic bottle blowout, filling and capping machines have a capacity of 125 bottles per minute. (*b*) Labeling machine spots, glues, labels, and wipes the bottles two at a time. Note lateral rams. (*Flow,* August, 1948, *p.* 50.)

more single-purpose machines (simpler in design). Other improvements desired in the industry are better grouping of controls and lubricating points, standardization of parts, and better temperature controls.[6]

[6] What's Wanted in Packaging Machinery, *Modern Packaging,* May, 1947, p. 104.

a. Cleaning Equipment. New containers are commonly cleaned by air cleaners. Hand-operated and automatic cleaners utilize vacuum, compressed air, or both. Rinsers utilize a spray of water to rinse inverted containers both inside and outside. Soaking and washing machines, employed for re-used glass containers, are more complicated.

Fig. 140. The rotary unscrambling table permits the contents of a case to be placed on the revolving table with individual items being fed in automatically. (*Island Equipment Corporation.*)

b. Unscramblers and Sorters. These devices are used to feed a variety of items such as caps, cans, jars, tubes, bottles, etc., to the packaging belt one at a time and in the desired position. Cartons of these items can then be dumped on the table and no hand sorting is required. Plungers may be used to remove empty tubes from cartons a row at a time and place them on sockets on the assembly belt which carries them through cleaning and in the correct position for filling.

c. Box and Cartoning Machinery. Whether the materials used are paperboard, fiberboard, wood veneer or plywood, wood, or plastics, the final formation of the box or carton will take place in the user's plant generally as close to the place of filling as is practicable.

For paper boxes, flat paper blanks (preprinted) are fed on a conveyor into the machine where a variety of operations fold, glue, and deposit on another conveyor the finished box ready to receive its contents. The same operations are performed for both parts of the box, the body and the cover.

One completely automatic machine makes plastic boxes. Flat stock is fed in one end and the completed box emerges at the other end. It is said to make transparent plastic boxes possible for articles that sell for as little as 10 cents.[7]

Box Making

Wood boxes and crates are assembled in special machines which nail and wire the wood members together. One machine drives all the nails into an 8-foot side of a crate at one time. Other machines form the individual sides, bringing these assemblies together automatically and ejecting the completed box.

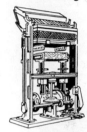

d. Filling Machinery. Free-flowing dry products are generally filled by volume. Usually this volume will be measured or weighed, although timed or regulated feeding may be used. For prevention of dust, the carton may be filled under vacuum or the product may be forced in by augers or compressed air plungers.

Free-flowing liquids may be packaged with a siphon filler. Though a siphon filler is slower than other types, it is simple and economical to operate. The pressure filler operates on the same order but is faster. The vacuum filler depends on a vacuum in the container being filled. This prevents the filling of a defective container.

Fig. 141. Electric-powered adjustable box-making machines produce from four to six boxes a minute. Precut lumber is placed in the jig which clamps and holds the pieces together while the machine drives in the necessary nails. (*"Flow Directory."*)

Viscous materials are generally inserted into containers by fillers of a rotary or constant-weight type. The latter utilizes pressure in the feed tank for its filling action and is usually hand operated. The former utilizes a series of piston pumps which rotate with the bottles. Certain liquid fillers may also be used by heating the feed line or by affixing a booster pump to it.

e. Bagging Machinery. Although this is another type of filling machinery, the use of bags introduces special problems. Glassine and cellophane bags have increased considerably in popularity within the last few years, and their application is constantly being expanded. Fiber and cloth bags are filled from rotary machines to which empty bags are affixed

---

[7] Plastic Box Machine, *Modern Packaging*, June, 1947, p. 102.

by hand. As the bags are filled to a specified weight, the flow of materials is stopped. The operator removes the full bag and puts it on a conveyor which takes it to a stitcher.

f. Capping and Sealing Equipment. Bottles may be capped by automatic machines which stop if either the bottle or the cap is missing. By the addition of a simple corking wheel the same machine may use

Fig. 142. Incoming conveyors feed cakes to wrapping machines at the American Lady Bakery, Denver, Col. (*Samuel Olson Manufacturing Company, Inc.*)

tapered corks. (A special machine is needed for the straight cork used in the wine industry.) These capping machines seal with a vacuum obtained mechanically or by steam condensation.

Bags and paper containers are sealed by glue, by wire staples or stitchers, by crimping, or by pressure or heat sealing of the edges. One firm releases a stated quantity of cranberries to a cellophane cylinder and then presses the edges together and seals it with heat. The top seal of one bag becomes the bottom seal of the next. Later they are cut apart.

Boxes and cartons are usually sealed with glue in a machine which brushes glue on the flaps, closes them, and applies pressure for a stated time to ensure a seal. This is done on a conveyor. Tin cans have lids placed on top, are sealed under vacuum and soldered, and then released to a conveyor which takes them to a unit which inserts a given number at a time in cartons. Wooden boxes and crates used in packing fruit and vegetables have the lids automatically placed in position and nailed down.

g. Wrapping Machinery. These machines cut a wrapper of the exact size needed from a roll of paper. The product to be wrapped is deposited on this as it moves along on a conveyor. Steel fingers crease the paper around it and fold in the ends. The top seam and then the ends are sealed by heat to form a tight bond.

h. Labeling and Marking Machinery. Identification and advertising of the product is usually part of the wrapper or the carton which receives the product. Tin cans, glass, and other containers not wrapped or printed have labels affixed to a side or front or have wrap-around labels. Where the position of the label on the container is not important, as on tin cans and other round items, the wrap-around type is used. This is put on by a rotary-type labeler. The straight-line type permits greater accuracy in spotting the label and can be used with a wide variety of shapes.

Code marking provides identification for individual batches or units of production. These are usually applied by a rotary wheel. One food product thus identifies its output by number of the branch plant, date of pack, and department number.

3. Methods of Closure

Correct closure methods are necessary to ensure a tight package that will not only provide all necessary protection for the container but enable it to reach the dealer with a salable appearance. The methods used will depend upon the type of materials being closed, the weight and size of the container, and the type of seal required.

a. Heat Sealing. This provides the tightest closure and is imperative where the imperishability of the product requires that air, moisture, and other damaging elements be excluded. It is used with glassine, waxed papers, and cellophane.

b. Gluing and Use of Other Adhesives. The importance of gluing increases along with the use of cardboard cartons and containers. Its importance at the present time can be judged by the results of a recent study in which it was revealed that 30.8 per cent of all damage to material packed in fiberboard shipping containers was due to unsealed container flaps.[8]

Proper gluing of containers, or cases as they are commonly called in industry, depends on proper selection and use of the adhesive. Proper selection of the adhesive requires consideration of four factors.

[8] F. R. Loetterle, Gluing Cartons and Shipping Containers, *University of Illinois Engineering Experiment Station, Circular Series* 56, 1949, p. 236.

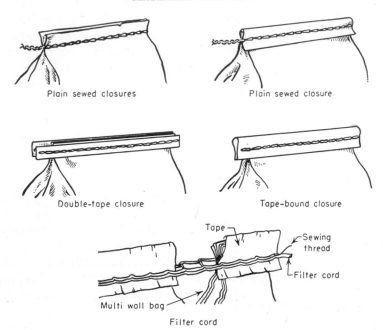

Plain sewed closures   Plain sewed closure

Double-tape closure   Tape-bound closure

Tape

Sewing
thread

Filter cord

Multi wall bag

Filter cord

FIG. 143. Types of sewing closures for fabric and paper bags. (*Union Special Machine Company.*)

a   *b*

FIG. 144. Bag-closing machines. (*a*) Fixed-base column type; (*b*) swinging-head type. (*Union Special Machine Company.*)

1. Type of box liner. These liners are the outside of a case, covering the corrugated or solid fiber center portion.

2. Sealing method. Are the flaps glued and closed by hand or by machine?

3. Compression time. How long are the flaps held down, allowing the adhesive to set and affect a bond without being under tension? Normal compression time on a machine is one minute or more.

4. To what ultimate conditions will the sealed container be exposed? Must the adhesive conform to government specifications for overseas shipments?

Gluing is used primarily for sealing the top flap of fiberboard cartons. The greatest single cause of failure is in the application of the glue, *i.e.*, proper amount, pressure applied until glue sets, clean equipment, etc. Glue has also been used with very successful results in preventing the shifting of cartons in rail shipments (see Fig. 150).

c. Stitching. The two main types of stitching are based on the binding agent used. The first type uses a cord or yarn to close bags. The other type uses a ductile wire to close fiberboard cartons.

Bag-closing machines are available for practically every type of textile and paper-bag material. They consist primarily of a stitching head, the type of support for the head, and the method of positioning the bag to the head

Fig. 145. Metal stitching machine used for closing of fiberboard cartons. (*Acme Steel Company.*)

during the sewing operation. The style of the stitching head depends on the material being sewed, the type of stitch needed, and the type of closure. The sewing head may be fixed to a machine base, mounted on a column or a swivel-arm support, or freely suspended in mid-air by a counterbalanced weight. The last two types are used for closing larger bags in limited quantities. Larger quantity operations generally demand a type in which the bags move under the closing head on conveyors. Roller, belt, and apron conveyors are commonly used for this purpose.

Wire stitching machines are used for the stitching of fiberboard cartons. The stitches are formed from a continuous coil of stitching wire. The machine cuts off a length, forms it into a U shape (usually $\frac{7}{16}$ inch wide), drives it into the carton, and clinches it in a single operation. Machines are differentiated by the types of supports for the clinching head. These are (1) the post type (used for stitching the bottoms of slotted-type cartons), (2) the straight-arm type (for putting stitches in side walls), and (3) the thin-blade type (similar to straight-arm type except that the arms are thinner and generally tapered for closing top flaps of cartons).[9]

d. Taping. Over 90 per cent of all gummed sealing tape manufactured is used for cartons. When properly used, it creates a permanent bond. The tape is made in different widths and with different weights of kraft paper.

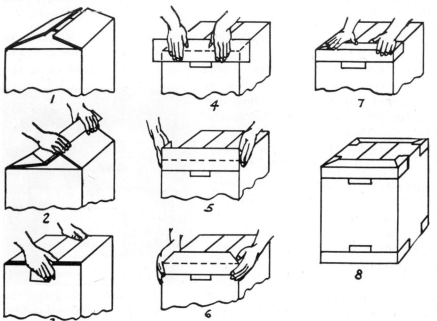

Fig. 146. Steps in the application of gummed tape. Strip should be long enough to provide a 2½-inch overlap at each end. As soon as the tape is in place, it should be rubbed down firmly and evenly.

The major causes of difficulty with the use of tape is the failure to moisten the tape properly and maintain pressure until the glue has had time to set. These further pointers have also been given for proper sealing of packages: [10]

1. Arrange material that is to be wrapped in an orderly fashion so that the finished package will look either square, oblong, or be in the shape of a cylinder.

[9] A. G. Denne, "Stitching Wire and Machines," *University of Illinois Engineering Experiment Station, Circular Series* 56, 1949, p. 221.

[10] Burton Lee Trodson, "Taping," *University of Illinois Engineering Experiment Station, Circular Series* 56, 1949, p. 228.

2. Always seal along the seams of the wrapping paper, chipboard, corrugated board, or protective wrapping.

3. See that the seam occurs where there is a fairly smooth surface in order to provide an adequate amount of surface for adhesion of the tape.

In other words, a little careful study of the product to be wrapped in a package will result in a properly sealed, properly protected package.

e. Metal Strapping. The two types of metal strapping are flat and round. The first is a flat band of high-tensile steel either galvanized or black enameled. A hand or machine unit is used to tension this band, apply a metal clip, crimp the clip to the band to hold the tension, and cut off excess strapping. The round type consists of high-tensile-quality galvanized wire held under tension by having the two ends of the wire twisted together.

The basic functions of strapping are: [11]

1. To strengthen and reinforce shipping containers.

2. To effect savings in over-all container and packing costs.

3. To bundle together into an easily handled package a number of durable items shipped without a container.

4. To prepare palletized units of merchandise for economical handling in transportation and storage.

4. Cushioning Materials

Damage to materials in transit may be classified as chemical or mechanical in nature. The latter is caused by failure of the outer container or by inadequate cushioning. Of the three principal causes of shock damage (in-transit vibration, impact, and dropping), dropping is generally the most serious in its effects.

The principal functions of the materials used in packaging are:

1. *To absorb and distribute shock.* This may be done by means of an inner container which holds the article rigidly in place away from the outer confines of the package.

2. *To transform and distribute shock.* This may be done by bolting the article (such as a washing machine) to a rigid base in a sawed-wood, wire-bound, or corrugated container (see page 186).

3. *To localize the stresses caused by shock.* A good example is a radio tube suspended by a webbing inside a corrugated container (see page 185; also see page 212).

In selecting the proper kind of cushioning means which will deflect properly the dynamic force to which it will be subjected and at the

---

[11] Harry M. Reed, "Closure Methods and Marking," *University of Illinois Engineering Experiment Station, Circular Series* 56, 1949, p. 231.

same time will support the load, the following qualities in the cushioning material must be considered: [12]

1. It must be of the proper density to support the unit without undue compression.

2. It must give in readily and uniformly under the stress it may experience.

3. It must withstand rough handling and repeated shock without deteriorating.

4. It must stand up under moisture conditions that may occur.

5. It must retain its form under repeated shocks.

6. It must not "dust" too easily.

If these qualities cannot be secured, than those factors which are most advantageous must govern our choice, with conditions 1 and 2 essential in all cases.

a. Excelsior. This finely shredded wood product is not recommended for packing of most industrial products. Aside from a fire hazard it tends to lose its resiliency when wet. When made up into padding, however, its usefulness improves. This is used, for example, in the wrapping of fine furniture where it is shipped with no other protection.

b. Shredded Paper. Shredded newspaper is most commonly used, though it is limited in resiliency and complications arise when used for shipments with a foreign destination. Shredded wax papers are more resistant to moisture. Glassine and kraft papers are also shredded. Extremely delicate instruments are often packed in shredded parchment, which provides even greater resiliency. Companies using a large quantity of ordinary paper shredding often install their own shredding or macerating machines.

c. Crepe Cellulose Wadding. This wadding is used both for cushioning against shock and for protection of surface finishes. Small parts are easily wrapped and put in cartons. When used for overseas packing, it should be water-resistant or be placed in a waterproof wrapper or container.

d. Flexible Corrugated Paper. This material consists of a corrugated face with a test liner on one side. Its advantage is its ability to be folded in any direction and still provide a substantial amount of cushioning protection. It is available in a variety of kraft and corrugated facings, including crepe-back and waterproof liners. As it is generally used from a roll, it permits speedier wrapping, even of unusually shaped packages (see Fig. 147).

e. Other Cushioning Materials. In addition to the ones already described, which are more commonly used, a number of other materials

[12] A. M. Underhill, "Basic Principles of Package Cushioning," Packaging Series 33, p. 8, American Management Association, 1950.

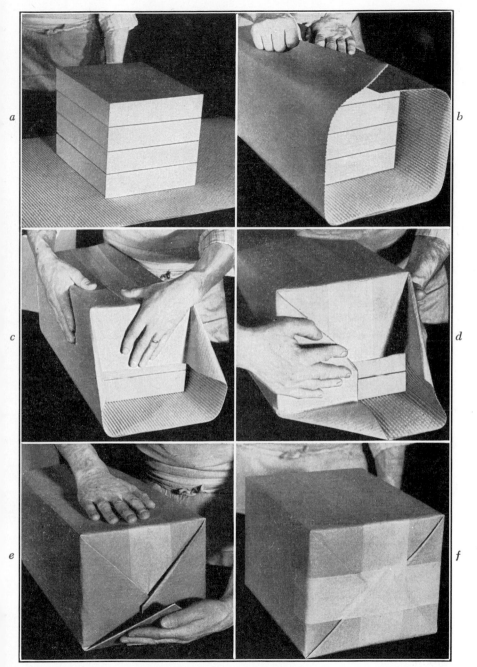

Fig. 147. Steps in wrapping tight package with corrugated paper. (*a*) Place article on sheet of corrugated paper. (*b*) Fold side of sheet over top and overlap. (*c*) First fold easily and smoothly, sides even, edges neat. (*d*) Make side folds snug. (*e*) Bottom's up, ready for final seal. (*f*) Job is neat, secure, and cheap, with extra cushioning at end. (*Sherman Paper Products Corporation.*)

find application in special instances. Wood hull and sponge rubber have limited uses. A new product, milkweed floss, is a Mexican fiber which is combined with rubber. Wood wool, which was originally started as a substitute for Kimpak, has increased its sales since the end of the Second World War.

5. Other Product Protection

Articles may be protected from shock by means other than cushioning materials. This is accomplished not so much by the particular type of

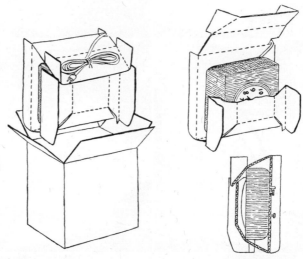

Fig. 148. Tapered walls to support the top, bottom, and side edges provide key to standardization of shockproof carton for clock cases. (*American Management Association, Packaging Series 33, p. 22.*)

container that is used but by the special design of the unit to deflect, absorb, or localize the effects of any impacts or shocks.

a. Bracing. This may consist of wood braces or cardboard folded to provide an extra cushioning effect. Cardboard arms were used at Telechron, Inc., to suspend clocks within a carton. As a result of a standardization program, 29 filler inserts (shown in Fig. 148) made it possible to package 52 different clock models in just three unit and master carton sizes. This affected 96 per cent of the clock production of the plant and resulted in savings in packing labor and materials of from 20 to 30 per cent in each group.[13]

[13] R. B. Aldrich, "Case Histories of Packaging Developments at Affiliated Companies," Packaging Series 33, p. 17, American Management Association, 1950.

Where diagonal distortion of the container may damage the article being shipped, it should be braced to a limited number of points. Articles with legs are generally supported by braces taking the strain and weight from the legs. The method of handling will have to be considered in the location of this bracing. A heavy electric motor bolted to a skid base and covered with a plywood or wire-bound box or crate may have to have braces at the side to permit handling by overhead crane. This is particularly important for overseas shipments.

b. Full-floating Suspension. Although the cardboard braces mentioned above provide a high degree of protection for even very fragile articles, sometimes additional steps must be taken to ensure safe delivery. This means a full suspension of the article. Figure 128 provides a good example of the free-floating suspension of a delicate article, in this case a radio transmitting tube, by means of straps or webbing materials.

c. En Masse Floating. Another means of absorbing shock is the use of a resilient inert mass. In fact, many of the cushioning materials are used for that purpose. Sponge rubber and pulp paper have also been used for this purpose.

6. Wrapping and Packaging Materials

These materials are used as a wrapper or container to enclose the article or articles for one or more of the following purposes: [14]

1. To protect against contamination.
2. To provide mechanical protection.
3. To prevent removal of corrosion preventive.
4. To unitize sets or to group identical parts.

They come to the user in the form of bags, flat paper tubes, or paper in rolls ready for use.

a. Kraft Paper. The natural color of this paper is brown but it is often bleached. It is used primarily for its strength and low cost. As the most widely used of all packaging materials, it constitutes over 50 per cent of all paper and paperboard produced. It is used as a wrapping paper or in the shape of bags or tubes. It also forms the base of a number of treated papers.

b. Processed Papers. A number of various characteristics may be imparted to basic pulp paper by processing and various ingredients being added during production. The most common result is a "greaseproof" paper that is resistant to the penetration of grease. It is generally made

[14] Packaging research section, Manufacturing Research Division, International Harvester Company.

by a machine process of hydration by which water is forced into the cellulose fibers of the paper.

"Glassine" paper is made by redampening and supercalendering grease-proof paper under high pressure and heat. It may be further treated to provide a tarnishproof, alkalineproof, or rustproof and moldproof paper. It may also be coated with wax, lacquer, or rosins, or it may be laminated.

   c. *Vegetable Parchment.* This material is neither vegetable nor parchment, but originally it had the appearance of parchment. It was formerly made from cotton fibers, but it is now made of wood pulp. Its outstanding characteristic is its high greaseproof quality and its wet strength. It will resist almost any type of oil, grease, turpentine, or shortening, etc. It is used largely for containers and liners for these products as well as for a number of food products. This last is also due to the fact that it is odorless, tasteless, and noncontaminating to foods.

   d. *Treated Papers.* Either the plain kraft or the various process forms may be further adapted to special requirements by various treating, coating, or impregnating processes. The most important of these are the waxed and the heat-sealing papers.

The wax paper is made by coating or impregnating the basic stock with wax. This is done by one of three processes. In the first, a wax emulsion is beat into the paper stock. Another method is to impregnate the finished paper with wax, which gives a non-heat-sealing paper. Still another method is to coat one or both sides of the paper with wax ("wet-wax method") which makes it highly resistant to both grease and water.

Vapor phase inhibitor paper (VPI) has been developed to arrest the corrosive action of oxygen and moisture on packaged metals. The VPI is a chemical developed by Shell Development Company of California which exudes a vapor. This vapor prevents corrosion when both moisture and oxygen are present. Hermetic sealing of the package is not necessary. In fact, one company states that a single piece of VPI paper only 4 inches square is sufficient for a part 6 inches in diameter when packaged in a cellophane bag.[15]

   e. *Plastic Films.* Plastic films, such as cellophane, acetate, pliofilm, and sarran, may be used in sheet form or for impregnating, coating, and sealing paper stock. A recent development is polythene (or called poly-ethylene), which is a clear plastic material. It is available in a wide range of thicknesses and is durable, flexible, translucent, odorless, and moisture-resistant.

   f. *Fabric Materials.* Cotton bags are used for bulk products. Their main advantages are re-use, sanitation, and the fact that they may be

---

[15] See Aaren Wachter, "V.P.I. Papers," *University of Illinois Engineering Experiment Station, Circular Series* 56, 1949, p. 81.

provided with a printed pattern for customer appeal. They do not provide the protection afforded by multi-wall paper bags against moisture, vapor, and heat.

Burlap bags are made from India jute fiber and are used where a high resistance to puncture is desired. Extra protection may be obtained for its contents by using a paper liner or by asphalt lamination.

QUESTIONS

1. Give some indication of the size and importance of the packaging industry.

2. Why is the layout of a packaging area so important to the efficient movement of materials?

3. What are the main types of packaging machinery? Describe in detail how any three of them perform their respective functions.

4. Describe the methods of closing packages.

5. What instructions should be given for the proper use of gummed sealing tape in the sealing of packages?

6. What are the basic functions of strapping?

7. What are the principal functions of cushioning materials?

8. What factors affect the selection of cushioning materials?

9. List and describe the most commonly used cushioning materials.

10. How can articles be protected from shock and impact while in transit?

11. Describe the characteristics of the main types of wrapping papers.

PROJECTS FOR FURTHER STUDY

1. Discuss the use of various cushioning materials and methods for the safe transit of delicate instruments.

2. Obtain a description (plus photographs and drawings if possible) of packaging tables in the shipping departments of several local department stores. After a class discussion, have each student prepare suggestions for the improvement of layout, packaging method, and materials used.

3. Obtain from local suppliers price lists of various types of packaging materials.

CHAPTER 15

RESEARCH IN PACKAGING AND
MATERIALS HANDLING

1. Development of Research Facilities

Inasmuch as interest in materials handling and packaging as major factors in cost reduction is of comparatively recent date, the development of research facilities in these areas has come largely since the beginning of the Second World War. New problems of handling, product protection, and transportation caused by the exigencies of war provided the impetus needed for their rapid development.

Testing of materials, their qualities and characteristics, and of containers themselves, has a considerable longer history. The beginning of the First World War was a significant date for several developments in container testing. In 1914, the War Department called upon the Forest Products Laboratory to set up general specifications for overseas packages. The purpose was to redesign many containers along more economical lines.

However, this laboratory performed tests on containers as early as 1905. It is also known that as early as 1886 the U.S. Forest Service had been conducting tests to determine the physical and mechanical properties of native woods. These tests showed that laboratory tests on shipping containers were practical. They also indicated that the species of lumber was only one of the factors to be considered in the construction of efficient wood containers.

In 1910, the U.S. Forest Service established the Forest Products Laboratory at Madison, Wis., in collaboration with the University of Wisconsin, which donated land, labor, and materials. In 1915, the Laboratory began a series of tests with organizations concerned with packaging. Among these were the National Association of Retail Grocers, the National Association of Box Manufacturers, and the National Association of Wholesale Grocers. The testing methods developed by the Forest Products Laboratory have been adopted as the standard for containers by manufacturers, shippers, associations, and others dealing with packaging.

Some of the more prominent agencies besides the Forest Products Laboratory are the American Society for Testing Materials, the Shipper

Container Institute, the Technical Association of the Pulp and Paper Industry, the Freight Loading and Container Bureau, and others.

a. Corporation Research. Materials-handling research at the International Harvester Company began with a small unit at the Milwaukee

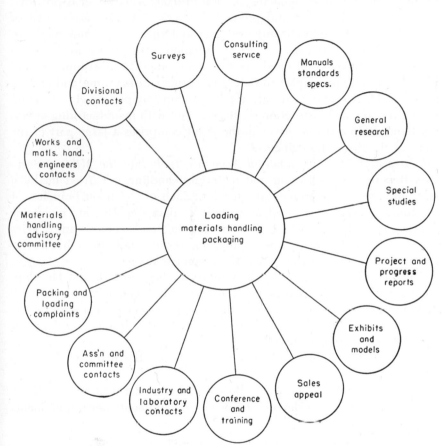

Fig. 149. Loading, materials-handling, and packaging research functional chart. (*International Harvester Company.*)

works in 1930 and was extended to the other plants of the company in 1936. When the manufacturing research department was set up in 1944, the materials handling and product protection section was made a part.

This research department has its own building in south Chicago comprising 230,000 square feet of space. The various subdivisions include the administrative, plant engineering, mechanical engineering, materials handling and product protection, welding, metallurgical, protective finishes (oils, varnishes, paints), inspection methods, forging, foundry and manufacturing standards sections.

The section pertaining to packaging, shipping practices, and materials handling consists of two supervisors, three materials-handling research engineers, and eight technicians. A total of 9,000 square feet is provided for research of handling and product protection. A wide assortment of testing devices is used in testing container materials and packing methods. Scale models of rail cars are used to demonstrate proper loading and tie-down methods. Full-sized tractors and other farm equipment are brought in and taken apart to determine proper dismantling and crating methods. These methods are given to the factory by personnel instruction or through detailed instruction sheets. Contact with manufacturing operations and divisional executives in the plant comprises a large part of the work of the research engineers.[1]

b. Research by Governmental Agencies, Including the Military Services. Research in packaging and materials handling is carried on by a large number of governmental agencies. Each of the main branches of the military services as well as various civilian departments maintains personnel and facilities for testing of materials and methods and carries forward an aggressive research program, coordinated through the Defense Department's Research and Development Board.

The coordinating agency in the military is the Research and Development Board of the Department of Defense. Military packaging research and development is coordinated through the Packaging Panel of the Material and Equipment Committee of the Research and Development Board of the Department of Defense.

Amongst civilian branches of the government the main coordinating groups are:

1. The Federal Specifications Board. The Board issues specifications, one section of which is devoted to packaging and container requirements for the commodity covered by the specification.

2. The Commodity Standards Division of the National Bureau of Standards. The Commodity Standards Division prepares standards for containers and materials-handling equipment. It also conducts or supervises basic research in laboratories of its own and also cooperating groups both military and civilian.

3. The Forest Products Laboratory. Since 1905, the Forest Products Laboratory has gradually become the center of research in characteristics of all wood containers.

A wide program of basic research is carried on in a large number

[1] See more detailed description in *Modern Materials Handling*, May, 1950, p. 50.

of individual laboratories. Container testing laboratories are located in the following centers:

Container Research and Development Division
Quartermaster Food and Container Institute for the Armed Forces
1819 West Pershing Road
Chicago 9, Ill.

Air Materiel Command
Engineering Division
Wright-Patterson Air Force Base
Dayton, Ohio

Squier Signal Laboratory, SCEL
Fort Monmouth, N.J.

Engineer Research and Development Laboratories
The Engineer Center
Fort Belvoir, Va.

U.S. Naval Supply Research and Development Facility
Supply Engineering Division
Naval Supply Depot
Bayonne, N.J.

Department of the Army
Rock Island Arsenal
Rock Island, Ill.

Naval Clothing Depot
29th Street and Third Avenue
Brooklyn 32, N.Y.

Picatinny Arsenal
Dover, N.J.

Naval Ordnance Materials Handling Laboratory
U.S. Naval Base Station
Hingham, Mass.

Transportation Corps Board
New York Port of Embarkation
First Avenue and 58th Street
Brooklyn, N.Y.

Naval Air Material Center
U.S. Naval Base Station
Aeronautical Materials Laboratory
Philadelphia 12, Pa.

Los Alamos Scientific Laboratory
Sandia Bas Branch
P.O. Box 5,800
Albuquerque, N.M.

In the military services, work in packaging and materials handling is done by various departments:

1. The Air Materiel Command maintains as part of the Engineering Division a complete packaging laboratory to evaluate all materials, packaging techniques, and packaging. At the present time, emphasis is being put on transportation of dangerous materials by air, metal containers, shock and vibration, and crating of components for domestic shipping.

2. The Department of the Army maintains a packaging activity in each of its seven technical services. Most of these services are performing

research and testing in the field of containers and packaging. The various services provide courses in materials handling and packaging within their training schools. Experiments are also conducted in methods of loading, warehousing, and packing and crating.

3. The Department of the Navy carries on research in packaging and materials handling at its Naval Supply Research and Development Facility at Bayonne, N.J. Investigations are conducted in the fields of stevedoring, car and truck loading, equipment design and usability (materials handling), and packaging and preservation—primarily from the standpoint of military logistics support. This includes testing and research of pallets, skid tests of fork trucks, and humping of freight cars with test loads. In addition, laboratories operated by the Bureau of Aeronautics, the Bureau of Ships, and the Bureau of Ordnance carry on programs of packaging materials application and research.

The results of much of this research is currently available to industry. A complete list of Simplified Practice Recommendations may be obtained from the National Bureau of Standards of the U.S. Department of Commerce.

A series of military (MIL) specifications outline requirements for containers and packaging of materials. These are available from the Army through the Specifications Branch of each of the respective services, *i.e.*, Quartermaster, Ordnance, etc. They may also be obtained from the U.S. Navy Bureau of Supplies and Accounts, Washington, D.C. In addition, a number of training manuals and technical manuals developed by the Department of the Army are available from the Superintendent of Documents.

c. Research by Associations. One of the most significant developments of recent date in packaging research has been the formation of the national safe transit program originally sponsored by the Porcelain Enamel Institute, Inc. This program is under the direction of a committee made up of manufacturers, container firms, and carriers. A testing program of the group is based upon the conclusion that the only basis for predicting safe transit of products was by exposing the packaged unit to standard performance tests prior to shipment. Separate procedures were devised for package units under 100 pounds and for other units of from 100 to 1,000 pounds.

Members may install their own testing equipment or may rely on established laboratories for conducting the specified tests. Equipment required includes two simple pieces for heavy units and a third piece for light units, which, including a shock recorder, would cost approximately $2,000. A complete procedure for one of the testing projects follows:

Testing Procedure for Project 1-A [2]

This procedure for Project 1-A of the National Safe Transit Program covers testing of packaged products, both single and multiple packed, weighing under 100 pounds as prepared for transportation.

Test cycle shall consist of:

1. Vibration test
2. Drop test

Tests shall be conducted in the order indicated.

Vibration-test Equipment

L.A.B. Package Tester or other equipment producing equivalent results.

Test Procedure and Performance Limits

The packaged product shall be placed on the table of the vibration tester; fences may be attached to the test table suitable for the product being tested. Vibration frequency shall be such that the packaged product leaves the table momentarily at some interval during the vibration cycle (equivalent to acceleration of "1g + "). The test shall be run for a minimum of 1 hour.

Note: A simple method of determining "1g + " is to advance the cycle of vibration until a thin piece of cardboard can be inserted between one bottom edge of the packaged product and the platform of the machine.

Drop-test Equipment

The apparatus shall consist of the following:

1. Divided table top drop tester such as Acme Drop Tester or other equipment producing equivalent results.
2. Hoist with suitable sling tripping device. Surface on which package is to be dropped must be a flat firm base (such as steel, concrete, etc.).

Test Procedure and Performance Limits Procedure

The procedure for identifying faces, edges, and corners of containers shall be as follows:

1. Facing one end of the container, with the manufacturer's joint, if any, on the observer's right:

Designate the top of the container as 1
The right side as 2
The bottom as 3
The left side as 4
The near end as 5
The far end as 6

2. Identifying edges by numbers of two faces that form that edge.

Example: 1-2 identifies the edge formed by the top and the right side. 2-5 the edge formed by the right side and the near end.

3. Identifying the corners by the numbers of the three faces that meet to form that corner.

[2] As of Jan. 1, 1950.

Example: 1-2-5 identifies the corner formed by the top, right side, and the near end.

The packaged product shall be dropped from the prescribed height (see performance limits) in the following sequence which constitutes a drop-test cycle:

a. A corner drop on the 5-1-2 corner
b. An edge drop on the shortest edge radiating from that corner
c. An edge drop on the next shortest edge radiating from that corner
d. An edge drop on the longest edge radiating from that corner
e. A flatwise drop on one of the smallest faces
f. A flatwise drop on the opposite smallest face
g. A flatwise drop on one of the medium faces
h. A flatwise drop on the opposite medium face
i. A flatwise drop on one of the largest faces
j. A flatwise drop on the opposite large face

Performance Limits

1. Weight of packaged product—50 pounds and under. Articles—single or multiple packaged products such as washing-machine tubs, table tops, stove panels, etc. Drop 24 inches.

1a. Weight of packaged product—over 50 pounds and under approximately 100 pounds. Articles—as in 1. Drop—12 inches minimum or 72 inches on Conbur (optional).*

2. Weight of packaged product—50 pounds and under. Articles—completely assembled products (and allied parts) such as roasters, cookers, hot-plates, etc. Drop—18 inches.

2a. Weight of packaged product—over 50 pounds and under approximately 100 pounds. Articles—as in 2. Drop—12 inches minimum or 72 inches on Conbur (optional).*

3. Weight of packaged product—50 pounds and under. Articles—hollowware. Drop—12 inches minimum.

3a. Weight of packaged product—over 50 pounds and under approximately 100 pounds. Articles—as above. Drop—12 inches minimum or 72 inches on Conbur (optional).*

The packaged product shall be considered to have satisfactorily passed this test, if upon unpacking, the product is free from damage.

The number of packaged products to be tested is left to the judgment of the manufacturer; however, the sample should be sufficiently large to assure valid results.

Testing facilities for packaging research are provided in England by the packaging laboratory of Patra House, which was opened in its new location at Leatherhead in October, 1948. This association was formed in 1931 as the Printing Industry Research Association. In 1937, it was re-

* If the use of Conbur Incline Testing Device is elected, the sequence of the test will be as described under Drop Test.

named Printing and Allied Trades Research Association with research being done principally on the optical and mechanical properties of paper. Packaging problems were first included in the research program in 1942 and 1943.

At the present time, the work of Patra can be divided into three main headings in each of its two divisions, printing and packaging: (1) research; (2) advisory service; (3) information service.

Research work on packaging is concentrated on the protective quality of packages, on studying and improving the protection afforded by packages and packaging materials against (1) mechanical damage to contents and to the package; (2) water vapor; (3) liquids; (4) gases (carbon dioxide, etc.); (5) insects; (6) molds.

As part of the information service, Patra operates a package testing laboratory which carries out routine tests on packages of all kinds. Packages are tested for strength; for protective qualities against mechanical damage, water vapor, and gas resistance; for resistance to the penetration of liquids; and for resistance to attack from insects and molds. The laboratory carries out its tests on a fee basis, charges being lower for members than for nonmembers. In addition, the laboratory staff produces two monthly publications, *Printing Abstracts* and *Packaging Abstracts*. The latter have recently been expanded in scope to cover all forms of packaging materials, including glass jars, metal cans, and drums, in addition to those made of flexible materials hitherto included. This publication is now available to nonmembers on annual subscription basis. The technical library includes some 4,000 books and periodicals, which are lent to members each year. Special research reports, technical papers, bulletins, information leaflets, and a bimonthly journal are also used to convey the results of the tests to its members.

2. Types of Testing

Testing procedures consist of tests made of the containers, which generally test the strength of the unit and its ability to protect its contents, and more exhaustive tests of the nature of the materials themselves. These are tests of fiber strength, resistance to weather conditions, strength of woods, and study of basic material characteristics.

The two general classifications of container testing are the field service test and the laboratory test. Many shippers argue that a service test of containers in transit (*i.e.*, observing the package and its content after it has been shipped) is sufficient to determine its utility. However, these containers in transit are subjected to constantly changing conditions and hazards and it is sometimes difficult to ascertain the exact cause of the failures observed in the tests.

A more general viewpoint on the value of the two types of testing is reflected by the comment of R. C. Lambrect, industrial head of the Electrical Motors Division of General Motors Corporation. He stated, "Laboratory work on loss and damage prevention is a necessity and while we use drop tests, etc., in working out container design, we feel

TABLE 5. REPORTED CAUSES OF DAMAGE IN STUDY OF 733,308 TEST BOXES

Item No.	Cause of damage	No. of boxes reported damaged	No. of boxes reported damaged by cause groups	Total damage, per cent
	Excessive slack in load:			
1	Excessive lengthwise slack...............	1,017 ⎫	1,128	14.4
2	Excessive crosswise slack................	111 ⎰		
	Poor car preparation:			
3	Nails, wire, boards, straps not removed.....	634 ⎫	642	8.2
4	Dirty car............................	8 ⎰		
	Poor arrangement of cargo:			
5	Poor arrangement of cargo...............	346 ⎫	491	6.3
6	Partial layer..........................	145 ⎰		
	Inadequate bracing:			
7	Weak or broken bracing.................	33 ⎫		
8	Poor design of bracing..................	678		
9	Poor car-door bracing...................	310	1,158	14.8
10	Poor bracing material...................	13		
11	No bracing............................	124 ⎰		
	Cars needing repair:			
12	Leaky car............................	499 ⎫		
13	Broken car walls.......................	25	681	8.7
14	Broken floor or floor racks..............	157 ⎰		
	Rough handling:			
15	Rough handling of car in transit..........	...	1,339	17.1
16	Rough handling during loading...........	...	176	2.2
	Miscellaneous:			
17	General crushing, rubbing, and punctures...	...	559	7.1
18	Crushing due to stacking................	...	263	3.4
19	Open manufacturer's joint...............	...	77	1.0
20	Case flaps unsealed.....................	...	1,311	16.8
	Total................................	...	7,825	100.0

* W. B. Lincoln, Jr., Shipping Container Study, *Modern Packaging*, April, 1948 p. 168.

TABLE 6. RESPONSIBILITY FOR CAUSES OF DAMAGE OUTLINED IN TABLE 5 [*]

Railroads		Shippers		Box quality	
Item No.	Per cent of responsibility	Item No.	Per cent of responsibility	Item No.	Per cent of responsibility
3	23.8	1–2	26.4	17	62.2
4	0.3	4–5	11.5	18	29.3
12	18.8	7–11	27.2	19	8.5
13	0.9	16	4.1		
14	5.9	20	30.8		
15	50.3				
Total.....	100.0	....	100.0	....	100.0
Per cent of damage reported	34	....	54.5	....	11.5

[*] W. B. Lincoln, Jr., Shipping Container Study, *Modern Packaging*, April, 1948, p. 168.

no answer is final until field service tests are made and the results tabulated." [3]

The Army–Navy joint packaging boards have also made considerable use of field service testing. They have sent test shipments to many parts of the world to check on durability, weather resistance, etc. In addition, these tests are often supplemented by laboratory tests. An attempt is made to duplicate the actual shipping conditions, including weather, climate, and handling.

a. *Field Tests.* Criteria for the conduct of field service tests were recently offered by the technical manager of Inland Container Corporation. In a recent article,[4] he listed the following basic requirements for sound performance tests:

1. Isolation and identification of the hazards shipping containers encounter in service.

2. A determination of the degree of severity of each of these hazards, preferably stated in fundamental engineering units.

[3] R. C. Lambrect, How Packaging Research Pays, *Railway Age*, Aug. 6, 1949, p. 247.
[4] W. B. Lincoln, Jr., Shipping Container Study, *Modern Packaging*, April, 1948, p. 168.

3. The necessary instrumentation studies to develop and prove the suitability of testing devices and procedures as a means of evaluating container performance characteristics, using the term "performance" in the sense previously discussed.

With this foundation available, he stated that it was then possible to determine: [5]

1. Characteristics and standards for materials, combined board, boxes and completed packs.

2. The inter-relation between these various factors.

3. The influence of fabrication practices in the box plant upon complete pack characteristics.

4. The influence of design upon complete pack characteristics.

In a recent study of a large number of packages sent by rail it was found that 0.9 per cent of the boxes shipped were damaged in transit to the extent of causing the consignee to file damage claims against the railroads.

Responsibility for the cause of damage found under this report was allocated as follows:

	Per Cent
Railroads	34
Shippers	54.5
Boxmakers	11.5
Total	100.0

Inadequate bracing and improper bulkheading was found to be one of the larger causes of damage. Some form of permanent flush-door blocking as well as adjustable bulkheads was indicated as needed.

Carloading impact tests were conducted at the Naval Supply Depot, Bayonne, N.J., in February, 1946, with the assistance of the Association of American Railroads.

The purpose of these tests was to analyze and compare the reaction of lading to impacts under the following four methods of shipment in a freight car:

1. Conventional load—bonded block pattern
2. Glued unitized load—bonded block pattern
3. Palletized load—material not secured to pallet
4. Glued palletized load

Test boxcars loaded by all four methods with W5C fiberboard boxes of bottled beer were subjected to a series of impacts at varying speeds. A complete motion-picture record was obtained. Complete statistical data recorded at the

[5] *Ibid.*

a   b

Fig. 150. Carloading impact tests. (*a*) Displaced cartons from palletized loads after the fifth impact; 58 bottles were broken. (*b*) Glued palletized load after similar treatment. All bottles in glued cartons intact. (*Official U.S. Navy photographs.*)

time of the report coupled with a series of photographs form the basis of this report.[6]

Total breakage of bottles was as follows:

Test number	Bottles broken	Damaged cardboard boxes
1	87	23
2	91	22
3	58	0
4	5 *	

* Found in cases placed loose in the doorway void.

b. Laboratory Testing of Containers. A first requirement of this type of testing is to reproduce the exact forces in the same degree as encountered

[6] "Carloading Impact Tests Data, Report No. 1, 26 March, 1946," U.S. Naval Supply Operational Training Center, Naval Supply Depot, Bayonne, N.J.

in field operation. The first consideration is whether to test the container alone or with its content. Another question to be determined is the representative number of specimens to be used. The number of testings to be given to a particular container must also be determined.

The types of test more commonly used to test the mechanical characteristics of containers are:

1. *Drop test.* This test is used to measure the ability of the container to withstand rough handling or its ability to protect its content. Two types of dropping apparatus are commonly used for this test.

FIG. 151. Fork trucks used to elevate end of large crate to make drop test. Other end is supported on rigid 12-inch support. (*International Harvester Company.*)

The divided table top is usually used for drops of short distances (21 to 48 inches). This consists of a table or flat surface with two trap doors which open and fall away quickly, allowing the box placed on the table to fall to the floor. Usually for greater distances, the second type, a hoist sling apparatus, is used. With this device a rope on a hoist is looped through a tripping mechanism. The package is attached to the other end of the rope and when the mechanism is released, the loop flies off and the crate falls to the ground.

In this test a specimen is dropped on its face, its edge, and its corners (often in a predetermined order).

2. *Incline impact test.* This test is used for the same purpose as the drop test, but generally for heavier packages weighing over 300 pounds.

Included in this apparatus are a two-rail inclined track which accommodates a dolly, a moving carriage on which the test specimens are placed, and a rigid bumper. It is now almost universally standard to have the track inclined at 10 degrees. The bumper, which is a backstop, is placed at an angle of 90 degrees to the inclined track.

The test is carried out by placing the crate on the dolly and raising it to the predetermined height on the track, depending upon the objective of the test. When the dolly is released, it plunges downward into the bumper. The container being tested is located coincidental with the edge of the dolly or projected 2 inches beyond the forward end. The

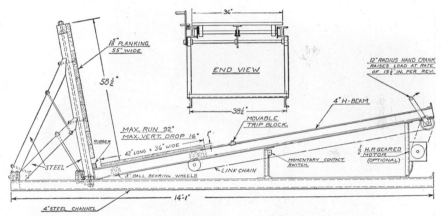

FIG. 152. Automatic Conbur tester used for incline-impact test. (*L. A. B. Corporation.*)

testing may be done on the face, corner, or the edge of the container. An impact recording machine is attached to the container in order to measure the amount of force exerted at the point of impact. This provides for accurate measure of the force and, therefore, of the consequences of the impact.

3. *Compression test.* This test measures the rigidity of the container or its ability to resist crushing from external forces which it may be subjected to from either static loads—as the top of a crate at the bottom of a stack of crates—or dynamic loads. Dynamic loads are the type applied to the ends of a container in moving cars. Here, as in the other two tests, pressure is applied to the diagonally opposite corners and edges and to the faces.

The testing machine consists of two parallel steel platens, one above the other. The container is placed on the bottom immovable platen and the top platen presses down on the container. This unit is generally operated by hydraulic pressure. A recording gauge on the apparatus records the load being applied and the strength of the crate.[7]

[7] T. J. Gross, The Compression Test, *Modern Packaging*, April, 1946, p. 147.

The compression test like no other test can furnish information regarding manufacturing practices entirely independent of the materials involved. Being extremely sensitive to fabrication defects, it provides a perfect mirror to reflect faulty equipment and inefficient methods in a box-maker's plant.

4. *Hexagonal revolving-drum test.* This test contains baffles, guides, projections, etc., mounted on the inside of the drum, in such a manner as

Fig. 153. Two-way ride recorder used to register intensity and duration of impacts. (*The Impact Register Company.*)

to raise, drop, slide, twist, and tumble on a revolving drum or as to simulate actual transportation hazards. This is one of the most versatile tests, although its complete validity has sometimes been questioned. There are two types of drums in common use. One, 7 feet in diameter, is used for containers weighing less than 250 pounds; another, 14 feet in diameter, is used for containers heavier than 250 pounds.

5. *Weaving test.* This test utilizes an oscillating table or car which moves horizontally forward and backward through any distances up to 8 inches to reproduce the swaying action of a moving train. By clamping the container to the table and by fastening weight to the top equal to the weight to be carried by the container, it will reveal the weaknesses in rigidity and resistance to racking or skewing.

6. *Impact shear test.* This test uses the same oscillating table, but leaves the container free to move horizontally back and forth between two bumpers subjecting it to the same type of shear impact as that of a stopping and starting freight car.

FIG. 154. Compression tests are made of various wood products and forms. This photograph shows a glued laminated-wood arch under test. (*U.S. Forest Service, Forest Products Laboratory.*)

7. *Vibration test.* This test not only measures the effect of sharp jars, such as the sudden stopping and starting of a car, but it also measures the continuous vibrations and bumps sustained by a moving train. The machine used for this test is a vibrator, a table $5\frac{1}{2}$ by 4 feet with vertical and horizontal travel of $\frac{1}{4}$ inch.

Very often prior to the mechanical tests which have just been listed, the container will be subjected to water immersion, water spray, or exposure to fixed conditions of air temperature or humidity. There are other tests which also test the quality of the material used in containers.

c. Material Characteristics:

1. Crushing tests are used to determine the peak pressure to which any particular type of corrugated cardboard can normally be subjected.

Fɪɢ. 155. Revolving drum for testing boxes and crates. (*U.S. Forest Service, Forest Products Laboratory.*)

The puncture test uses the Beach Puncture tester which measures the puncture resistance of fiberboard or other material to be tested. The apparatus involves the use of a pendulum on the end of which is a rod bent in the form of a 90-degree arc. On the end of the rod is fixed a solid metal triangular pyramid 1 inch in height.

The board to be tested is held between two clamping plates which are approximately at the levels of the axes of the pendulum. The pendulum is held by a trigger and a stop in a horizontal position. When the trigger is released, if there is no specimen between the clamping plates, the pendulum will swing through an arc of 180 degrees to the horizontal

Fig. 156. Combination vibration and pendulum impact package tester. Maximum height of pendulum lift is 20 inches. Note the recorder affixed to side of test case to measure the force of the impact. (*L. A. B. Corporation.*)

Fig. 157. Shipping package tester, 1,000 capacity, has a throw of 1 inch with a maximum speed of 300 rpm. (*L. A. B. Corporation.*)

position. The puncture resistance of the board, when in the machine, would then be the difference between 180 degrees and the distance moved by the pendulum.

2. In the tensile strength test, a strip of the specimen material is gripped by clamps at each end. The grips are then pulled apart to determine what pressure is needed to separate the material. The bursting strength test consists of two concentric disks. One fits into the other; the material to be tested is placed between the two disks. Pressure is then exerted on the two disks and is built up until it bursts the material between them.

3. The liquid and vapor penetrability tests may be conducted by submersion or by pressure sprays. This is used for the testing of moisture-proofing agents and papers and is an important part of research for export packing.

QUESTIONS

1. What specific tests are used in connection with (a) cardboard containers, (b) crates, (c) reinforced plywood boxes, and (d) wood boxes?

2. What are the general classifications of container testing?

3. What type of research is carried on in connection with materials handling? With containers and packaging?

4. What research is carried on by equipment manufacturers?

5. What research is carried on by the users: (a) corporations, (b) Army, (c) Navy, (d) other governmental agencies, (e) private groups, and (f) associations?

6. Outline the work of Patra House; of Forest Products Laboratory.

7. Why are field tests important?

8. What means are employed to simulate field conditions?

9. What are the basic requirements for sound performance tests?

10. Describe the purpose of each of the devices used for laboratory testing of containers.

PROJECTS FOR FURTHER STUDY

1. What type of research is carried on by corporations in (a) materials handling, (b) containers, and (c) packaging and crating methods.

2. What type of research is carried on by the railroads in this field?

3. What corporations have research programs concerned with handling and packaging?

4. Prepare a list of suppliers of testing equipment.

5. What equipment is needed to set up a package testing laboratory?

Part V

ANALYSIS

CHAPTER 16

HOW TO SOLVE A HANDLING PROBLEM

One of the biggest questions facing industry today is how to solve its handling problems and improve its handling methods. The foregoing chapters have stated the fundamentals of materials movement as well as the essential characteristics of the methods, materials, and equipment by which they are applied to specific problems.

These problems may be divided into two types. The first is a restricted application where a specific material is to be moved between two points. An example would be the movement of punchings from one press to another or the movement of a product down an assembly line. The second is a general application where a broader approach to the problem is taken. The first is often dictated as a matter of expediency; the second is to be preferred and will provide the only complete answer to the handling problem.

1. Approach to the Problem [1]

This is essentially a production analysis with the emphasis put upon the aspect of materials movement. This study should precede any extensive purchase of materials-handling equipment. The review of existing production methods should include an examination of every movement of materials.

Basically, materials within a factory are moved, stored, and processed. The time spent in processing is often a surprisingly small part of the total time the goods are within the factory. Storage (or idle time) constitutes the largest time element by far. In many plants, the total man-hours spent on the movement of materials is in excess of the man-hours spent in shaping, cutting, bending, joining, or other processing of these materials.

a. What to Move? The first step in the analysis of production from a materials-handling standpoint is to find out what materials are to be moved. This may sound like a simple question, but there are few factories in which the list of items to be moved will be short or simple. Almost

---

[1] This section adapted from John R. Immer, When You Mechanize!, *Mechanical Handling*, May, 1951, p. 180.

invariably, production involves bringing together a large number of shapes, sizes, and weights. In the case of meat packing, you start out with a single product and end up with a large variety of products and by-products, each of which has peculiarities from a handling standpoint.

Question	Answer
What to move?	1. Parts or materials list 2. Item characteristic list 3. Production schedule
Where to move it?	1. Process sheets 2. Flow-diagram studies 3. Flow-chart analysis 4. Templets and scale models
How to move it?	1. Operation analysis 2. Time and motion study
What equipment to use?	1. Equipment characteristic sheet 2. Cost studies

The *parts list* or *bill of materials* is the first source of this information. The parts list includes a list of all assemblies, subassemblies, and individual parts for each of the products manufactured by the company. It provides complete identification, number of items required per finished product, type of materials, and whether manufactured within the company or purchased from the outside. The materials list provides the same information for the parts to be manufactured within the company. Both of these lists are part of normal processing procedures and should be available in every manufacturing firm.

The *item characteristic list* is a convenient form for grouping a large mass of information necessary to the planning of handling methods and the movement of materials. It puts on paper all the information needed about the materials to be moved. In addition to the description of these materials, it indicates the quantity to be transported at one time. This in itself often shows up wasteful methods, such as the movement of cartons one at a time from one department to another. This information also serves as the base of later studies to show the flow of materials through the plant and provides a basis for a rough computation of direct handling costs.

The *production schedule* discloses the number of manufactured units to be produced. This number multiplied by the quantities per production unit (as indicated by the parts list and the bill of materials) completes the picture of the materials to be moved. This schedule should be available from three to six months in advance of current production. Even where these production figures are extremely fluid and subject to considerable change, it is necessary to establish a range of quantities for use as a planning figure. In one large automobile factory, projected production figures are given to the materials-handling division which then makes necessary plans for the receipt of purchased materials and for the necessary facilities for storage and movement of all materials within the plant for the coming period.

| ITEM CHARACTERISTICS LIST | | | | | | | | | | | |
| Item | | | | Transporting Unit | | | | | How Moved | | | |
Description	Size	Weight	Quantity	Type of Unit	Quantity Per Unit	Size	Weight	No. Units Required	From	To	Distance	Equipment

FIG. 158. The Item Characteristics List is a valuable tool for compiling information relative to the movement of materials. (*Mechanical Handling, May,* 1951, *p.* 182.)

b. Where to Move It? Most industrial materials are moved a much greater distance in processing than is necessary. The materials-handling division of a large manufacturing firm recently told its management that it had spent $600,000 during the previous year on unnecessary rehandling of materials in process. Of course, it hurriedly added that none of this wasteful handling would occur again.

Process sheets, or list of operations, show the operations to be performed on each of the individual parts manufactured within the company. In addition to providing the number and description, the charts should indicate the name and number of the department in which each operation is to be performed. In some cases, this will include a more specific designation of the machine or work center involved. In any case, the charts show the type of machine and special tools, dies, or fixtures required. These lists frequently show only processing operations with no mention made of movement between operations.

Flow-chart analysis is one of the most valuable tools in pointing out the difficult relationships of manufacturing processes. Again, a convenient form is provided for putting down on paper a large amount of information. The way in which this is done shows the flow of materials and makes any excessive handling stand out.

There are a number of types of flow-chart techniques available to the analyst. One is the process chart which uses the conventional symbols: ◯ operation, ◯ movement, ▽ storage or delay, and ☐ inspection. Other symbols are used, but these remain the simplest to construct. Another type of chart uses the same symbols preprinted on a prepared form. The analyst simply connects the appropriate symbols and writes in the description at the side.

Flow-diagram studies provide a more visual means of showing the flow of materials. Generally, though not always, these are drawn to scale. In fact, a regular blueprint of the factory floor may be used quite effectively. On this will be drawn the aisles, working areas, and storage areas. Machines may be located on the plan or general departments only may be shown. By referring back to the process sheet or the flow-chart analysis, the site of each operation is spotted on the plan. These are then connected by lines following the aisles or the routes by which the materials themselves are transported. This is a particularly useful technique when the path of a number of materials must be charted, as in the average job shop.

Templets are two-dimensional representations of machines, generally prepared to the scale of $\frac{1}{2}$, $\frac{3}{8}$, or $\frac{1}{4}$ inch to the foot. They are made of paper, cardboard, plywood, tape, or plastics. In the layout of one press shop, they were made of stiff paper and held in position by rubber cement. As a new layout was prepared, a sheet of transparent plastic was laid over it and the lines of the flow diagram drawn on a sheet of tracing paper laid on this. When completed, another arrangement was tried and checked in the same manner.

Templets are quickly made and provide great flexibility. Their main disadvantage is the lack of the third dimension. Another disadvantage is the difficulty in obtaining a permanent record of the layout. This has been overcome somewhat by the use of transparent templets. These are arranged on a sheet of transparent plastic material, on which the walls and other permanent features are drawn with a grease pencil. When the layout is completed, a sheet of undeveloped sensitized paper (blueprint or black-and-white print paper) is carefully drawn under the layout. A lamp is held over this for the correct exposure time and the sheet is removed and developed in the usual manner.

Scale models are three-dimensional scale representations of machines and may be very simple (showing the general shape only) or very complex and detailed as the need may be. The simplest forms are inexpensive to prepare. (One plant with 200 machines made a scale model of the plant for $300.) The effectiveness of scale models in showing complex relationships often makes a large investment more than worth while.

Photographs of a new layout are sometimes issued to the installation crew instead of scale drawings.

c. How to Move It? One approach to this problem is to analyze the present method of handling. By putting a detailed analysis of this method on paper, inefficient methods and expensive aspects are revealed. By isolating and then considering each element one at a time, the needless elements can be eliminated.

Operation analysis is an easy way of showing up the wastefulness of wrong methods of handling. The chart which uses two figures ($\bigcirc$ operation, $\bigcirc$ transportation) enables a skilled analyst to follow each step of the operation. Particular attention is given to the distance of each reach or movement of the worker. A number of principles relating to the efficiency of motion have been developed. These serve as an effective guide for the analyst.

Time study makes it possible not only to study each element individually but to ascertain its time value. It shows the amount of time taken for each element. This serves as the basis for evaluating each method as its measurement of time provides an objective unit of measure. Its other function is to provide a test for the efficiency of each of the types of handling equipment to be considered.

d. What Equipment to Use? So far, the techniques and forms required are those with which every progressive production-engineering department is familiar. They are part of the tools of every production engineer. They might also be said to comprise the groundwork and base of any materials-handling analysis or survey. Certainly no major project involving extensive mechanization should be undertaken without the careful consideration of each of them, substantially in the order as outlined. That is not to say that there will be written evidence of each of the answers described above. The trained production engineer working with processes with which he is familiar may seldom construct a process chart on paper in order to develop an efficient flow pattern. He will tend to do this mentally, however, and resort to sketches on paper when the picture gets too complicated for his mental imageries. The function is there just the same.

The selection of the specific type of equipment to be employed in a mechanization program involves a large number of technical considerations. Even large manufacturing firms with extreme degrees of specialization in their engineering staffs will seldom be able to consider effectively the merits of all the handling equipment available to them. Their experience and knowledge are probably adequate as long as (1) only familiar types of equipment are considered, (2) conventional methods of handling are involved, and (3) production methods are not drastically changed.

Beyond this range, additional sources of specialized information must be called upon. These may be special sources developed within the firm or agencies called in from the outside. Many large firms are setting up materials-handling sections staffed by engineers familiar with the techniques outlined above *plus* a wide knowledge of the various types of materials-handling equipment. Foremost among the outside sources of information are the equipment salesmen—many of whom have already solved for others the same problem which now confronts you. Technical magazines offer a storehouse of solutions to specific problems as well as descriptions of the latest equipment and methods used by other firms.

An extensive mechanization program is often preceded by visits to other companies which have similar problems. Consultants are another valuable source of information.

EQUIPMENT CHARACTERISTIC SHEET

Equipment	Direction					Frequency			Path			Elevation				Area Served			
	Vertical-up	Vertical-down	Incline-up	Incline-down	Horizontal Only	Continuous	Intermittent	Occasional	Fixed Path-perm	Path-portable	Non-fixed Path	Overhead	Working Height	Floor Movement	Under-floor	Point	Limited Area	Limited Path	Unlimited Area
Belt Conveyor		×	×	×		×			×	×		×	×					×	
Elevator Conveyor	×	×				×										×			
Chain Conveyor		×	×	×		×			×	×			×	×	×		×		
Roller Conveyor			×	×	×	×	×		×	×		×	×	×			×		
Trolley Conveyor		×	×	×		×			×			×					×		
Monorail Conveyor			×	×			×		×			×					×		
Enclosed Conveyor	×			×	×		×		×	×		×			×		×		
Chute		×	×	×	×	×	×		×	×		×	×				×		
Fork-Lift Truck	×	×			×		×				×			×					×
Tier Mech. (Elevator)	×	×					×	×			×			×			×		
Hand Truck					×		×	×			×			×			×		
Hoist, Powered	×	×					×	×					×				×		
Jib Crane	×	×			×		×	×	×				×				×		
Bridge Crane	×	×			×		×	×	×				×				×		
Mobile Crane	×	×			×		×				×			×					×
Elevator	×	×					×	×								×			

Fig. 159. The Equipment Characteristics Sheet points out the major types of equipment which may be used to accomplish a certain type of movement. (*Mechanical Handling, May,* 1951, *p.* 183.)

Equipment characteristic sheets make the problem of selection of equipment easier by limiting the kinds to be considered for a specific handling problem. Many companies have devised their own sheets to fit the special nature of their own handling problems. Considerable care has to be exercised in limiting the fields of application of each type of equipment. After the sheet is completed, it should then be used as a guide only. The danger in the form is that the limitations listed will become accepted without further consideration.

Cost studies are the final determinant for the type of equipment to be used. These often involve information on present handling costs which are not usually available. This necessitates special cost studies to determine more accurately present handling costs. Time studies provide the basis of detailed analyses and are a valuable source of cost information. Time cards and regular departmental cost records may also furnish clues to handling costs. Ratios of the expense of handling personnel to volume of materials moved should be studied. These figures will also help to outline the importance of the operation from a cost standpoint. This, in turn, will limit the amount of study that can economically be given to the project as well as the amount of new equipment which may be justified.

2. How to Organize a Program for Better Handling

It has been emphasized that better handling is the result of careful planning. To accomplish the most efficient layout and method, the ordinary steps of executive control must be carried out. These are (1) delegate responsibility for the function, (2) provide the necessary authority for the discharge of that responsibility, (3) ensure that periodic reports of progress are received, and (4) evaluate the efficacy of the program.

The successive steps in organizing a program to ensure the most efficient movement of materials are as follows:

a. Make One Man Responsible. There is a growing trend to designate a materials-handling engineer. In larger factories this may be a departmental head or a materials-handling manager (see Chap. 22). In even the smallest plant, there must be someone directly responsible for the function and who (although he very likely has many other duties) will continually ask the question: How can we improve our handling methods?

b. Set up a Committee. This serves the twofold function of keeping the problem continually in front of every department and of ensuring the consideration of the interest of each in the planning that is done.

c. Develop Idealized Flow Lines for Production. These may be sketches superimposed on general building outlines or may be drawn without regard to existing structures. In either case they should be devoid of all detail. The main purpose is to show the most efficient layout for that production problem.

d. Set up a Master Plan for Materials Movement. This is essentially the adaptation of the idealized flow lines to restrictions caused by the existing structure or other conditions peculiar to that plant. This becomes the practical objective of the company for its handling program.

e. Outline What Is Needed to Accomplish This Objective. It is usually desirable to divide the outline into a number of phases and to develop one phase at a time. This will include a list of equipment needed as well as any changes in layout required for each phase.

f. Establish a Sequence of Priority for Each Phase and Select the Most Urgent. The phase considered the most urgent in view of the need for increased production, elimination of bottlenecks, and cost savings should be selected.

3. How Much Does Handling Cost?

There are a lot of figures available, but practically none that offer any solution to the cost within an individual plant. Percentage figures have a limited application but should be used with care and then treated as only a rough estimate. Even figures of the total tonnage handled compared to that of the finished product may still be no guide to the actual cost of moving that tonnage.

The cost of handling is something that must be calculated within each plant. The following is an effective method for ascertaining this cost and presenting it in a figure that will serve as a practical index of the handling efficiency of the plant.

a. Cost of Handling Departments. In many companies, certain handling functions are performed by separate departments. Therefore, the cost of operating these departments is readily available. Some of the functions often set up within the accounting framework in this manner are receiving, shipping, storage (raw material, in-process, and finished), toolrooms, packing and crating, and internal transport. It is an easy matter to isolate and identify these handling costs.

b. Individual Accounts Chargeable to Handling. Many accounting systems provide for classifications of accounts which should be included in the cost of handling. Although they are a part of the cost of other departments, it is often fairly easy to extract this information to include in the cost of handling. Some of these accounts are equipment costs and maintenance for handling devices, and the wages of truck operators, handlers, checkers, and order fillers.

c. Handling Performed as Part of Other Operations. So far, cost information has been obtained from accounting records. In many cases this information may provide a picture of handling costs which will satisfy management. It is not, however, the complete story. A system of materials movement which increases the handling time for the individual operations may retard production and increase over-all production costs.

The most practical way of determining this type of handling costs is by an analysis of the time studies of the production operations within each department. It is seldom necessary to analyze all the operations performed. It is generally adequate if a representative number of them are carefully selected to provide a cross section for each department. The analysis of these operations will then provide a percentage figure for machining time, handling, and jigging or positioning. This percentage figure can then be applied to the labor bill of the department, and the result is a usable figure for the internal handling costs of its operations.

d. Total Shown as Percentage of Factory Costs. The cost of handling for the factory will be the total of the three types of costs outlined above. The important figure, however, is the ratio of these costs to fabricating costs. This is the total of manufacturing costs less the cost of raw materials, purchased parts, and assemblies. In other words, it is the percentage of the total increment added to the product by the manufacturing process.

4. The Cost Accountant and Materials Handling

The lack of accurate information on the handling of costs is due in large part to a general inadequacy of cost records. It was stated in 1946 that 85 per cent of all industrial companies did not allocate cost on a product basis.[2] During the Second World War, the Quartermaster Corps found that a large number of small industrial firms had practically no cost accounting system at all.

The first step, then, in ensuring accurate knowledge of handling costs is to see that an adequate cost accounting system is in operation. This will be discussed in greater detail in the following chapters. It will also be shown how the accumulation of handling costs can be shown under each of the main accounting systems in common use.

The second step is to provide account numbers and classifications which will provide the required cost data. The specific form and type of data will depend upon the type of manufacturing process involved. It should be detailed enough to provide all the cost information outlined on page 278.

The final step is to show the importance of the information gathered. This will be done primarily by a constant comparison with the costs of the operations of the previous period or with that of other firms engaged in the same type of work where this information is available.

[2] Martin Black and Harold Eversole, Report on Cost Accounting in Industry, *Journal of Accountancy,* November, 1946, p. 443.

In this connection, it is important to establish a set of standards of operation to serve as a basis of comparison. Sources of waste will show up most clearly where variations from the normal can be made to stand out. Pictorial charts are sometimes very effective in pointing out the variations to management, but, where used, they should be simple and of a type easily and quickly prepared.

The importance of isolating, measuring, and comparing the individual elements of production (and this certainly includes materials handling) can scarcely be overestimated. Handling costs must be brought out of the wilderness of indirect costs where they have lain concealed and must be brought into the open where each and every facet can be examined and weighed on its merit. Costs have to be known before savings can be shown.

QUESTIONS

1. How do you solve a materials-handling problem?
2. Explain the part production analysis plays in this solution.
3. How can a firm determine the specific types of handling equipment needed?
4. How does one achieve better handling within a company?
5. What are the elements in the cost of handling?
6. What type of handling costs is the most difficult to ascertain?
7. How should handling costs be shown?

PROJECTS FOR FURTHER STUDY

1. Outline a practical program for better materials handling for a local factory for which general information is available.
2. Apply the handling approach to a local factory or company where handling is involved.
3. Using this approach as a check sheet, examine some of the more complete accounts of handling systems as reported in recent issues of technical publications.

CHAPTER 17

METHODS OF ANALYSIS

The most effective approach to a materials-handling problem is an analysis of the situation creating it. Although general analyses of such problems have been made for a long time as part of general production studies, it is only within recent years that emphasis has been put on materials-movement analysis as such. A number of methods of analysis are available to the materials-handling engineer, who must be able to select the most appropriate one for the problem at hand.

Although these methods vary considerably in the form, structure, and tools used in connection with them, there are a number of elements common to all of them. The basic steps in materials-handling analysis are:

1. Assemble pertinent data and information.
2. Identify each factor that will affect the analysis.
3. Ascertain relationship and weight of each factor.
4. Show this relationship by graphs, diagrams, etc.
5. Select handling methods which may be used.
6. Compare advantages and disadvantages of each of these methods.
7. Select the method which most completely satisfies all requirements.

1. Factors in Materials-handling Analysis

a. Product, Quantity. This will consist primarily of production schedules and bills of material. The quantities of both present and future schedules on the materials to be handled will largely dictate the type of analysis which may be justified and finally the capital investment and degree of flexibility which may be economically considered. The bills of material are necessary to indicate the component parts which have to be handled within the production departments or in receiving and warehousing operations.

b. Product Description. This includes consideration of weight, size, shape, and other factors which may affect the handling, movement, and storage of materials within the plant. Special care has to be given to processes with characteristics which affect handling or any personnel who may come in contact with these materials.

c. Flow of Materials. Flow is dependent upon the sequence of operations and is one of the prime determinants of materials-movement expense. In most plants it offers the best opportunity for lowering handling costs.

The most important characteristic of this factor is that no added investment in equipment is necessarily needed. Rearrangement of equipment will involve a certain expense in labor and in minor purchase of accessories which is quickly returned by the lower movement costs between operations and the resulting increased production.

d. Handling Equipment. This may involve a study of existing equipment in order to utilize it more effectively. An example would be the scheduling system set up for the movement of materials between departments by trailer trains (see Chap 11). It may also include consideration of new equipment and its incorporation into the handling system of the plant.

e. Physical Plant. In most instances, the physical plant serves as a limiting factor to the methods under consideration. Walls, columns, floor surfaces and weight capacities, location of utilities, placing of openings, and the locational requirements of special processes and equipment restrict the selection of equipment and the method of handling which might otherwise be employed to provide lower materials-movement cost.

f. Investment Policy. Although this policy will be determined in many instances by more long-range considerations of the competitive position of the company, a policy for the amortization of new equipment is often arbitrarily set by top management. Many companies are depriving themselves of much-needed handling economies by too strict a policy of limited-period amortization for handling changes and equipment.

2. Motion Analysis

The movement of materials within a workplace is often not considered as part of the materials-handling picture. One reason for this is that the handling costs are included as part of the operation and it is not possible in most cases and seldom practical to isolate this item of expense. This aspect of handling is taken care of at Oldsmobile by including materials handling in the work of a methods section, which then proceeds to analyze thoroughly *all* the handling aspects of a job.

The movement of materials within the work area must also be considered in the installation of any handling system. The labor costs, for example, of removing parts from a carton might easily obviate any other savings the system might otherwise show.

3. Flow Analysis

The consideration of a materials-handling problem, particularly of a production department, involves first of all the determination of where the materials move and the paths they follow. The specific methods and techniques used for the analysis of this flow were discussed in Chap. 4.

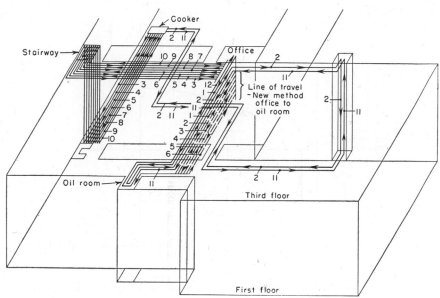

FIG. 160. Flow diagram for preparation of lard oil flux. (*E. Burke Neff.*)

The charting of the path followed by an operator preparing lard-oil flux resulted in a reduction of 70 per cent of the distance traveled and 38 per cent of the time. This study, made by a student in the School of Business Administration at the University of Minnesota, was part of a course requirement involving an analysis in a local plant.

The lard-oil flux was used in soldering the ends on cans for whole hams and is supplied by the factory. The solid lines in Fig. 160 show the steps of the operator under the former method. Dotted lines show the new travel required. This job is the part-time duty of a worker whose main function is to supply materials to line operators. The reduced time and distance give him more time for this more important task.[1]

[1] E. Burke Neff, An Improved Method of Preparing Lard-oil Flux (unpublished study), School of Business Administration, University of Minnesota, 1950.

4. Graphic Analysis

Almost any analysis of materials handling involves the presentation of a large mass of facts and pertinent information. From a cost standpoint, the purpose of the analysis is to ascertain how each of these forces or items of expense affect the total handling cost. This generally involves a certain number of fixed or variable items according to the nature of their function.

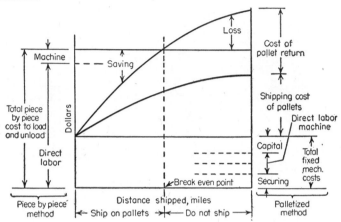

FIG. 161. Break-even chart in general form for inter-plant shipment on pallets. (*Modern Materials Handling, November*, 1949, *p.* 18.)

The most effective way of showing the relative weight and importance of each of these cost factors is by means of charts and graphs. The following graphic analysis of the economies of palletized shipments developed by Walter F. Friedman is illustrative of the effectiveness of this method.

Figure 161 shows the general form of the graph constructed to show the elements in this problem. Two shipping methods are compared. In the piece-by-piece method, cartons are palletized and carried to boxcar by fork truck. The individual cartons are then stacked manually in the car.

In the palletized method, the palletized shipment is loaded directly on the pallet to the boxcar. Cartons are strapped to the pallets and no manual handling is required at the boxcar.

The total handling cost under *A* consists of the manual labor required to load and unload the car plus the charge for the machine used in the operations. Accessories and capital charges are not involved because all the facilities (pallets and securing materials) remain with the shipper.

Under method *B*, fixed-cost elements include direct labor and machine costs and, in addition, the cost of securing the load and the capital investment charges on the pallets while in transit and return. To these fixed costs must be added the elements of variable cost. These are the shipping charge at the commodity rate of the pallets shipped with the commodity load and the shipping charges for the return of the pallets. These elements are functions of the distance shipped and returned. The shipping charge for the commodity being shipped is the same under

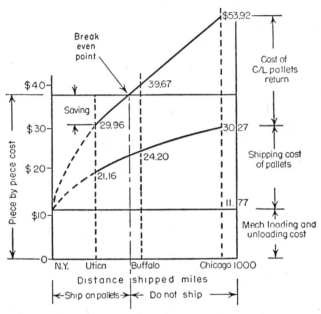

Fɪɢ. 162. Break-even chart for inter-plant shipment of cases of asparagus on wooden pallets. (*Modern Materials Handling, November,* 1949, *p.* 18.)

either method and therefore does not have to be considered in this analysis.

In the graph (Fig. 161) the distance shipped is indicated on the horizontal axis and the dollar cost on the vertical axis. Since there are no variable cost elements in method A, the cost in this method is shown by a straight line parallel to the horizontal axis. Variable charges, increasing with the distance shipped, are shown on the graph by a curve. Where these two lines meet is the break-even point beyond which it will not pay to ship on pallets.

In Fig. 162, the elements of this graph are applied to a specific problem which involves the shipment of 1,320 cases of 24 No. 2½ cans of asparagus. Each case weighs 52 pounds. The capital charge was based on the use of 22 wood pallets per carload with a 30-day turn-around time for the pallets at the receiving end. The combined cost of the various items is shown on the chart. In this analysis the chart shows the break-even point just short of Buffalo. Changes in the shipping cost of pallets or their return would affect the break-even point and the shipping distance with which pallets could economically be used.[2]

5. Safety Analysis

The most efficient handling operation is generally the safest. According to the National Safety Council, 22 per cent of all disabilities to

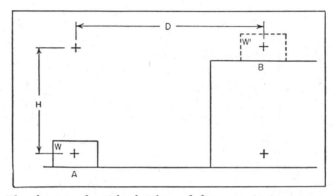

Fig. 163. The elements of weight, height, and distance exist in every movement of materials. They are basic to the handling problem and are the primary sources of materials-handling accidents. Handling accidents are due to exposure of the above types. (*Modern Materials Handling, March, 1950, p. 13.*)

workers result from handling objects. The first step in the analysis of handling from a safety standpoint is the understanding of the causes of accidents.

a. Elements in Movement of Materials. The basic elements existing in every movement of materials are shown in Fig. 163. Movement is horizontal, vertical, or a combination of the two. It is essentially a movement of weight, although in special instances, bulk, shape, and the characteristics of the materials are involved. In the diagram, height (H) and distance (D) are shown with the weight (W) to be moved.

The difference in the cause of accident by manual and mechanized handling is contrasted in Fig. 163. In manual handling, the controlling factor in exposure to accidents is the weight of the object. With mechanized handling, however, distance and height become the controlling fac-

[2] Walter F. Friedman, Are Palletized Shipments Economical?, *Modern Materials Handling,* November, 1949, p. 16.

tors in exposure to accidents. The greater distance traveled by the object increases the probability of collision with other objects or personnel.[3]

The causes of these mishaps with either manual or mechanical methods of handling materials are quite well known, and, as a consequence, are preventable.

b. Steps in Safety Analysis. The study of past accident occurrence data to isolate material-handling accidents is the first step in handling analysis. The next is to classify and group all material-handling accidents by location and type of handling exposure. These may be grouped by:

1. Specific department
2. Production line
3. Shift
4. Machine or operation
5. Type of material handled
6. Type of handling equipment used

The next step is an investigation of all operating items cited as causes of accidents. Each exposure should be evaluated on the relation of each item to (1) plant layout, (2) practices and procedures, (3) housekeeping, and (4) methods. This will complete the fact-finding steps in the analysis.

The basic steps in this analysis may be summarized as follows: [4]

Step 1. Study all accident occurrence data and isolate material-handling accidents. Prepare lost-time accident analysis, showing percentage of material-handling accidents to total. This should cover at least a twelve-month period.

Step 2. Study material-handling accidents to determine locations and types of problems. At this point, depending upon circumstances, accidents may be grouped by type of material handled, etc., as shown above.

Step 3. Inspect and study operating items disclosed in step 2 as sources of accidents. All investigations should consider the four factors of plant layout, practices and procedures, housekeeping, and methods.

Step 4. After completing step 3, prepare detailed descriptions of the problem backed up with facts and figures. Evaluate problems and prepare objectives.

Step 5. Study solutions of the problems on the following basis: (1) Consider methods of making existing procedures safe before promoting new systems of handling. (2) Consider simple improvements rather than extensive changes in layout or purchase of expensive materials-handling equipment. (3) Consider alternate methods of eliminating hazard. This may require considerable research and return visits to the plant.

[3] Leroy Faulkner, Accidents Cost Money!, *Modern Materials Handling*, March, 1950, p. 13.

[4] Adapted from "How to Analyse Your Materials Handling Accident Problems," by Leroy A. Faulkner, supervisor, Industrial Safe Practices, Liberty Mutual Insurance Company, *Modern Materials Handling*, April, 1950, p. 22.

Step 6. Discuss suggested solutions to the problems with supervisory personnel and management to obtain reactions and additional information for final presentation.

Step 7. Submit report to management. Include statement of the problem, description of conditions creating the problem and recommendations which if adopted will minimize the possibility of accidents.

The presentation to management must list handling hazards and the corrective measures to be taken. These will be considered in the light of the scope of handling changes warranted, availability of capital, and its effect on the over-all operational efficiency.

6. Equipment Cost Analysis

This type of analysis is illustrated by the comparison of the operating costs of gasoline and electric industrial trucks. Within a company or indi-

COST COMPARISONS--CLARK GASOLINE AND ELECTRIC POWERED TRUCKS									MODEL 4024	
BASED UPON 250 WORKING DAYS PER YEAR									NO OF UNITS 10	
	4 HOURS WORK PER DAY		6 HOURS WORK PER DAY		8 HOURS WORK PER DAY		16 HOURS WORK PER DAY		24 HOURS WORK PER DAY	
	GAS	ELECTRIC	GAS	ELECTRIC	GAS	ELECTRIC	GAS	ELECTRIC	GAS	ELECTRIC
INVESTMENT										
TRUCK COSTS	29520	38320	29520	38320	29520	38320	29520	38320	29520	38320
BATTERIES	—	15500	—	15500	—	15500	—	31000	—	31000
CHARGER	—	6900	—	6900	—	6900	—	6900	—	6900
CHARGER INSTALLATION	—	500	—	500	—	500	—	1500	—	1500
FUELING FACILITIES	1000	—	1000	—	1000	—	1000	—	1000	—
FREIGHT	1000	1000	1000	1000	1000	1000	1000	1250	1000	1250
TOTAL INVESTMENT	31520	62220	31520	62220	31520	62220	31520	78970	31520	78970
FIXED CHARGES ANNUAL										
DEPRECIATION TRUCK INVESTMENT(1)	6300	9350	6300	9350	6300	9350	6300	9600	6300	9600
INTEREST ON INVESTMENT(%)	—	—	—	—	—	—	—	—	—	—
TAXES & INSURANCE (1%)	315	620	315	620	315	620	315	790	315	790
TOTAL ANNUAL FIXED CHARGES	6615	9970	6615	9970	6615	9970	6615	10390	6615	10390
VARIABLE CHARGES ANNUAL										
GASOLINE (2)	1600	—	2400	—	3200	—	6400	—	9600	—
ELECTRIC POWER (3)	—	540	—	810	—	1080	—	2160	—	3240
BATTERY DEPRECIATION (4)	—	3100	—	3100	—	3100	—	6200	—	7750
OIL (5)	185	—	275	—	375	—	750	—	1125	—
GREASING & INSPECTION (6)	1875	1875	1875	1875	1875	1875	3750	3750	5625	5625
PARTS & MAINTENANCE (7)	2000	1000	3000	1500	4000	2000	10000	4400	18000	7200
TOTAL VARIABLES ANNUAL	5660	6515	7550	7285	9450	8055	20900	16510	34350	23815
TOTAL ANNUAL CHARGES	12275	16485	14165	17255	16065	18025	27515	26900	40965	34205

NOTE 1 – TRUCK DEPRECIATION BASED UPON 5 YEARS LIFE
NOTE 2 – GASOLINE COSTS BASED UPON (a) CONSUMPTION 1 GALLON PER HOUR (b) 16 CENTS PER GALLON.
NOTE 3 – ELECTRIC POWER COSTS BASED UPON (a) 1 GALLON GASOLINE EQUIVALENT TO 54 KWH CURRENT. (b) COST 1 CENT PER KWH.
   COST 1 CENT PER KWH (c) BATTERY & CHARGER EFFICIENCY 50%.
NOTE 4 – BATTERY DEPRECIATION BASED UPON 1500 CYCLES OR AMP HRS.
NOTE 5 – OIL COSTS BASED UPON (a) CONSUMPTION 1 QT. PER 8 HOUR-SHIFT (b) 15 CENTS PER QT
NOTE 6 – GREASING & INSPECTION COSTS BASED UPON (a) ½ HOUR LABOR PER SHIFT PER TRUCK (b) $1.50 PER HOUR
NOTE 7 – PARTS & MAINTENANCE BASED UPON

GASOLINE POWER   20 CENTS PER HOUR (ONE SHIFT OR LESS)
   25 CENTS PER HOUR (TWO SHIFTS)
   30 CENTS PER HOUR (THREE SHIFTS)

ELECTRIC POWER   10 CENTS PER HOUR (ONE SHIFT OR LESS)
   11 CENTS PER HOUR (TWO SHIFTS)
   12 CENTS PER HOUR (THREE SHIFTS)

FIG. 164. Cost comparisons of gasoline- and electric-powered trucks. (*Prepared by W. B. McClelland for Clark Equipment Company.*)

vidual plant this question is one which often can be answered only by detailed equipment cost records for the operation of this equipment. In lieu of this, there must be available reasonably reliable estimates for all the cost expense items that comprise the total cost.

The cost comparisons shown in Fig. 164 were developed by W. B. McClelland for the Clark Equipment Company, manufacturers of both electric- and gasoline-powered units. Annual costs are shown for the use of 10 units of each type, assuming a 250-day work year. For the sake of this illustration, other expense items had to be assumed. Although the figures will vary in different companies, the general form of this analysis provides a valuable check list for the factors to be included in this type

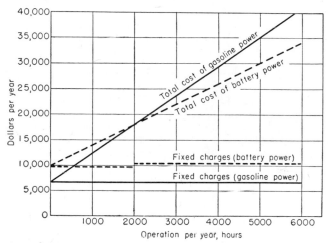

FIG. 165. Chart showing the total annual charges developed in Fig. 164. (*Prepared by W. B. McClelland for Clark Equipment Company.*)

of analysis. The nature of these charges is discussed in greater detail in Chap. 19.

7. Palletization Analysis

The considerable savings in handling costs accruing to the use of pallets demand that they be considered in every handling analysis of articles of pallet size or under. Even in the handling of bulk commodities their use can reduce handling costs.

The graphic analysis described above has been developed to show the economics of moving goods on pallets. The materials-handling and product-protection section of the International Harvester Company has developed a form for the orderly presentation of the information required in palletization analysis (Fig. 166). The Unit Load Data Sheet (Fig. 167) has been prepared to aid in the establishment of load design and to serve as a reference sheet in operations. Load patterns can be laid out on paper in the crosshatched areas and the weights calculated. If the commodity is available, load patterns can be constructed, measured, and

MATERIALS HANDLING PALLETIZATION ANALYSIS DATA

PART NAME	PART NO.	MODEL	PROD. PER DAY	BANK IN PIECES	PIECES PER PALLET	TYPE & NUMBER OF PALLETS REQUIRED			WEIGHTS HANDLED		INITIAL CONTAINER OUTLAY		CONTAINER COST ATTRIBUTAL		SHIPPING DEPT. LABOR COST		WAREHOUSING DEPT. LABOR COST		RECEIVING DEPT. LABOR COST		TOTAL MATERIAL AND LABOR COST		STORAGE AREA REQUIRED IN SQ FT		REMARKS
						DOUBLE FACED 42 x 42	SEPARATOR TYPE 42 x 42	BOX TYPE 42 x 42	No. of Lbs. Per PALLET	TOTAL IN TONS	PRESENT	PROPOSED	PRESENT	PROPOSED	PRESENT	PROPOSED	PRESENT	PROPOSED	PRESENT	PROPOSED	PRESENT	PROPOSED	PRESENT	PROPOSED	
TRANSMISSION CASE	8846-DA	A & B	200	12,000	24		500		2610	654	0	$9,635.	$695.	0	$785.	$245.	$3208.	$654.	$785.	$1130.80	$2878.	$1724.80	2040	1530	

Fig. 166. Form used for analysis of factors affecting palletization. (*International Harvester Company.*)

weighed. They can then be drawn on paper or photographed. The load should be designed to weigh the amount previously decided upon to be the most desirable.[5]

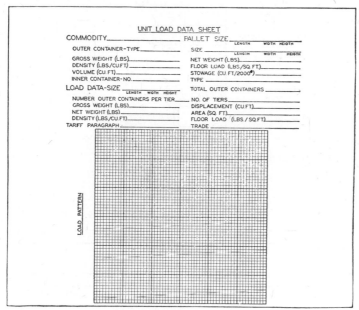

Fig. 167. Unit Load Data Sheet. (*Prepared by W. B. McClelland for Clark Equipment Company.*)

8. Analysis of Operations

It is often necessary to determine how much handling is involved in machining, processing, and assembling operations. Where a problem of balance is involved, this is a necessary step, as the reduction of handling times on bottleneck operations may be the means of increasing output.

On a series of operations in a shop, this analysis may be used to get a more accurate estimate of the adequacy of existing handling methods. It is also effective in comparing the effectiveness of two handling methods. The example shown in Fig. 168 was developed by C. G. Chantrill & Partners (Management Engineers, London) to ascertain more accurately the costs of handling under a proposed method.

The proposal was to eliminate an existing overhead traveling crane. The summary chart at the bottom shows the extra handling time with the use of the crane as well as the percentage of internal handling time within the department.

[5] W. B. McClelland, Cleveland, Ohio.

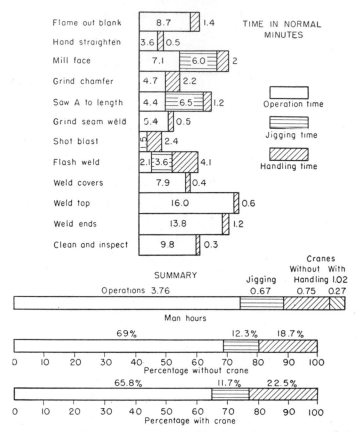

Fig. 168. Handling analysis of operations used to show the percentage of **time** spent on handling. (*C. G. Chantrill & Partners, London.*)

QUESTIONS

1. What are the basic steps in materials-handling analysis?

2. What are the main factors involved in a materials-handling analysis?

3. What is the importance of graphic analysis to materials handling?

4. What are the essential differences between motion analysis and flow analysis?

5. What basic elements of movement are involved in a materials-handling operation?

6. Outline the steps involved in a safety analysis.

7. What determines the elements to be considered in a cost analysis for spe cific types of materials-handling equipment?

8. Discuss the cost elements in the use of industrial fork trucks.

9. What factors are involved in palletization analysis?

PROJECTS FOR FURTHER STUDY

1. Prepare a chart showing the economy of shipping goods on pallets from your local community. Use the chart in Fig. 162 as a guide. Obtain local commodity standard rates, and figure each pallet at 100 pounds. Where other figures are not available, use the ones given in the example in the text.

2. Prepare a safety analysis of the shipping and receiving area of a local plant or store.

CHAPTER 18

TYPES OF SURVEYS

Just as in recent years other things have been held out as a universal panacea, materials-handling surveys are the current prescription for all production ills. This trend has been accentuated further by the large number of instances in which impressive savings have resulted.

The movement of materials from one operation to the next is today the great frontier for the cost-conscious executive. The emphasis in previous years has been, for example, on increasing the speed of machines, the use of more efficient cutting tools, and other ways of increasing individual machine production. One such study saved 0.10 minute per cycle. A simple change in the method of handling cut the handling time in half with a saving of 0.25 minute per cycle.

1. Who Makes Materials-handling Surveys?

The industrial engineer is the man most qualified by training and experience for this task. He must be acquainted with fundamental principles of production flow and of motion analysis. He has to be able to gauge the importance of cost factors entering into the picture. He should have a knowledge of the various types of equipment and an understanding of how these will affect production flow.

a. Company Engineers. Most generally these surveys will be conducted as a part of the regular work of the industrial engineer. In the smaller firms this may be *the* engineer for the entire plant or a time-study and methods engineer. As the plant grows in size and management sees cost-saving possibilities in the subject, these operations may become more specialized. This will include variations up to a separate division reporting to a vice-president in charge of manufacturing.

b. Equipment Venders. A great deal of "engineering" is done as part of the sales-service program of equipment manufacturers. Thus, the salesman selling monorail conveyors cannot sell just a piece of equipment but must plan the layout, change manufacturing layouts, and evolve a new *system* for handling. In many instances, it is the *system* and the engineering which produce the savings which, in turn, justify the cost of the installation.

Recognizing the importance of this service in selling, companies have vied with one another in developing forms and procedures to be used for materials-handling surveys. Yale and Towne developed the "How" plan for surveys. Towmotor evolved the "group analysis" approach and a series of handling studies (this has no connection with the "Group Analysis" developed by the Preben Jessen Company of New York). Clark Equipment Company has made a comprehensive survey of the bottling industry. These are but a few of the surveys being made by equipment manufacturers.

c. Consultants. This service is available from consultants as part of the production analysis commonly made by general industrial engineering consulting firms or from those specializing in materials-handling problems. Many of the general firms have actually been making "materials-handling" studies for a number of years under the guise of "production surveys" where the importance of the former subject was recognized and given due attention.

2. When Are Surveys Needed?

A number of conditions which reveal the need for a survey have been described. Many of these are slanted toward the personal interest of the compiler, but they all sum up to the same general conclusions.

A survey is needed when management realizes that handling costs are too high and begins to think there might be a way of lowering them. Stronger competitive factors may necessitate a drastic reduction in unit production costs. A materials-handling survey may be the answer.

A survey is needed when accidents in the handling of materials occur. These are signs of improper methods and procedures, inadequate training or instruction, or of improper equipment and facilities—both of handling equipment and of the general manufacturing plant.

A survey is needed when management wants to ensure that its own methods of handling are the best obtainable. In this connection an outside consultant is brought in. One company with one of the most complete and progressive engineering staffs in the industry regularly employs a consultant to make such a check. Results produce improved methods or provide assurance to management of the efficiency of its own staff.

Symptoms that indicate bad handling methods include:

a. Confusion and Lack of Order. The layout of processes and the arrangement of machines should be such that materials and stock are carried ahead in direct lines, and not back and forth or with paths crossing and intermingling.

b. Handling by Hand. Lifting, carrying, and placing by hand should be limited to machine feeding on short runs, special operations on light parts or light stock, and to small volumes of supplies or of special material.

c. Handling Too-heavy Objects by Hand Truck. While such materials as barreled pigment, filled drums, etc., weighing ½ ton or more each *can* be handled by hand truck, the hazard rises rapidly with the weight above a few hundred pounds. Such products are generally best handled by powered trucks or other lifting and conveying equipment especially suited to the purpose.

d. Unmarked or Narrow and Crowded Traffic Aisles and Material-storage Space. For dense or powered traffic, aisles should be at least 3 feet wider than twice the width of the vehicle used. Storage space for materials, stocks, and parts on production floors should be clearly marked off, properly located in relation to the machines or operations and aisles and not encroached upon for other purposes.

e. Overloaded or Carelessly Loaded Box Trucks, Carriers, etc. These conditions indicate poor supervision and poorly trained and careless workmen.

f. Bad Maintenance. This is evidenced by such details as wobbly truck wheels, rickety truck bodies, noisy powered equipment, worn and uneven floors, worn crane cables, stretched and worn chains, uneven plant railway tracks, and worn and broken tools.[1]

3. What Should Be Accomplished?

To answer this question, one must differentiate the major types of surveys. There are two major types, specific and general. Surveys of a specific handling problem should result in a solution satisfactory from the following standpoints:

1. Move the desired quantity at the required rate of speed for the lowest cost.

2. Satisfy any requirements relating to the special characteristics or size of the materials and the hazardous nature of the materials, the processes, or the surroundings.

3. Integrate the new equipment into the handling methods and equipment of the rest of the plant.

4. Establish the desired degree of control over the operation. This is often the major objective in the specific survey.

The general survey is concerned with the broadest possible interpretation of handling and movement of materials. Its primary objective is to provide the lowest possible handling costs for the over-all operations of the company.

Only by a general survey can a company achieve the maximum benefits from materials handling and be assured that its company-wide handling costs are the lowest possible. Although the specific survey is often needed to solve particular handling problems, the over-all approach is the one that produces the big savings.

[1] R. P. Blake, "Industrial Safety Subjects," Subject 6, Division of Labor Standards, Department of Labor.

General surveys are carried on by company engineers or by consultants brought in for the purpose. In either case there is often a considerable time lag between the start of the survey and even the initiation of a program. This is primarily due to the fact that a large mass of operating information has to be considered before specific objectives can be outlined. Frequently much of this information is not available and must be developed before the survey can proceed.

Where the survey is being conducted by the company itself, one man (a senior staff member) assumes complete responsibility and delegates the individual assignments for the various phases of the project. Where this staff member has a number of other responsibilities (as is usually the case), an assistant may actively direct the project under his guidance.

Along with this centralization of responsibility a large amount of coordinating work is required with the various departments having interests affected by materials handling. This is accomplished by a committee which is composed of representatives from each of these departments. In the larger company (having a number of manufacturing plants), this committee may become the moving force within the company for the development of improved handling systems and methods. The work of these committees is discussed in greater detail in Chap. 22.

Consultants are often called into the picture where a company does not have the trained personnel to carry out adequately the over-all analysis of operations desired. More often, a company has the engineering personnel, but they are occupied with other developmental work and not available for a project of this size. Even here, in some instances, consultants are brought in if for no other reason than to ensure that the company is using the most efficient methods available.

The following results should be expected from a general survey: [2]

1. The most efficient and economical system for the movement of materials.

2. Increased production and elimination of bottlenecks and obstructions due to the faulty flow of materials.

3. Increased utilization of plant space.

4. Safer operations. Handling hazards should be reduced or eliminated where possible.

5. Decreased processing time. By reducing the in-process time, factory turnover is increased and the result is the maximum utilization of manufacturing facilities.

[2] For a list of operating ratios which are affected by a general survey, see Chap. 19.

4. What Surveys Are Made?

Equipment venders are constantly making studies of specific handling problems as a regular part of their sales activity and are frequently called in for consultation at an early stage in the development of a project. In many firms (not always the smallest ones), much of the basic planning for the system of handling to be installed is made by the venders themselves. The result is frequently a system that is adequate as far as the equipment is concerned, but the equipment is not necessarily the type that is best suited to the particular problem.

a. Warehouse Handling Surveys. A materials-handling survey of its warehouse was recently made by the Quincy Market Cold Storage & Warehouse Company. The following steps were involved in this survey: [3]

1. Study the physical conditions of the warehouse.
   a. Measure the floor space.
   b. Look at the blueprints. (It is inadvisable to study the blueprints of an old building, as changes have usually been made.)
   c. Test floors and elevators for load capacities.
2. Analyze the commodities handled and stored.
   a. Know the activity of every item and quantities received.
   b. Measure and weigh the items.
3. Gather information concerning the types and kinds of material-handling equipment available.
   a. Have salesmen and manufacturers submit specifications.
   b. Visit other plants where equipment is in use to obtain firsthand information of their experience with the equipment.
4. After these three steps are considered, the actual work of installing the system may commence.

b. General Merchandise Warehouse Surveys. A more elaborate type of survey is indicative of the work and planning often required before a major materials-handling study is ready to go into the building and installation stage. The increased realization of the importance of advance planning of an over-all nature has led companies to consider this as part of a complete developmental plan.

Typical is the following account of the planning done for the new warehouse by L. Bamberger & Company of Newark, N.J., an affiliate of R. H. Macy & Co. of New York City.

Research work in connection with this project was carried on over a period of many years by L. Bamberger & Company, and several architectural and engineering firms were engaged on this problem from time to time. Several schemes were developed and then abandoned for one

[3] James J. Gallery, Palletization in the Multi-storey Warehouse, *Distribution Age*, June, 1948, p. 26.

reason or another. Centralization of the six individual and widely separated units of the warehousing and delivery facilities was the primary objective. The exact location of such a centralized operation was of considerable importance, and a study was undertaken to determine the theoretical center of merchandise distribution.

At one time, complete plans and specifications were prepared for a multi-storied building, but this project was discarded in favor of a one-story structure of 400,000 square feet. This required considerable acreage

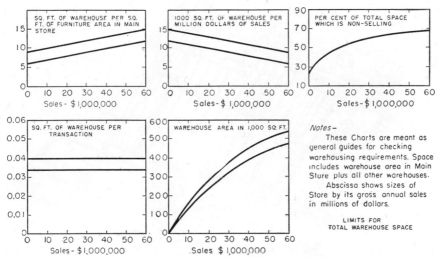

FIG. 169. Limits for total warehouse space used in development of most efficient layout and handling system for merchandising warehouse. (*Abbott, Merkt & Company.*)

with a railroad siding. Fortunately, a suitable site was located very close to the theoretical center of distribution, as determined by the survey. Having acquired the site, over 20 architects and engineers were interviewed and Abbott, Merkt & Company was selected to handle the design of the new depot.

The Bamberger executives in charge of receiving, warehousing, and delivery operations had performed individual research over the years in regard to methods and procedures as well as physical layout. These executives worked hand and glove with the engineers in developing plans.

However, before even preliminary layouts were made (there were eventually 12 or more possible plans developed), a nationwide inspection trip was made by the engineers in company with the Bamberger operating executives. Outstanding warehouses were visited from coast to coast, copious notes were taken, and the opinions of operating personnel solicited. This trip took 3 weeks and tended to crystallize in the minds of the executives their ideas in regard to modern warehousing.

The initial design was started and, as mentioned above, several designs or schematic drawings were prepared before the final layout evolved. The engineers conferred constantly with the Bamberger operating executives and every detail of the plans and specifications was discussed at length and mutually agreed upon. The result of this planning is shown in Fig. 170.

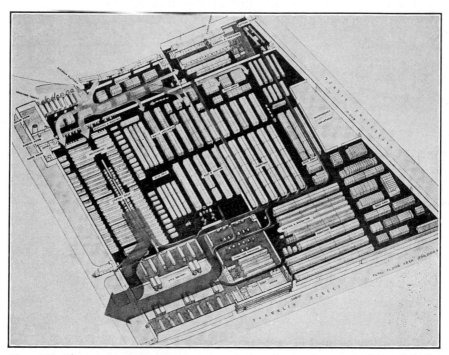

Fig. 170. The result of the planning. Straight-line flow and minimized handling for merchandise stores. Arrows show the flow of materials in new warehouse of L. Bamberger & Company in Bloomfield, N.J. (*Abbott, Merkt & Company.*)

c. *Surveys of Operational Hazards.* Improvement in materials handling is often a gradual process, a piece-by-piece elimination of handling hazards and improvement in methods. The following list [4] considers some of the hazards in handling and suggests preventive measures:

Operation, Hazard, or Injury	*Preventive Measure*
1. *Incoming cars or trucks.* Struck by train, car, or truck.	Proper clearances between sidings and tracks and fixed structures. Gates, warning signals or signs, guard rails. Under (or over) passes.

[4] *Ibid.*

Operation, Hazard, or Injury	*Preventive Measure*
	Supervision of car movements. Proper location of traffic-ways and doors to buildings. Adequate yard lighting; elimination of tripping hazards. These measures apply for motor traffic except that roads may quite easily be relocated and truck and car operators may be on plant payroll and thus under the direct control of the plant executives.
2. *Unloading cars or trucks.* Torn, pinched, or crushed hands and feet; bruises, strains, falls; injury to health from dust fumes or chemicals.	Proper tools and equipment; careful training and supervision of men in safe methods of work; personal protective equipment; adequate lighting.
3. *Emptying and cleaning tank cars.* Suffocation or poisoning on entering tanks; burns from acid drips; falls from cars; explosion of flammable gases; electric shock from extension cords.	Testing of air in cars; steaming out, washing out, or ventilation of cars; use of fresh air helmets; use of life line and watcher outside car; training, supervision, proper ladders, platforms and tools, and equipment; safeguarded extension cords and lights; protective clothing.
4. *Opening baled, crated, or barreled materials.* Cuts and abrasions from sharp edges; nail wounds; strains from lifting; tool wounds.	Adequate space for work; proper tools; training, supervision, housekeeping and order; hand, foot and leg protection; lighting.
5. *Piling materials.* Falling materials; strains from lifting; falls; foot injuries.	Equipment to aid piling; methods worked out to suit materials and conditions; training in proper ways to lift and to pile materials; adequate storage space, orderliness, lighting.
6. *Transporting materials and articles through the process.* Struck by trucks; hand pinched, torn or bruised under or between articles; articles falling on feet; falls over loose articles; strains; getting caught by powered conveying machinery.	Planned and routed traffic; clear aisles; trained power vehicle operators; hand truck of proper type; adequate spaces for placing at machines or other stations; housekeeping and order; complete guarding of all hazardous moving parts. Good maintenance of equipment and floors.
7. *Preparing for shipment.* Strains; tool injuries; falls.	Order; training; proper equipment; adequate space; supervision.

Operation, Hazard, or Injury	Preventive Measure
8. *Handling acids, caustics, hazardous substances, volatiles.* Burns; dermatoses; eye injuries; inhalation of toxic fumes.	Special equipment for handling the substances; personal protective equipment; special trained men, testing for susceptible individuals.
9. *Handling stock or articles at machines or processes.* Abrasions, cuts, bruises and sprains of hands and arms; foot injuries; dermatoses (chiefly in chemical and allied industries); eye injuries from flying particles; burns (welding or forging).	Gloves, wrist and hand leathers, aprons, safety shoes, goggles; reduce handling by layout of machines, processes, and by motion study; substitute less toxic substances; special handling methods suited to specific condition.

QUESTIONS

1. By whom are materials-handling surveys made?
2. How can you tell when a survey is needed?
3. What specific items should one look for which might indicate improper handling methods?
4. Why are surveys made?
5. What should a survey accomplish?
6. Discuss some of the types of surveys most commonly made.
7. Describe the steps followed in the survey made by the Bamberger Company.
8. Discuss some of the hazards involved in (*a*) loading rail cars and trucks, (*b*) handling of materials in process, and (*c*) handling around machine operations.
9. Discuss the preventive measures which may be taken to reduce accidents in (*a*) loading rail cars, (*b*) handling of materials in process, and (*c*) handling around machine operations.

PROJECTS FOR FURTHER STUDY

1. Make a survey of the operational hazards of a local plant or shipping and receiving department.
2. Prepare a survey of handling methods for a small truck terminal. Local deliveries are discharged from small trucks on one side. Large trailer trucks are loaded on the other side with goods for various cities.
3. A group of presses is employed in successive operations of a wide variety of products of similar size and shape. The sequence of operation varies slightly with each product. Prepare a report on the various means of handling which may be employed. Discuss the pros and cons of each method.

CHAPTER 19

COST ACCOUNTING SYSTEMS

To understand materials-handling costs, it is necessary to have a working knowledge of the way in which these costs are derived. This involves an examination of the cost systems now most commonly used in industry and a brief discussion of their operation. These may be classified in several different ways.

On the basis of their computation they are classified as (1) predetermined or (2) historical. The latter involves the recording of actual costs as they occur. The former involves a standard and a computation of the variance from it. Costs may also be classified according to the type of operations as (1) production order or (2) process order. Most systems employ both types in one form or another.

A third method of classifying costs separates them into (1) accounting costs which are an integral part of the accounting system and (2) statistical costs derived from cost records which are not necessarily part of the regular system. The latter includes special cost studies which are of inestimable value in the determination of handling costs.

1. Production Order System

The first project of a cost accountant under this method is to set up an overhead per cent to be applied to each job as it is processed. This per cent is based on either machine hours, labor hours, or the labor cost of a department. Theoretically, if the exact machine hours were used and the exact costs of production ended up as predicted, there would be no trouble in distribution of the total overhead. However, if one encounters a period of widely fluctuating production hours and a different cost setup is involved, there is the problem of distributing the variance. The theories of distributing variance are:

1. Variances closed into "cost of goods sold" and the "inventory" account.

2. Shown as a total "cost of goods sold" of that period.

3. Shown as deferred credit or charge on the balance sheet.

There is good reasoning for the development of each of these theories.

However, it is not our duty here to consider the arguments pro and con for the application of these accounting principles.

As the work enters the process in this system, there are two methods of recording costs.

1. Send production order to each department for recording.

2. Have central accounting department take care of all the recording.

When the job is finished, an entry is made either by the final department or by the central accounting division. This entry records the merchandise into the finished goods records of the company.

a. Depreciation. With this brief presentation of the systems of accounting, their application to materials handling can then be considered. Most important is the depreciation figure used in the write-off of handling equipment. The figure arrived at in the depreciation analysis of a company is put into the overhead per cent that is applied to the various projects. This is one of the costs referred to by cost analysts as the "bucket" (miscellaneous items of expense).

The rate of depreciation on new equipment is that set by the Bureau of Internal Revenue and this cost enters into "overhead." The per cent applied to "overhead" is not affected. Therefore, management may not be able to realize the true saving or loss from the purchase of the equipment. Savings from the reduction of labor hours per units of material handled would not show up in this account.

One way to correct this would be to keep a card file for each handling device. Management would then have at a glance the cost of the machine as well as the investment involved. Also, each card should show every operation the machine performs; then, if a new machine is considered, an instant check is available on potential savings.

The actual computation of depreciation in most firms is the straight-line method. This depreciation rate is the cost of the machine plus installation cost, minus salvage estimate, divided by the number of years of operation. Other accounting theories on depreciation are discussed later in this chapter.

b. Taxes. Like depreciation, taxes are put into the overhead cost of operations and any deviation in taxes will show little reflection in the per cent of overhead applied. Taxes are affected in any operation by the introduction of a new machine or method. First, the mill tax of the locality will be levied on the increased investment, and, second, savings involved may not be so large when income tax on amounts invested is taken into consideration. It is, therefore, important for a firm to use a "tax sheet" to keep a record of taxes before and after a method improvement. By using this sheet, management will have, at a glance, the tax implications involved.

c. Cash Outlay. The financial accounts such as "cash in bank" and "accounts receivable" show the liquidity of a firm irrespective of accounting system used. But the firm's problem of cash outlay is *will the program pay for itself?*

The cost records of a production-order system, discussed above, show the cost of each order. If management wants a further analysis, each order will have to be analyzed to ascertain the average cost per unit of material and labor. After this is done, management will know its present cost situation, and comparison may be made with the new system. Of course this operation could be saved by having material and labor costs recorded on a joint sheet.

A firm using this accounting system generally has a type of production which does not require records of average costs of material and labor. They are most interested in the cost for a particular order or job. A number of firms have set up controls in the form of various ratios. A very complete list was provided in a recent speech by Walter C. Puckey, a director of Hoover, Ltd., London.[1]

In any case, the more controls that are available within reason, and the better the measuring sticks used in these controls, the more satisfied we are that the schemes submitted are sound investments. Let us look at a few controls we can use. Here is a list of the more important:

1. Ratio of turnover to stores stock
2. Ratio of turnover to work in progress
3. Ratio of stores stock to work in progress
4. Average "through-put" time of a job
5. Average footage traveled by a job
6. Ratio of delivery costs to turnover
7. Ratio of packing costs to total cost of product
8. Average number of items on shortage lists
9. Achievement against quoted delivery times
10. Ratio of trucking cost to total cost
11. Ratio of stores cost to total cost
12. Utilization of floor space per unit of turnover
13. Horsepower per worker utilized

2. Process Order System

The process system is used where a company has a homogeneous product such as the canning industry or the flour milling industry and allied fields. This system can be explained as follows:

[1] Walter C. Puckey, Material Handling—a Job of Production Engineering, a talk presented at Mechanical Handling Exhibition, London, June, 1950, *The Journal of the Institution of Production Engineers,* June, 1950, p. 244.

1. As goods come in, an entry is made to the "inventory" account and recorded in a stock ledger sheet or inventory record sheet. (This assumes the use of perpetual inventory method.)

2. When goods are sent into production, a summary sheet on which all issues are recorded will show a debit to "work in process."

3. When goods are finished in a department, no entry will be made until the end of the month. Then an analysis is made of how many units were processed and finished. The result is an average cost per unit. For example:

a. Assume 600 units cost $600 for Department 1.

b. Department 1 sends 400 units to Department 2.

c. Department 2 sends all 400 units to "finished goods" after adding $300 more, labor and materials.

Department 1	Department 2	Finished Goods
(a) 600 (b) 400 *	(b) 400 (c) 700	(c) 700
	(c) 300	
Total	700	

* 400 × average cost of $1 = $400.

With this description of the system as background, the next question is where do we find the material-handling costs? Whenever any specific cost is desired, a service or production department can be set up. The individual items of expense are recorded and added to the cost of the product. Because of the integrated nature of materials handling, it is generally too cumbersome a system for detailed accumulation of costs. Like the production order method, this cost is buried in the overhead accounts of the various departments. Labor costs of handling would be indirect labor costs, and of course the other material-handling costs are billed as other items under the general overhead account.

a. *Depreciation.* Depreciation under the process system is recorded under the overhead account. The same general basis as described on page 270 is used under the process system to record and figure these overhead costs. The overhead item of depreciation is applied a little differently in this method.

The composite figure for depreciation is taken as just one item in the overhead costs of a department. Inasmuch as no percentage figures are involved here, a department head or cost analyst will see the depreciation figures every month. When a new method is devised, a manager has a tangible figure for comparison. No percentage is involved, and savings will show up in actual figures. When more than one machine or depreciable item is involved, there should be a card for each machine or tool. Composite figures can easily be secured.

b. *Taxes.* Taxes under the process cost system are basically treated the same as under the production order system. As taxes are compiled, they are entered into the "tax expense" account. This account is closed into the overhead account at the end of the month. The problem of property taxes is solved by using the yearly figure and dividing by 12 to get a monthly figure. As far as income taxes are concerned, they should be basically the same as the actual costs under the production order system. Therefore, profits would be the same under both the production order and process methods.

As far as the savings on purchases or developments are concerned, the profit figure on savings should be reduced by the per cent that applies to the particular income bracket of the firm.

c. *Cash Outlay.* The cash outlay problem is the same here as in the production order system. The cash accounts are on the same basis, as only the cost accounts would be affected. As the basis of depreciation would be the same, there would be no difference in the adjusted basis for the equipment. Inasmuch as an average figure is obtained at the end of the period, management has a sound basis for determining whether or not the average cost of a product is affected by the cash outlay for the new materials-handling device or system.

3. Standard Cost System

In both of the above systems, costs are obtained after the product is completed (the production order system) or the cost may not be available until the end of the month (the process system). The disadvantages of this are numerous. First of all, management is not so much interested in past costs as they are in whether or not future operations can be carried out efficiently. Second, extraneous factors can force costs out of line without management being aware of the condition until the end of the month or until the end of the production-order period. An example of this is the use of new labor or the transfer of a skilled worker to a nonskilled job due to the nature of operations for that particular month. Third, when the perspective on profits is poor, the firm may lack information to enable it to cut costs and reduce expenses. "Standard cost" systems have been devised as an attempt to overcome these deficiencies in the other two systems.

Setting up the standards to be used as the base of the system is an engineering function. Standards are determined for (1) quantity and price for material; (2) time and rate for labor; (3) for hours and rate for overhead. These figures are expressed in terms of per unit as well as on a total over-all basis. Past records are analyzed, and time studies are taken and used to arrive at a budget for the period.

After the system is set up, the operating function is carried out by the accounting department. Once this standard is set, material as it is purchased is recorded as standard costs per unit and any variance in price is recorded as "material price variance." When the goods are issued into production, they are recorded into "goods in process" at standard costs, and when transferred from this account to a "work finished" account, a quantity variance may develop. This may arise by more or less material per unit than called for by the standard.

It will be noted that all prices and quantities will be handled by production as standard, and adjustment to actual prices and quantities will be made in two places only, i.e., (1) when purchased and (2) when transferred from "work in process" to "finished goods." The symbols used in standard cost presentation are:

Q_a Actual quantity Q_s Standard quantity
R_a Actual rate R_s Standard rate
T_a Actual time T_s Standard time
P_a Actual price P_s Standard price
H_a Actual hours H_s Standard hours

a. Overhead. Overhead entails a little more complicated analysis as there are three types of variances that arise due to overhead variance. These are:

1. *Budget variance.* This results from the difference between budget or standard overhead and actual overhead.

2. *Capacity variance.* This arises from the difference between standard budget hours and rates and actual hours times the standard rate. This changes the number of hours over which this account will be prorated.

3. *Efficiency variance.* This is the difference between the standard hours per actual units and the actual hours per actual units. Once installed, this system is actually cheaper than the others to administer. More important, management is able to see their costs as they occur. This is the most important aspect of any accounting system. In addition to the example given above, a number of "hybrid" systems have been formulated to fit the type of production found in specific firms.

The best aspect of the standard cost system is its adaptability for ascertaining the costs of materials handling. As part of its regular function of setting up the system for standard costs, the engineering department should include an analysis of handling operations and establish standards for each of them. Thus, specialized cost information on handling could be obtained at little additional expense. A constant check could also be maintained on this type of expense.

b. Depreciation. Depreciation when computed as in the other two systems is also listed as an overhead item. In this case, management can have its engineers allocate a reasonable depreciation figure to the handling function. A cost technician will often establish this figure. In some firms the depreciation cost of material handling might be set as the depreciation on the equipment actually used to handle material.

c. Taxes. Taxes are figured as in the other two systems and, like depreciation, are recorded as an overhead item. Taxes applying to materials handling could be costed as a materials-handling item. Income taxes would be the same here, as government rules would be followed in profit determination. In this case, it is easy for management to compare the tax differentials arising from two periods of operations by comparing budgets.

d. Cash Outlay. Cash on hand and other liquidity factors show up the same in any system, but the problem of whether or not an outlay pays for itself is something else. Under the standard system, any profit variation will show up as favorable or unfavorable variance, but a word of caution should be had as some other factor could influence the variances.

4. Depreciation

In the administration of the Federal tax laws, some rules are laid down by the Department of the Treasury which are not altogether in agreement with accepted accounting principles, but which may be necessary to prevent the evasion of income taxes by the taxpayer. For example, the regulations state that "a taxpayer is not permitted under law to take advantage in later years of his prior failure to take any depreciation allowed under the law or of his action in allowance plainly inadequate under the known facts in prior years."

The total allowable depreciation equals the cost less the scrap value of the fixed asset. The depreciation actually allowed may easily be less than the total allowable deduction. Occasionally the income tax authorities allow more depreciation than that later found to be allowable. Any excess of the allowable over the allowed depreciation is lost to the taxpayer; any excess of the allowed over the allowable depreciation decreases the allowable depreciation in the future.

5. Obsolescence

In the case of depreciable property, the annual depreciation deduction may be increased by an allowance for extraordinary obsolescence; this begins the year when it is reasonably certain that the property is being affected by revolutionary inventions, abnormal growth or development, radical economic changes, or other factors, which may force the abandonment of the property at a future date prior to the end of its normal useful life. In effect, the obsolescence deduction results from a decrease in estimated useful life of property.

As a practical matter, obsolescence deduction will usually be limited to comparatively few years. Though a taxpayer may be of the opinion that his property may be obsolete in 10 years, a mere opinion will not warrant the deduction. The taxpayer may have to wait another 7 years for events which bear out his opinions and make it possible for him to substantiate an obsolescence claim with a reasonable degree of certainty. The remaining cost of the property would then be recoverable over the remaining 3 years, through a deduction for a depreciation including obsolescence.

Accountingwise there are a number of other theories besides that of the straight-line method. Without going into detail, one can sum up the other two main theories quickly. The *sinking fund method* tries to see that the last years are the years that the greatest depreciation is taken and that the beginning years take less of a load. The *annuity method theory* develops the thesis that the largest load should be taken in the first years. There is one other way of figuring depreciation instead of using the yearly basis. One could use the number of units that will be produced. Then, when the monthly budget is set up, the production rate can be used for depreciation for the period.

It should also be mentioned here that most small firms, as a practical matter, will use a composite plan for all their fixed assets by establishing a set per cent for the whole of the assets.

6. Interest

Neither cost accountants nor financial accountants can agree on whether to classify interest as a cost of operation or just as a financial matter of classification for the balance sheet. Actually, it is a cost of operation from the financial man's views in the same way that interest is the owner's return from money invested in the business. Yet from the engineer's or the cost man's view, interest is definitely a cost of operation of a business. As evidence of lack of agreement on this issue, one author wrote a book explaining that it should be an expense; he later wrote another book explaining why it should not be so. Possibly the best remedy to the problem is to look at the side that fits the personal needs of the firm.

QUESTIONS

1. What are the cost systems most commonly used in industry today? Compare their presentation of information as to handling costs.

2. What is the basis for depreciation of equipment under each of the cost systems?

3. How is "cash outlay" treated under each of the cost systems? How does this affect the purchase of new equipment in a company?

4. Describe how taxes are treated in each of the cost systems. How does this affect new equipment purchases?

5. Discuss the merits of the production order system from the standpoint of revealing handling costs.

6. Show how the historic cost system operates.

7. What are the advantages of the standard cost system?

8. Explain the operation of standard cost systems.

9. Compare the accounting problems involved in the depreciation and the obsolescence of materials-handling equipment.

10. How does the classification of interest affect the selection of equipment?

PROJECTS FOR FURTHER STUDY

1. In cooperation with the accountant of a local plant or warehouse, prepare a report on the determination of specific account numbers in order to provide more accurate handling costs.

2. Write a report on the effects of taxes and interest on the computation of savings for a proposed handling system.

CHAPTER 20

DETERMINATION OF HANDLING COSTS

1. Cost Accounting as a Tool of Management

Cost and operating reports are a valuable guide to the executive in providing him with the detailed cost information which will enable him to test the effectiveness of materials-handling proposals. The major objectives of such reports are: [1]

1. To furnish the maximum amount of information from both operating and cost angles.

2. To present in the most practical way the facts that reveal actual working conditions and situations; to facilitate effective supervision of plant operation; and to aid in attainment of high standards of efficiency and therefore realization of maximum net profit.

3. To aid in determining policies.

In the costing of materials-handling equipment, these things are of particular interest to management:

1. Length of time for savings to pay for the project
2. Implications of tax structure
3. Availability of cash for the expenditure
4. Necessity and morale factors

To present these things to management in a clear, concise, and easily comprehended way, the development and use of standard forms is advised. By following a set procedure in their preparation, the completeness of the presentation can be further increased. The following method has been found to be effective in this respect.

1. The methods department or industrial engineering department sets up complete comparative figures of costs under the old and the new method.

2. Cost department verifies this with past costs and prepares a statement including this data.

3. This statement is submitted either to a comptroller or some public accountant for tax and amortization implications.

[1] Theodore Lang, editor, "Cost Accountants' Handbook," p. 3, The Ronald Press Company, New York, 1945.

4. The draft with the financial review and clarification is sent back to the cost department for preparation for management presentation.

2. Setting up Accounting Statements

Accounting statements must be based upon adequate cost records. This necessitates the setting up of account numbers and classifications which

Proposed Cost Statement for New Equipment Purchase

Present Method of Operation			
Labor Expense................. _____	Labor Hours.......... _____		
Material used.................... _____	Material units........ _____		
Overhead (including depreciation.. _____			
Total.................................. _____	Labor Units_____ Material_____		
Operation with New Equipment			
Labor Expense................. _____	Labor Hours.......... _____		
Material used.................... _____	Material units........ _____		
Overhead (excluding depreciation) _____			
Total.................................. _____	Labor Units_____ Material_____		
Total Expense Under Present Method .... _____			
Total Expense With New Equipment .... _____			
Gross Saving .... _____			
Gross Saving................... _____	Net Saving x 60 per cent =		
less depreciation as per tax schedule .... _____	actual saving per internal revenue		
Net Saving Per Year........ _____	x 60 per cent = _____		
Actual saving Per Year.. _____			
less 10 per cent of Purchase as interest expense............... _____			
Saving as to Cash Outlay.. _____			

FIG. 171. Proposed cost statement for new equipment purchases provides management with the net saving as to cash outlay.

will provide accurate handling-cost information. The isolation of handling costs is the first step toward reducing them. The next step is an orderly presentation to management which will show these costs in their proper perspective.

The cost statement in Fig. 171 has been devised to show the additional effects of taxes, interest, and other financial aspects which will affect the cash outlay of the project and the net savings that may be expected to result therefrom.

No hard and fast rules can be set as to the specific account numbers that should be set up. This will depend upon the importance of materials movement in the company (see Chap. 6) and the cost of collecting the data. The latter will have to be considered in terms of the savings which may be derived.

3. Interpretation of Data

Much time will be saved for management in its perusal of proposals if its engineering department knows from past experience or policy set forth in written (or verbal) form just what criteria will be used in their acceptance. For projects of lesser magnitude, a definite written policy will permit these to be decided upon by a lower echelon in the administrative ladder and will permit quicker review by higher officers.

Having established this policy or set up these criteria, management can expect projects to contain all the pertinent information or data on each project. They can then arrive at a decision without further delay. This not only speeds up the process of managerial consideration but also ensures that all necessary factors have been considered. The development of this form also makes it easier to visualize the problem under consideration and essay more thoroughly all the factors which may be involved.

4. Showing Handling Costs by Applied-percentage Method

Although much of the real handling expense of a plant is hidden deeply within production operations, customary practice in most firms today recognizes certain expense items which are part of the handling-cost picture. As already shown, the specific method of accumulating and showing handling costs will depend upon the type of accounting system used.

a. No Cost System. A certain percentage figure is applied to materials as they are received, processed, or completed. In one case, materials-handling costs are considered simply as part of all the indirect labor and expense items of the company. This general percentage figure was arbitrarily set a number of years ago and has not been changed since.

A fairly accurate system of this type (and satisfactory in certain operations) can be developed by a small firm with no record of receiving costs, handling from one process to another, or other handling costs. They can have their public accountant survey their operations and make reasonable estimate as to the percentage to be applied to the material as it is received.

A larger firm that has departmentalized its cost and production centers but still has no service cost system may also easily establish a percentage to be applied in the same manner. By using accrued data, management can take all handling costs and divide them by total purchases. This includes the handling costs in the material at an early stage. Inventories.

both ending and beginning, thus have the costs of handling included in them. These entries are carried on the books by debiting Inventory (perpetual) and Expenses and crediting the normal accounts as is usually done. Every time a shipment comes in, the Material-handling Expense Account is credited for the applied amount and Inventory is debited. The proper method is to have the Material-handling Expense Account controlled by a subsidiary ledger which shows the items, such as depreciation, handling labor, etc., that apply to the handling of materials.

The following are some of the necessary entries that are involved when goods are received.

JOURNAL ENTRIES

I: *Debit:* Inventory (perpetual)   *Credit:* Vouchers Payable
II: *Debit:* Materials-handling Expense   *Credit:* Vouchers Payable

SUBSIDIARY ENTRIES

III: *Debit:* Depreciation (materials-handling expense–general ledger)   *Credit:* Reserve for Depreciation (general ledger)
IV: *Debit:* Materials labor (materials-handling–general ledger)   *Credit:* Payroll (general ledger)
V: *Debit:* Other Sundry Handling Expenses   *Credit:* Entry to Record

The only difficulty with this method is with the disposal of the balance of Materials-handling Expense Account. Since this is just an estimate, this balance should be either an addition or subtraction of the Inventory and Cost of Goods Sold Accounts. This difference should be distributed between the two accounts in proportion to the way in which the goods move out over the period. For instance, if two-thirds of the goods moved out, then two-thirds of the balance should go to Cost of Goods Sold and one-third to Inventory. In the following period, the balance will count the same as materials coming in. Add this to the total units purchased, and figure the ending inventory to find the proper proportion.

An advantage of the method is that the depreciation of equipment is included in the handling account and is added to the cost of the material. As this method involves a nondepartmentalized company, other expenses are often inaccurate as to the timing of charges to cost of material. One effect is to reflect a different profit the first year of application, but after that year both beginning and ending inventories will be influenced. This first year will show a higher inventory than normal, and a footnote should point this out to management. The higher profit arising from this condition should also be pointed out to management in the footnotes of the Profit and Loss Balance Sheet.

b. Production Order System. The applied-percentage system works as well in the types of cost systems described in Chap. 19. In the production order system the cost of material handling is added to the actual cost of the basic material as it is transferred from one department to another or from one order to another. It provides management with a firm foundation as to what its over-all material-handling costs are. If this were its sole advantage, the system would more than pay for itself.

The percentage is applied as in the no cost system. The same method of arriving at the percentage figure is used. As the material goes into process, it has the material handling cost added to its value. This is done by taking as many items out of the former overhead account budget and budgeting them under the materials handling account. Items in this category are depreciation of materials-handling equipment, indirect labor of materials handling (applied directly in detail) and other sundry accounts that are directly applied to materials handling.

c. Historic Cost System. The per cent is applied in this system as in the other two. Likewise, the handling cost should be developed in a budget and closed out in the same way as in the other systems. At the end of the month instead of having some of the "cost of material" in an overhead account they are more properly classified as part of the material cost.

d. Standard Cost System. In the standard cost system this budget is simply another standard to meet. Any variance is fully distributed and is not shown on the balance sheet. To do this, the budget would be included in the standard cost for material. Another way of accomplishing this would be to apply this percentage to materials at the end of the period.

The main advantage of the method applied to this system is that an efficiency variance and a price variance both can be computed. Management can therefore distinguish cost variances arising from price variation from that caused by the variation in the amount of material being moved. In industries with wide fluctuations this distinction is of considerable value. In more stable industries the added cost of the system probably would not be justified.

In the variance distribution, the variances for labor and overhead would be distributed as usual. The material variance could not be computed until the full cost of materials handling was added to the material cost. The variances could then be computed as usual.

5. Cost Factors in the Selection of Equipment

The form shown in Fig. 172, Analysis of Annual Costs—Materials-handling Equipment, has been developed by W. B. McClelland to estimate the annual costs of different methods of handling which may be under consideration. It calculates the cost for each method assuming 8, 16, and 24 hours per day operation. This is done to analyze the fluctuations of fixed and variable costs as volume of production varies. The form could be extended to provide comparison of operations for 4 or 6 hours per day.

ANALYSIS OF ANNUAL COSTS—MATERIALS HANDLING EQUIPMENT
BASED UPON_____WORKING DAYS PER YEAR

ACCOUNT	METHOD 1			METHOD 2			METHOD 3			REMARKS
	8 HRS. DAY	16 HRS. DAY	24 HRS. DAY	8 HRS. DAY	16 HRS. DAY	24 HRS. DAY	8 HRS. DAY	16 HRS. DAY	24 HRS. DAY	
INVESTMENT										
INVOICE PRICE OF EQUIPMENT										
INSTALLATION CHARGES										
MAINTENANCE FACILITIES										
FUELING OR POWER FACILITIES										
ALTERATIONS TO PRESENT FACILITIES										
FREIGHT & OTHER TRANSPORTATION										
DESIGN WORK										
SUPPLIES										
OTHERS										
CREDITS										
TOTAL INVESTMENT										
FIXED CHARGES										
DEPRECIATION (YEARS)										
INTEREST ON INVESTMENT (%)										
TAXES (%)										
INSURANCE (%)										
SUPERVISION PERSONNEL										
CLERICAL PERSONNEL										
MAINTENANCE PERSONNEL										
OTHER										
TOTAL FIXED CHARGES										
VARIABLE CHARGES										
OPERATING PERSONNEL										
POWER AND/OR FUEL										
LUBRICANTS										
MAINTENANCE LABOR										
MAINTENANCE PARTS & MATERIALS										
OTHER										
TOTAL VARIABLE COSTS										
TOTAL ANNUAL CHARGES										

Fig. 172. Form devised by W. B. McClelland to estimate the annual costs of different methods of handling. (*Clark Equipment Company.*)

a. Determination of the Capital Investment Required. This is the estimated gross amount by which the accountant will debit his asset account and it should include all costs involved before the actual operation of the system.

The various items comprising this capital charge are:

1. *Invoice price of equipment.* This figure is the estimated total of the invoices to be received from manufacturers and can be obtained from the proposals of the various bidders.

2. *Installation charges.* All labor, materials, burden, and other costs involved in removing the plant accessories from the receiving carrier, and then placing and conditioning them ready for operation.

3. *Maintenance facilities.* The invoice prices, installation costs, etc., required for equipment to repair and maintain the handling devices.

4. *Fuel and/or power facilities.* Invoice price, installation costs, etc., for facilities necessary to provide power and/or fuel. If propelled by internal-combustion engines, gasoline facilities must be provided. If batteries are the source of power, then charging equipment and battery handling devices must be obtained.

5. *Alterations to present facilities.* Labor, material, and burden involved in any necessary alterations to existing property. This may include strengthening of floors, replacing a gravel storage yard with concrete, or changing the locations and size of door openings.

6. *Freight and other transportation.* All transportation charges on equipment, material, etc., necessary for each method. It may include transportation and expenses of personnel making investigations pertaining to the subject project. For greater exactness, these items might be subdivided in accordance with the first five items above and the following two.

7. *Design work.* All labor, material, and burden involved in the engineering work required.

8. *Supplies.* All expendable items such as hooks, cables, etc., needed to use the handling equipment efficiently.

9. *Other charges.* Any capital costs not already included.

10. *Credits.* The net realizable income from the sale of items abandoned or replaced. This figure will be the difference between sale price and the cost of preparing these items for sale with a further deduction of their book value. This could be a debit if the book value exceeded the net amount realized from the sale.

If these items can be profitably used elsewhere, the accountant should transfer the book value to the new location and make corresponding adjustments to the respective accounts.

If the book value for items abandoned does not equal exactly the net realizable salvage value, an error has been made in the depreciation rate, and the difference should be adjusted to earned surplus. In that case neither a debit nor a credit should be considered here.

The total of the above accounts will be the estimated increase in assets or the total capital investment.

b. Determination of the Probable Fixed Charges. The next step is to determine the probable fixed charges for each of the methods or types of equipment being considered. The accounts or items to be included here are:

1. *Depreciation.* The rate of depreciation for each class of equipment is generally a policy of top management, in some cases the board of directors. It is also controlled by tax allowances. This term as usually used at this point includes two different elements of cost technically discussed

as depreciation and obsolescence. Depreciation is deterioriation due to wear and tear. Obsolescence is a cost occasioned by better processes or equipment becoming available. Equipment becomes obsolete for two basic reasons:

a. The user of the equipment may devise new processes making present facilities worthless or his customers may demand a change in product of such a nature that present facilities cannot be used.

b. The producer of the equipment he owns may offer new models, the economy of which prompts abandoning present facilities in favor of

ESTIMATED DEPRECIATION CHARGES – MATERIALS HANDLING EQUIPMENT

Method No.				Type of Handling Equipment								
Description	Property	Original Installed Costs	Estimated Salvage Value	Amount to Depreciate	Estimated Life Years	Annual Depreciation Charge						
						1st Year	2nd Year	3rd Year	4th Year	5th Year	6th Year	7th Year

FIG. 173. Form devised by W. B. McClelland for estimating depreciation charges. (*Clark Equipment Company.*)

new ones, even though the mechanical condition of that equipment indicates more years of productive life.

In case the depreciation policy dictated to the materials-handling man is not the same for all items of equipment being considered, he might use the sheet shown in Fig. 173, Estimated Depreciation Charges—Materials-handling Equipment. With this sheet he can calculate the estimated annual depreciation charge for each piece of equipment and arrive at a total figure which his superiors would accept.

If the policy is to depreciate such equipment on a use basis (such as per ton handled, per hour operated, etc.) instead of an annual time basis, this account should then be included under variable charges.

2. *Interest on investment.* It is an open question whether interest on investment should be included on an analysis sheet such as this. Some persons say that interest on investment must be included in every procurement. Others say it is not logical to include interest on investment. This side claims that one should summarize actual expenditures for each case and then compare the return on investment with each potential method.

3. *Taxes.* Property taxes considered on all facilities.

4. *Insurance.* Insurance charges of all types considered.

5. *Supervision.* The cost for persons permanently required to manage and control the operation.

6. *Clerical.* The cost for persons continuously required to provide the necessary paper work.

7. *Maintenance personnel.* The cost of the persons required full time to provide inspection and maintenance.

8. *Other expenses.* Any expenses not listed above which occur on a time basis.

The sum of these accounts will provide an estimate of the cost of making each method available for use, the stand-by charge, or the fixed charges which are predetermined at the time procurement is made.

c. Determination of Variable Charges:

1. *Operating personnel.* The cost for those persons actually assigned to operate the equipment whose time is charged to this operation only when so assigned. This account should include the wages received as well as other expenses involved in keeping an employee on the payroll, such as social security, payroll charges, medical care, etc. Incidentally, the actual wage paid is not the only cost of keeping any person on the payroll regardless of his station in the organization.

2. *Power and/or fuel costs.* If the equipment is propelled by internal-combustion engines, this account will indicate the cost for gasoline. If propelled by electric motors, it will be the public utility charge.

3. *Lubricants.* The amount paid for oil and grease used with the units involved.

4. *Maintenance labor.* The cost for maintenance labor which fluctuates with the use of the equipment. First, there is the maintenance work on the accessories involved; *i.e.,* on industrial trucks, cranes, conveyors, or whatever kind of equipment is being considered. Second, there is the maintenance labor on the supplies required for use with this equipment. Pallets provide a good example. If expendable pallets were involved, the accountant would probably not set them up on his books as a fixed asset but would carry the inventory as a deferred charge instead. As these pallets were used, he would transfer the value from the inventory account to an expense account. In such a case, little or no maintenance labor would be required. If, however, durable pallets were involved, he might capitalize the cost of the pallets required for continuous operation of the plant. He then might charge to depreciation the estimated cost due to obsolescence. Any charges for repairing the pallets or cost of replacing those destroyed or lost might be considered a variable charge. The accounting practice for perishable tools might be acceptable for costing such supplies.

THE BUILD-UP OF *Handling Cost* ON YOUR PRODUCT

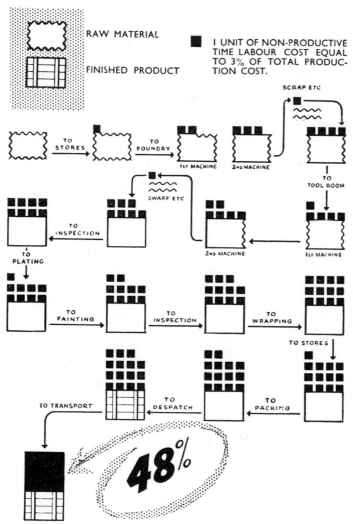

FIG. 174. Example of the accumulation of handling costs on a product as it progresses through various manufacturing operations. (*Conveyancer Fork Trucks, Ltd.*)

5. *Maintenance parts and materials.* The cost of repair parts to keep the accessories in operation as well as cost of parts and materials to keep the supplies in usable condition. The discussion concerning accounting for maintenance labor applies also to this account.

6. *Other costs.* Any variable costs not included in the previous accounts.

The sum of these accounts will provide an estimated cost of using the equipment which is available. The fixed charges indicate the cost of making the equipment available for use. They will be combined to form the total estimated annual cost.

d. Determination of Total Annual Charges. Management usually thinks in terms of tons of consumable merchandise actually produced. The weight of the salable merchandise plus the weight of the containers gives the tonnage which must be handled. The materials-handling man can sometimes benefit by resolving his costs into:

1. Cost per unit of salable merchandise shipped.

2. Cost per unit shipped for which the carrier must be paid, including container and merchandise.

6. Cost Factors in Selection of Gasoline and Electric Industrial Trucks

The relative merits of gasoline- and electric-powered industrial trucks have become one of the most discussed aspects of materials handling. There are a large number of factors to be taken into account before making a decision between the two. The factors fall into two main groups. The first group can be measured in terms of dollars and cents. The second consists of all other factors and considerations which will affect the selection. The second group is discussed in greater detail on page 153.

The figures shown on the form in Fig. 164 and the results portrayed on the graph in Fig. 165 were developed from a particular situation and it was not intended that they would have general application. In most instances, the individual figures for each of the cost accounts provided in the form will have to be developed from an individual firm's own experience.

This study was developed by an equipment company manufacturing both the electric and the gasoline types. Different levels of production are provided to show the relative ratios of fixed and variable charges in each instance.[2]

QUESTIONS

1. List the objectives of cost reports.

2. What specific questions does management raise on the cost of materials-handling equipment?

[2] Sections 5 and 6 are based on material developed and reviewed by W. B. McClelland.

3. Why are account numbers so important in getting accurate cost information?

4. How is the applied-percentage method applied to a production order system to show handling costs?

5. How can the applied-percentage method be applied when there is no cost system?

6. Discuss the application of the applied-percentage method to the historic cost system.

7. How is the applied-percentage method used with a standard cost system?

8. What are the major cost factors in the selection of equipment?

9. What is meant by "capital investment required" for the new handling system?

10. What items are included in the determination of the capital charge?

11. What items are included in the estimated increase in assets account?

12. What items are included in estimating probable fixed charges?

13. How are variable charges of a cost report determined?

14. What problems arise in computing maintenance charges?

15. How can the presentation of handling costs as a total annual charge help the materials-handling engineer?

PROJECTS FOR FURTHER STUDY

1. Using specific cost figures furnished by the instructor, prepare a cost analysis.

2. Set up the necessary accounts for the receipt of goods where no cost system is used and a percentage figure is applied.

CHAPTER 21

HOW TO SELL BETTER HANDLING METIIODS

To those who have complete responsibility for production, materials handling is simply another of the myriad factors which must be considered and assigned its importance or place in the industrial structure. The use and acceptance of new methods and equipment for handling must be balanced against their effect on other factors of production. In the matter of expenditure they must compete with all the other demands which are constantly being made upon the treasury of the company.

1. Educating Management

Industrial efficiency starts at the top! The same is true of materials handling. The company whose executives are aware of the cost-saving potentialities of improved handling methods and systems tends to develop these systems rather quickly and painlessly. In other companies, methods may be improved but each step is an uphill fight. Engineering staffs may know of better ways to do it but the time required to "sell" management may not make the effort worth while.[1]

Materials handling has a special claim on management's attention. It is not only *a* method but in many cases *the* method which offers the greatest opportunity for cutting production costs. For many companies, it is practically an untouched horizon.

In the first place, the handling and moving of materials constitutes a large part of any production activity and the major part of distributing, transporting, warehousing, and supply activities. Second, most progressive firms have already spent considerable time on increasing individual machine production, improvement of morale and labor relations, analysis of materials utilization, time and motion study, and the other studies which have in their turn contributed to a steady increase in productivity. Further increase in research in these fields will produce only slight increase at best.

[1] See John R. Immer, "Layout Planning Techniques," p. 308, The Role of Top Management in Materials Handling, McGraw-Hill Book Company, Inc., New York, 1950.

How, then, to make management more aware of what improved handling can do? Educating management for materials handling calls for effective and brief means of presentation. Motion pictures are about the most painless and effective means of telling this story to those whose time is limited. In many an organization a 30-minute period in the middle of the day may be taken off not only by the engineering staff directly concerned but by production management itself. Often "production management" at this point will include production superintendents and foremen.

Another effective means of spreading the gospel of better handling is through the technical magazines and papers. This is being done by editorials, articles, and reports, and even the advertisements serve a useful purpose in this connection.

2. Educating Materials-handling Engineers

A distinction must be made between "training" and "education." The former involves the teaching of specific methods and ways of doing things. The latter goes much further and provides an understanding of the fundamental forces and principles at work. One teaches "how" to do something; the other teaches "why" it is done. There are many well-trained materials-handling engineers. These men, many with a lifetime of experience with specific kinds of equipment, install thousands of conveyors, cranes, and specialized types of handling equipment with never a question of their technical knowledge and ability, both of which are well tested. The result is a high standard of performance as far as the equipment itself is concerned.

The integration of this equipment into the total pattern of the production processes of the company is an entirely different problem. This is concerned more with flow lines, cost of alternate methods of handling, methods analysis, and cost studies. It also involves an understanding of production processes, accounting methods, organizational problems, and an appreciation of what management wants from its materials-handling engineers.

Management wants these men to know how to move materials most efficiently and at the lowest cost. It also wants them to know what it costs to move and handle materials. They should know the easiest way of moving materials from one operation to the next. It expects them to be familiar with all the tools of the industrial engineer, the accountant, and of management in order that they should be able to devise the most efficient method, compute its cost elements, and present it in a clear, concise manner. They must also be familiar with the work of the various equipment engineers referred to above and have a broad knowledge of materials-handling equipment and methods.

The enthusiastic reception and endorsement of materials handling by nonmanufacturing companies (shipping, warehousing, processing, etc.) has widened the demand for materials-handling engineers. This means primarily that the training of the materials-handling engineer must be of a broader nature to include the handling of any materials in any industry. This means more reliance upon fundamental aspects and principles of handling and an understanding of basic techniques rather than a knowledge of handling methods. This last is an important part of his education as well, but it is not enough in itself.

3. Educating Workers and the Public

Just as many companies have profited by making their workers "motion conscious," additional rewards go to the plants where they are "materials movement" conscious. Such a program often results in the workers themselves pointing out improvements in handling that should be made. Where control over specific operations is less rigid, as in the warehousing, distributing, and transporting industries, this cooperation of the workers is especially important.

The value of the attitude of the public toward the handling and moving of materials may be difficult to assess in dollars and cents. In the long run it can have very positive effects in its demand for more efficient methods in public ventures and in the decreased resistance to change.

The importance of this factor has been emphasized by many of the personal experiences of the author in countries outside the United States. It is difficult for the American engineer to appreciate or to understand the amount of resistance to improved methods of handling that exists in many foreign countries. One project, for example, was turned down because "it had never been done before."

4. Instruments of Education

Although much has been written about specific phases of materials handling, very few attempts have been made to date to bring together this knowledge and information so as to present an organized and coherent picture. Although magazines and trade publications have in the last decade produced thousands of articles of the type, How We Move Steel at the XYZ Company, many of the most significant advances and methods of handling have remained unreported.

The primary source of information is the individual plant or firm which has been faced with a materials-handling problem. It is impossible for one person to visit every installation where a new method of handling has been evolved. The next best thing is to rely on the editors of technical magazines who spend the greater part of their time in search of outstanding installations and ideas. Although they are generally written from a narrow point of view (to suit the special interests of their readers), their technical accuracy at the present is usually high.

a. Individual Companies. The final authority on any phase of materials handling is the company which uses it. A considerable part of the credit for the phenomenal spread of technological improvements in the

FIG. 175. Scale model of machinery permits detailed study of handling needs of machine before it is installed. (*Northern Electric Company.*)

United States is due to the generosity of individual firms and their willingness to share these developments with others. In no other country is there such an openness about methods and techniques.

It is common practice for a company, before starting on an extensive handling program, to send representatives to other companies which have already solved the same problem. The experience of L. Bamberger & Company described in Chap. 18 is typical. The study made by Merchants Motor Freight Company of St. Paul, Minn. (Chap. 32) is another example of how the benefits of the system work both ways.

The fact that the other companies may be competitors is no deterrent in most instances. One farm machinery company developed an improved type of paint-spray booth which a leading competitor heard about. The competitor wrote for details on the installation. Complete blueprints and specifications as well as a detailed account of its operation were sent. Finally, the competitor sent one of its engineers to the other plant for

2 weeks to study its operation and construction before duplicating it in their own plant. In the meantime, the first company had an engineer gathering ideas from still another firm—a competitor of both of the firms referred to above.

An example of how the veil of secrecy operates in the opposite direction is contained in an experience of the author while traveling in a

FIG. 176. Detailed scale model is used to study handling methods of new plant before it is built. (*Northern Electric Company.*)

foreign country a few years ago. Being intrigued by a large door, he stepped into a room where a fairly commonplace metal-processing operation was taking place. The chief engineer, acting as guide for the tour, said that he was sorry they had gone in this room as it was a very secret method which had been developed by their own engineers at considerable cost to the company. The method, incidentally, was one which a competitor had discarded 15 years before as being obsolete. With a free exchange of information, this and a number of other methods observed in the two plants would have been replaced long ago.

b. Company Publications. The most valuable of these are the ones published by materials-handling equipment companies. While these are restricted to a description of the equipment manufactured by the company, they often provide a more detailed description of an installation than will be found in technical magazines. Many engineers have kept their back copies for a number of years and have a ready reference for the use of this equipment.

The articles usually are well illustrated and have a large amount of technical detail which, of course, is of value to the materials-handling engineer considering the value of a similar installation. Another advantage is that any additional details (on the equipment especially) are readily available from the publisher. Inasmuch as the name and location of the company in which the equipment was installed is usually given, it is also easy to check on the results obtained.

c. Magazines. Magazines are the main source for all types of information and knowledge in regard to materials handling, plant layout, and packaging. The only difficulty (and this is a serious one) is locating the article for the particular subject in which you are interested. Ordinary bibliographical references are not detailed enough to reveal some of the most valuable material on dispatching, cost analysis, and maintenance procedures when these are incidental parts of articles which are listed only by the type of process or one or two main types of equipment. If these articles are to be of reference value to the practicing materials-handling engineer as well as to the student, a more detailed reference system is needed.

Such a system was recently developed by the author to provide detailed indexing of specific phases of materials handling, plant layout, and packaging. A four-digit classification was developed which showed for each article:

10.00: Type of equipment: materials handling and packaging
20.00: Industry (automobile, meat packing, clothing, etc.)
30.00: Type of operation described (assembly, machine, loading, etc.)
40.00: Type of materials being handled (by weight, size, shape)
50.00: Techniques of organization and management (time study, etc.) [2]

This information was put on IBM cards for machine sorting. Another machine would print to a tape all the articles which included reference to specific items of information needed. (Approximately 860 items were used for 12,000 articles.) Each item would appear on a single line, thus:

BLAWKNX PLAN CRANE HEDRM 5 HOOPER A STL 278 1 3 44
1120 2131 5415

[2] For complete classification, see Appendix B.

This line would read: "Blaw-Knox (name of company involved), Plan Crane Headroom (descriptive title), article less than a full page in length (5), written by A. Hooper, *Steel Magazine*, page 278, Jan. 3, 1944. Includes reference to: overhead traveling cranes (11.20), in iron and steel processing (21.31), and has information for layout or workplace or machine space requirements (54.15)."

The different types of magazines in the United States are currently featuring approximately 1,500 articles per year on almost every aspect of materials handling, packaging, and layout planning. This does not include company publications and trade journals with limited circulation.

Finance and management publications frequently carry articles or reports on materials-handling programs. A recent article appearing in *Fortune* was particularly noteworthy. In addition, a few of the equipment companies have featured advertisements in these publications to bring to the attention of top executives the savings to be derived from improved handling methods.

There is a magazine for almost every major, and many minor, trade and industry in the country. Some of those for the metal trade and processing industries have featured many excellent articles on the handling of their specific products. Although the others have occasionally produced studies of considerable merit, the fact that this is a relatively new subject to these magazines is reflected in their treatment of the handling function. There are a number of exceptions to this, however, particularly where the articles seek to show only specific handling methods.

Magazines devoted to materials handling are of fairly recent origin in the United States. *Modern Materials Handling* was founded in 1946 (as an offshoot of *The Palletizer* started at the beginning of the Second World War), and *Flow* was founded in 1945. In England, however, *Mechanical Handling* dates from 1932. It was formed as an offshoot of the older *Cassiers Journal*, which was started in 1891.

Industrial-management magazines have featured articles on plant layout and materials handling from their first issues, most of these dating from just before the First World War. Within recent years they have become an even more fruitful source of information. As a whole they have developed more specialized material on method and organization than the materials-handling magazines themselves.

The popular science magazines often carry stories of new handling gadgets and machines. In addition popular magazines of general appeal often have articles on handling and moving of materials. Although very limited in number, the breadth of the reading audience gives them an importance as an educating medium for materials handling.

d. *Daily Newspapers*. Financial journals frequently carry references to outstanding materials-handling installations. News of convention proceedings and exhibitions also attract attention. *Flow* magazine places advertisements in the *Wall Street Journal* from time to time. These stress the importance of materials handling as a source of potential savings in production costs. Individual equipment companies frequently place advertisements in daily financial journals.

e. *Books*. A large number of books have been written describing the use of specific types of materials-handling equipment. The most noteworthy of these were written about 1930, and although worthy of examination because of their description of basic types of equipment and their uses they are in need of being brought up to date. Two books brought out during the Second World War partly made up this deficiency but still left many important types of equipment undescribed. Cranes and conveyors are the exception to this statement, as recent books provide a more complete treatment for these types, which is lacking for other major types such as industrial trucks. The packaging industry is comprehensively covered by several encyclopedias of outstanding merit.

The background and understanding of analysis for materials handling has been covered to date largely in textbooks on layout planning and special sections in other books on industrial engineering. The section in the "Production Handbook" has long been the classic reference. It is only within the last year that a book on materials handling has appeared which began to provide a picture of what the materials-handling engineer should know.

The manuals and special booklets prepared by various equipment companies merit inclusion in this category as an aid to education and training. In many specialized areas these provide the most authoritative source of information.

f. *Films and Other Visual Materials*. As evidenced by the film list in the Appendix, a wide selection of visual training aids is available. Many of these are films on general production methods, prepared during the Second World War by some of the larger industrial firms. Several very fine presentations of the basic principles of modern handling methods have been issued by large firms as a service function. Many equipment manufacturers have prepared films showing specialized uses of their products as well as the savings to be derived from the use of this equipment. Inasmuch as many of these are strictly "sales films," they are not listed in the usual film indexes.

5. Visualizing Handling Problems

The executive responsible for final approval of a materials-handling project wants to get a clear picture of what he is approving. With the demands made on his time by other responsibilities it is essential that this presentation be concise and easy to comprehend as well as complete.

a. Blueprints. Despite the increased use of other means of presentation these still remain the standard stock in trade of the industrial engineer. The ease of carrying them into the manager's office is but one point in their favor. Larger scale drawings may be used to show the details of a proposal or method. Smaller scale drawings show the over-all picture at a glance. There are, however, some disadvantages to the use of blueprints.

More elaborate projects are often examined by accountants and other nonengineering personnel. In many companies, also, the approving executives may have a background in law, accounting, or sales and little or no engineering experience. To these persons the blueprint with its maze of lines may be difficult to understand if not completely unintelligible. More than one such project has been approved by an executive who had not the slightest idea of what he had authorized.

b. Other Types of Drawings. The problem of visualization has been solved in many instances by various types of drawings which include the third dimension. Various types of orthographic projection are used to accomplish this. Diagrammatic drawings, either of oblique or isometric projection, are used to illustrate simple installations or more complicated ones of limited scope. Schematic drawings either in angle projection or in perspective are generally used for larger projects or to show an over-all picture of a complicated installation. Where multi-story buildings are involved, cutaway sections are frequently used.

Where an extensive program of improvements is involved and a large number of persons are concerned with its approval, a regular commercial artist may be called in.[3] The increased visualization afforded by his sketches and drawings permits a quicker and more accurate appraisal of the merits of the proposal. The savings in the time required by the approving authorities to reach a decision more than pay for the expense of the drawings.

c. Templets. In addition to their very valuable use as a tool in evolving the most efficient arrangement of machines and equipment, templets are valuable from the standpoint of the presentation of the project. The fact that they are flat also makes it easier to carry them from

[3] See Immer, *op. cit.,* Chap. 19, Drawing for Plant Layout.

one office to another. In larger companies with acres of plant space to be shown, templet boards can be filed in large flat drawers (Ford Motor Company, Dagenham, England), filed vertically with unneeded sections raised out of the way like a double-hung window (The Bullard Company), or hung flat against the wall (Cadillac Motors Company).

Color is used with templets to show a wide variety of things. Some of the combinations employed within recent years are:

1. Present position of machines not to be moved, present position of machines to be moved, and new position of machines.

2. Machines on hand, placed on order, delivery within 60, 90 days, etc., and no order placed.

3. Machines used for product A, B, etc.

4. Conveyors: gravity roller, powered roller, slat (flush with floor), belt, monorail, and trolley.

5. At the end of the Second World War, machines belonging to the parent company, Corporation A, Corporation B, the Army, and the Navy.

By means of color certain aspects of a layout may be vividly brought to the attention of management. This provides a more comprehensive and complete presentation than black-and-white templets or line drawings.[4]

d. Scale Models. The use of scale models has become standard practice in both large and small manufacturing plants. In some instances they are used primarily for presentation of a proposed layout or handling method to management. In others, such as Oldsmobile, they are used as a tool in the analysis of methods itself. The models range from rough wood blocks (painted or plain) made by the plant carpenter to elaborate models of complex machinery prepared in considerable detail.

The problem of how to handle in the most efficient way some 1,000 tons of raw material per week was uppermost in the minds of the engineers in the planning of a new wire and cable plant of the Northern Electric Company Limited at Lachine, Quebec. A complete and very carefully detailed three-dimensional model was built to a scale of ½ inch to the foot. This permitted detailed study of all handling methods in the new plant long before it was built.

The educational value of scale models is shown more clearly in the examples contained in Figs. 177 and 178. They provide a vivid contrast of good and bad methods of handling.[5]

[4] Ibid., Chap. 20, Templets.
[5] See Materials Handling: 1949 Ways to Cut Costs, Modern Industry, Jan. 15, 1949, p. 40. This article contains a check list for good handling practice.

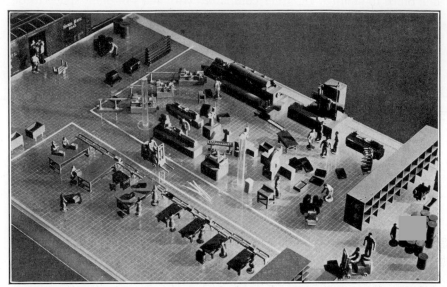

Fig. 177. See how many faulty materials-handling practices you can point out in this scale model. (*Modern Industry*, Jan. 15, 1949.)

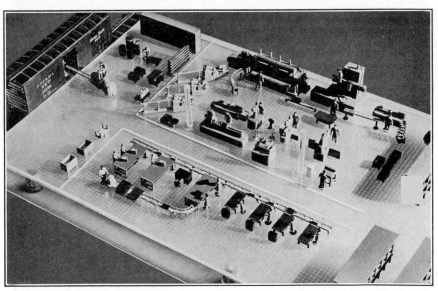

Fig. 178. Compare the handling methods above with those shown in Fig. 177. (*Modern Industry*, Jan. 15, 1949.)

6. Presenting Costs to Management

The various methods of analysis and survey with which the earlier part of this book is concerned may be used effectively in presenting the cost picture to management. Many of these techniques serve to show in a graphic or diagrammatic way the adverse characteristics of the old method and by comparison the advantages of the new method. To com-

Fig. 179. Artist's drawing of new Hoboken Pier No. 4 shows the general movement of traffic and some of the solutions provided for quayside handling and storage. (*The Port of New York Authority.*)

plete the presentation, cost analyses and intangible (or noncost) considerations are carefully prepared.

Although many production men are wary of using too many charts and graphs, these means are frequently the best way of presenting a project so that it may be quickly and completely understood by those responsible for approving it. Bar charts and pie charts may help show the comparisons in cost under the old and the new methods. Graphs will show trends in cost movements as well as the relationships of handling costs to other factors such as volume of goods moved, total production units, and direct labor accounts.

Many companies have developed standard forms for the presentation of data relative to a major proposal or change in method. These forms serve as a check list for cost factors to be included in the study and thus ensure completeness of the report from this standpoint. The standard presentation also makes it easier for the executive to weigh the merits of the proposal and thus make a decision more quickly and with a better grasp of the nature and extent of the proposal.

QUESTIONS

1. What is meant by "educating" management?
2. What does management expect from materials-handling engineers?
3. What interest does the public have in materials handling?
4. What can workers do to affect handling methods?
5. Where can information on materials handling be obtained?
6. Discuss the contribution made to materials handling by (*a*) magazines, (*b*) books, (*c*) daily press, and (*d*) films.
7. Outline a classification system for the organization of knowledge relative to materials handling.
8. Discuss the various means of visualizing the handling problem.
9. What are the limitations of blueprints and line drawings?
10. How can color be used in connection with templets and scale models to show a specific type of information?
11. Discuss the relative advantages of templets and scale models.
12. What problems are involved in presenting a materials-handling problem to management?

PROJECTS FOR FURTHER STUDY

1. Prepare a layout of a small woodworking plant manufacturing two main products on a quantity basis. Use colored templets to show the use of each machine.
2. Examine carefully the issues of one of the materials-handling journals for one year. Write a commentary on the type of article and the style of presentation.
3. Prepare a report on the purpose of the author and the type of presentation for three other books written recently on materials handling or plant layout.
4. Make a study of the sales literature of three companies all selling the same equipment.

PART VI

ORGANIZATION

CHAPTER 22

ORGANIZATION

Perhaps the most important observation which can be made regarding materials handling is: *maximum economy in the movement of materials is achieved by an over-all approach to handling.* This can be done only by careful consideration of the need for emphasis on handling when any question of organization is involved. This importance is not only in the particular organization chart which is derived or in the specific relationship of one position to another. The main consideration is that the over-all aspects of materials handling are reflected in this organization.

The exact type of organization will depend upon a number of other operating characteristics of the company. The size of the organization and the amount of specialization that may be involved will affect its position. As the size increases, there will be increased specialization of this function and a higher degree of research into specialized and more technical aspects both of materials handling and of packaging.

The small size of a plant or other firm having a materials-movement problem is not a deterrent to the development of efficient handling methods. In many cases it offers a greater challenge to the ingenuity of the materials-handling engineer and the salesmen of handling equipment. Also the economies of improved handling methods for these units may often be a matter of life and death to the companies concerned. This is also true of those economic activities in which the handling of materials plays an important part, such as warehousing and wholesale distributing, merchandising, and the various transporting mediums.

1. Factors Determining Importance of Materials Handling in the Organization

It is quite obvious that materials handling is of more importance in some types of economic activity than in others. The organization chart of the company should reflect this importance. The question, then, is: What factors determine this importance?

a. Relation of Value to Bulk. Where the weight or the bulk of the materials being handled is of very high ratio to value, the cost of handling is often the largest single item in the total cost of the product. In the operations of rock quarries, mines, sand and gravel pits, and in the processing of a large number of basic raw materials, handling costs are the dominant processing expense.

b. Weight and Size of Commodity. As the weight and size of the commodity increase, the need for specialized handling methods and equipment becomes greater. The amount of planning and attention that needs to be applied to the problem will increase in the same ratio. Machine

Fig. 180. No manual handling here. (*Scovill Manufacturing Company.*)

shops specializing in the machining of large castings will necessarily devote considerable engineering time and expense to the problem of moving materials from one operation to the next. At the A. O. Smith Corp., in Milwaukee, Wis., for example, successive machine operations are often performed on pieces weighing up to 100 tons. At Hunter's Point, Calif., the handling of large assemblies on ships is facilitated by means of special cranes capable of lifts up to 250 tons. Another company engaged in fabrication of steel trusses provides for special handling equipment at every stage of the production process. Scovill Manufacturing Co. in its new brass rolling mill at Waterbury, Conn., provides for complete mechanical handling of 1-ton billets and coils.

c. Nature of Process. Many processes consist primarily of moving materials through vats or areas where certain changes or additions to the materials are effected. This can best be done, particularly where mass production is involved, by means of special handling equipment and specialized planning. The Roto-dip unit of the Fisher-Ludlow Corp., Ltd., Birmingham, England, carries automobile chassis through a series of cleaning and degreasing operations, dip painting, and automatic drying on a single conveyor installation which requires only loading at the beginning and unloading at the end of the process.

d. Nature of the Industry. The mass production of materials has effected economies which have made available to the masses a wide variety of extremely complicated mechanisms such as automobiles, household appliances, television sets, etc. Without exception these achievements have been made possible only by a high degree of mechanized handling. It may be said, then, that: *wherever it is possible to concentrate the activities of a company on a limited number of major types of products, revolutionary changes in handling are imminent.*

2. Functions Involved in Materials Handling

It will readily be noticed in the following examples that there is a wide variation in the organization and in the specific responsibilities of materials-handling sections or divisions. It is important, then, to consider the specific functions by themselves. The question of their inclusion in a formal departmental setup is dependent on the operating requirements of each specific company. In most instances these functions are already being performed by other parts of the staff organization, and it is a matter of policy whether or not to utilize these services in their present position or establish a separate group under a materials-handling division.

a. Surveys and Analyses. This is a methods engineering function, whether it is retained by the methods department or done by a specialist on materials handling within the methods department or in a materials-handling division. The accounting and cost accounting departments are relied on for detailed cost figures. The purchasing department is checked for availability of materials equipment.

b. Engineering Drawings. Preliminary studies are invariably made by the materials-handling engineers or by draftsmen assigned to them for the purpose. In small companies the same men will also prepare more detailed drawings. In larger plants this is a function of a drafting department or more commonly a function under the direction of the plant engineer. Consultants may be brought in from the outside, but even here the drafting often is done by the company itself. In addition, detailed drawings on equipment and its installation are often furnished by the prospective equipment vendor.

c. Testing and Experimental Work. This work is often a function of the plant engineer and as such is often relegated further to the maintenance department. This generally results in very little testing or experimental work being done. This is one of the first functions that will be taken over by the budding materials-handling section.

The dissemination of the results of this work to the other operating sections of the plant is one of the more important aspects of this function. This also includes the formation of a central information file in order to benefit from experiments and publications of other companies. Where there is a plant librarian, she will have to be given advice on what books and other publications to procure. Where there is no central company library, the formation of a collection of source material (including pertinent manufacturers' catalogues) should be one of the first objectives of the new section.

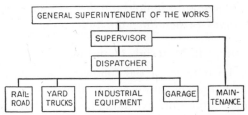

Fig. 181. Organization chart of transportation department. (*General Electric Company.*)

d. Installation. In most plants this is a function of the plant engineer. Conveyors and other fixed equipment are often installed by the regular plant installation crew. Major installations or complete new handling systems will more frequently be installed by an outside contractor. At the Fort Wayne, Ind., plant of International Harvester Company, an installation and maintenance crew is a part of the materials-handling section.

e. Maintenance. Materials-handling equipment as part of the operating plant has generally been considered as a part of the regular plant-wide maintenance program and as such the responsibility of a plant maintenance engineer who reports to the plant engineer.

This is another function that is frequently transferred to a materials-handling section at its inception. In fact, in many companies the recognition of the need for special maintenance requirements of materials-handling equipment has been the main immediate reason for setting up such a separate section.

f. Scheduling and Dispatching. Although this is generally a function of materials control or production control, the need for coordinating the movement of materials-handling equipment in a large plant justifies its separate position in the organization. The chart in Fig. 181 shows how this was incorporated in the organization of the transportation department of the General Electric Company.

g. Checking Results. This is a function of management and is carried out by giving special attention to routine reports on departmental costs or by rendering special reports on projects after a certain elapsed time. In one company a tickler in the files of the assistant factory manager calls for a report of each project above a certain amount one year from date of start of operations in the new method. This report compares the estimated savings with the actual savings.

3. Materials Handling as Part of the Industrial-engineering Department

From a purely functional standpoint, materials handling is simply another branch of industrial engineering. It is another aspect in the constant battle of management to increase production and decrease the unit cost of the product. When management is faced with additional complications arising out of rapidly increasing wage rates and rising prices for raw materials on one hand and a stiffer consumer resistance to higher prices on the other, this particular technique is often no longer considered just another part of industrial engineering. In order to emphasize its importance and to permit the more complete operation of its work, there is considerable justification for raising materials handling as far as the organization chart is concerned to a comparable level with industrial management itself.

When materials handling appears under the industrial- or production-engineering department, it is important to consider the relation of that department to the rest of the organization. One fact stands clear: the person finally responsible for materials handling must be high enough in the organization to cut across departmental lines. If the factory production departments are brought together on a fairly low level as regards the organizational chart of the company, the industrial-engineering department need not appear very high in the chart itself. If, on the other hand, the production organization is elaborate and extends high into the structure of the company, industrial engineering must occupy an equivalent position in order to surmount departmental barriers. Where production is headed by a vice-president, an equivalent ranking officer should head the engineering services.

a. Materials Handling Included under Methods Engineering. From a strictly functional standpoint this is where materials handling belongs. The purpose is to improve one type of operation, and the technique used is one of methods analysis. In the smaller manufacturing plant, the methods department is responsible for *all* changes in methods. There is a strong tendency for companies to have at least one engineer in this department formally or informally designated as the materials-handling engineer.

At the Square D Company (Switch and Panel Division), one engineer in the methods engineering department specializes on materials-handling work. Layout planning and larger handling problems are developed in committee discussion. Final drawings are made in the works engineer's office and the actual rearranging or installation is done directly by the maintenance department (which is directed by the works engineer) or

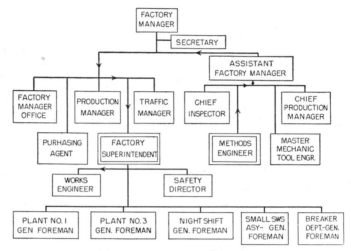

Fig. 182. Organization chart, Switch and Panel Division, Square D Company.

through outside contractors, in which case the works engineer lets the contract. Throughout the planning and construction the specialist from the methods department acts as adviser and consultant.

At Oldsmobile, materials-handling studies are treated as a regular part of the methods-engineering work. This, however, is divided into two sections. One section is concerned with current methods improvement on existing installations. The other is concerned with the development of new lines, departments, or new plants. As such, the whole gamut of methods techniques is utilized to achieve the most efficient methods and layout. This includes strong attention to the relationship of work areas and the method to be used for the movement of materials from one workplace to another.

b. Materials-handling Section. A rapidly increasing number of firms are setting up a separate section for materials handling under the industrial-management or production engineering departments. In one company such a section saved an annual demurrage charge of $18,000 the first year of its operation. Although most companies are hesitant in expanding this phase of their engineering staff, such sections usually have little difficulty in justifying their existence on the basis of savings made for the company through their operations.

In one company each of the sections shown in Fig. 183 consists of an engineer and one assistant. The materials-handling engineer and his assistant make their own preliminary drawings and on small projects may even complete the working or installation drawings. In this case, they will be developed in close cooperation with the plant engineer and installed by the maintenance department, which is under his jurisdiction. On larger

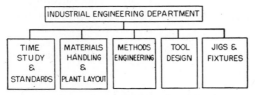

Fig. 183. Organization of industrial engineering department in small manufacturing concern.

projects, draftsmen from the plant engineer's office will do the detailing and may complete the working drawings for the project.

In companies having a number of branch plants, each of considerable size, a materials-handling section may be included in the engineering organization of each plant. One tractor works of the International Harvester Company has a materials-handling section consisting of a materials-handling engineer, an assistant materials-handling engineer, two analysts, three investigators, and one clerk-stenographer.[1]

4. Materials Handling the Responsibility of the Plant Engineer

The closer tie-in of materials-handling equipment to the physical plant is exemplified by the extension of this function to the plant engineer. In many plants the only major attention given to materials handling has been the maintenance of the equipment used in this function. This is then considered as part of the regular maintenance program of the company.

The increase in utilization of equipment for movement of materials has induced many of these same companies to set up a special section within the maintenance department in order to provide a more specialized service. In many instances, the need for additional records on equipment performance has led to setting up a records clerk. The results obtained

[1] John R. Immer, "Layout Planning Techniques," p. 307, McGraw-Hill Book Company, Inc., New York, 1950.

from scheduling and dispatching have often enlarged this office and resulted in the formation of at least a separate section though still under the plant engineer.

Even where materials handling is recognized as an industrial-engineering function and developmental work is assigned to that department, the technical details of the various projects as well as their execution are often left to the plant engineer's office. See the example of the Square D Company (Switch and Panel Division).

The bringing together under one department of the various functions involved in materials handling is also a natural step in the development of a separate materials-handling division. The Columbian Rope Company, for example, includes the following responsibilities under the plant engineer: [2]

1. To make engineering studies covering all phases of

 a. Materials handling
 b. Machine and equipment layouts
 c. General plant layouts

Any of the manufacturing activities of the company may be investigated for the above purposes. The studies should take into consideration the application of such methods and equipment as will give maximum cost reduction in relation to capital invested.

2. Based on the foregoing studies, the plant engineer will submit from time to time specific plans and recommendations with sufficient detail and economic analysis to enable the management to appraise them.

3. In addition to plans which may be initiated from time to time by the plant engineer, definite assignments for study and formulation may be made by the vice-president.

4. Upon approval of final programs for changes in materials handling and machine or plant layout, the plant engineer will be responsible for:

 a. Specification of equipment to be purchased by the purchasing department.
 b. Layout drawings. The actual work to be done by the design engineering division if desirable, but subject to the approval of the plant engineer.
 c. Installation according to his approved plans. The actual work of moving and installation will be done under supervision of the master mechanic, but will be subject to the approval of the plant engineer.
 d. Trial operation of the new equipment for material handling and pilot operation of new machine or process layouts erected to his plans. Arrangements will be made with the mill operating organization to cover this point as the need arises.

[2] A. K. Strong, plant engineer, Columbian Rope Company, Auburn, N.Y.

Under this heading a materials-handling section has been set up and will remain under the plant engineer's jurisdiction until management is convinced that a separate division is desirable.

It is noteworthy that the plant engineer reports directly to a vice-president in charge of manufacturing. This makes it possible to cut across organizational lines, as previously emphasized.

5. The Materials-handling Division

The need for centralized direction and control of materials-handling activities in order to derive their maximum benefits reaches its ultimate (and in many cases its inevitable) form in the separate division reporting to the vice-president in charge of manufacturing or production. It is significant enough to be called a trend that mass-production industries in which the movement of materials plays an important part are placing materials handling in a key location on the organization chart. In most instances this is only another outward evidence of the importance being accorded materials handling in American industry today. It is also recognition that management expects the major economies and greatest reductions in manufacturing costs to come from this function.

Not only must this function be placed high within the production organization in the individual plant but where two or more plants are involved a central supervisory group tends to develop. Whether it is organized as a top control group for materials-handling functions within a company or strictly as a research group it will still tend to have the following scope and type of activities:

Scope of Central Division

1. Receipt, storage, and movement of all raw materials, finished parts, and assemblies to production areas.

2. Movement of materials through production (machining, processing, assembly, and in-process storage).

3. Preparation of finished product for shipping (packaging, packing, and crating).

4. Final stores, order filling and shipping.

5. Inter-plant shipment of semiprocessed parts and assemblies.

Activities of Central Division

1. Experiment (conduct research) to determine the most efficient and economic means of moving, handling, and protecting materials.

2. Experiment with and establish standards on materials, equipment, supplies, and

a. Performance characteristics of equipment

b. Strength characteristics of packages and crates

3. Establish and issue standards, operating procedures, instruction sheets, manuals, and other means of disseminating knowledge of methods, techniques, and materials to the other divisions of the plants.

4. Make surveys of all handling problems relative to inter-plant shipments, receipts, and shipments, *i.e.*, all the things beyond the jurisdiction of a single plant.

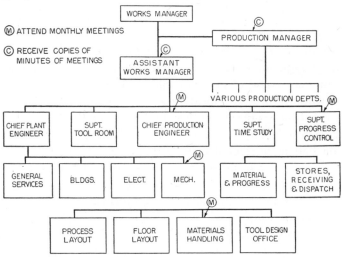

Fig. 184. New organization for better control of materials handling. Departments marked *M* are part of permanent committee which meets once a month. (*Hoover, Ltd., Perivale, London.*)

a. Central Operating Division. The form taken by the central co-ordinating materials-handling group will depend largely on a myriad of forces within the organization as well as on the amount of emphasis to be given materials handling as a separate function. It may also reflect the amount of line cooperation which management may, in a specific instance, expect to be given it by the other divisions of the company.

The example of the separate organization set up within the framework of the plant engineer's office (in reference to the Columbian Rope Company) is indicative of the trend toward centralization of materials-handling functions as evidenced by the Ford Motor Company of Detroit, Mich., the Johns-Manville Corporation of Waukegan, Ill., the General Electric Company of Schenectady, N.Y., and the Westinghouse Electric Corporation of Pittsburgh, Pa.

Within the Steel and Tube Division of the Timken Roller Bearing Company at Canton, Ohio, an operating department is directly responsible for all material handling as related to equipment other than standard railroad and conventional highway trucks. This includes:

1. The maintenance of materials-handling equipment [3]
2. An instruction and training program for both maintenance men and equipment operating personnel
3. Materials handling and movement within the plant, including:

a. Unloading, stacking, and moving raw materials as they arrive at the plant

b. Moving in-process materials from one operation to another in an organized fashion; this includes stacking of materials outside the buildings

The determination of materials-handling costs is still a function of the accounting and cost departments. In addition, excellent cooperation is obtained from these departments for the solution of any specific problems. Surveys are conducted on request by the industrial-engineering department in conjunction with the supervisors of the materials-handling department.

In the Akron, Ohio, plants of the B. F. Goodrich Company, the factory service division is responsible for the handling and transporting of all materials. The company's central office plans major handling and layout changes. Lesser changes are developed and completed by the personnel of each of the branch plants.[4]

b. Manufacturing Research Division. One of the outstanding examples of a central coordinating materials-handling unit set up as a research group is provided by the International Harvester Company. Here a materials-handling and product-protection section is set up in the manufacturing research department. Although this central group is amply supported by individual materials-handling sections within each factory or plant, it carries on an active program of company-wide coordinating action and instruction. The work and organization of this section is described in Chap. 15.

6. Approval of Projects

In most of the plants contacted by the author, materials-handling studies are the result of numerous informal consultations with interested departments or in many cases with individual workers; committee meet-

[3] This program is described in considerable detail in *Flow,* March, May, and July, 1949.

[4] See also *Factory Management and Maintenance,* July, 1950, p. 235.

ings of representatives from interested departments and the studied decisions of executives (plural) generally based on detailed and comprehensive cost reports and estimates. In addition, equipment salesmen are freely consulted and sales literature of suppliers carefully examined for ideas. (This is probably one reason why equipment manufacturers have developed so many excellent case studies of handling in various industries and applications. In few other fields have manufacturers of equipment provided the instructor with such a wealth of material of comparable quality.)

Larger projects are often preceded by years of study and research on the part of the engineering and production staff. For example, read the account of the research done by the executives of Bamberger and Company before they built their new warehouse (Chap. 18) and of the research for the development of truck terminals (Chap. 32). Extensive plant visits to other noteworthy installations of similar nature is also a standard part of the preparation. Consulting firms are also brought in for additional advice and suggestions.

a. Initiation. The reply received from The B. F. Goodrich Company is typical of the attitude of an increasing number of large companies.[5]

The best answer to your question is "The Team," which means any employee of The B. F. Goodrich Company. Any employee can put his material-handling idea on paper and set the suggestion committee to work evaluating his idea. Also any of the following divisions could initiate this action:
1. Suggestion committee
2. Factory service division
3. Time study and methods department
4. Engineering and design department
5. Machine and process development department
In addition, a superintendent of a large department finds his whole department needs a new layout to reduce materials handling. He and his staff will put together the facts and a preliminary plan with possible savings, and try to interest top management to appropriate the amount required for an engineering department study and new layout.

A valuable source of job knowledge is the man who does the work. A properly functioning suggestion plan is the best means of bringing to the fore ideas on materials handling. Where there is no such formal machinery for developing these ideas into projects, it devolves upon the methods engineer (whether or not specializing in materials handling) or the materials-handling engineer to discover and develop them.

[5] P. W. Watt, superintendent, factory service departments, The B. F. Goodrich Company, Akron, Ohio.

b. Authorization of Study. Small changes in method or minor equipment outlays are made normally within the operating budgets of the departments concerned and require no higher authorization (see account of Belden Manufacturing Company, Chap. 26).

Materials-handling projects often involve large-scale changes in layout and arrangement of equipment, which necessitates a large amount of

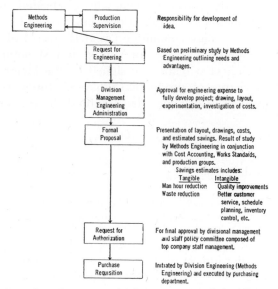

Fig. 185. Procedure chart for approval of major materials-handling project. (*Coated Abrasives Division, Minnesota Mining & Manufacturing Company.*)

engineering planning and development in itself. Many times this engineering development is a large part of the total cost of the project, particularly where extensive layout changes are involved. The Coated Abrasives Division of Minnesota Mining and Manufacturing Company of St. Paul, Minn., has developed the procedure shown in Fig. 185. Special projects are prepared at Munsingwear, Inc., on a standard form.[6]

c. Consultation. Material-handling studies affect in such an intimate way so many aspects of the operations of a company that any change should be made only after a very extensive process of criticism and review by all concerned. This is one justification for the use of scale models; it results in easier and quicker visualization of handling methods by both management and the workers. One company put a scale model of a pro-

[6] Immer, *op. cit.*, p. 291.

posed change outside the employees' cafeteria and asked for comments. Several worth-while and valuable suggestions were received.

d. Approval. Expenditures which can be made within the operating budget of a department are approved by the department head and require no higher authorization. More extensive changes, depending on the size and extent of the recommendations, may require the approval of the board of directors of the company.

Final approval of the project is generally predicated upon a group consideration of its merits and implications—financial and otherwise. This may be a materials-handling committee (as at Hoover, Ltd., London) or a general staff committee (Minnesota Mining and Manufacturing Company). Often the project will then be signed by the factory manager, a vice-president in charge of production, and sometimes by the finance director or comptroller as evidence that the funds have been allotted for that purpose.

QUESTIONS

1. What determines the exact type of organization for a specific company?

2. What factors determine the place of materials handling in the organization?

3. What major functions are involved in materials handling? Discuss.

4. How does materials handling fit into the industrial-engineering department?

5. Trace the trend of the materials-handling function toward its status as a separate division or department of the production organization.

6. Show how the plant engineer may exercise the materials-handling function.

7. Describe the material-handling responsibilities of the plant engineer at the Columbian Rope Company.

8. What activities will be carried on by the central materials-handling division?

9. Discuss the operating responsibilities of the central materials-handling division.

10. Trace the development of a materials-handling project to its approval by management.

11. Who initiates a study of materials handling in a manufacturing plant?

12. What personnel and departments should be consulted when a materials-handling project is being considered?

13. Whose approval is necessary for a materials-handling project? What will determine this?

PROJECTS FOR FURTHER STUDY

1. Using a local plant as a model, prepare an organization chart showing the exercise of the materials-handling function.

2. Prepare a chart showing how a project would be approved in a small plant consisting of approximately 100 machine tools. Castings require from 5 to 10 separate operations and weigh about 40 pounds apiece when finished.

3. Make a study of how the materials-handling function has been indicated (or not) in organization charts printed in recent textbooks on industrial management and organization.

CHAPTER 23

PRODUCTION CONTROL

1. Relation of Production Control to Materials Handling

Effective control over the flow of production through a plant requires the close control of the method of movement of materials as well as of the timing of the operations themselves. This involves a control over movement between operations. As the degree of this control increases, time lag of operations is reduced and banks of materials between operations cut down.

Modern methods of production require a very close integration of operations with a reduction in the amount of materials in process. This results in a shorter time lag between operations and a sharp reduction in the over-all processing time. In order to achieve this, there must be a rigid control over the movement of materials from the time they are received at the plant until they leave the shipping department.

The system used to transport materials through the plant will often be used also to provide for this rigid control over production. The path of a conveyor line, for instance, controls the direction in which the materials may move, and the speed of the unit controls the rate of production.

In the mass-production assembly of aircraft during the Second World War, assemblies often were moved at periodical intervals whether the work of that particular assembly station had been finished or not. Flying squadrons or trouble crews would then be brought to the area to bring the work back to schedule. In other plants the assemblies moved continuously, passing through a specific assembly area in the time allotted to that group for completion of its operation.

2. Materials-handling System and Scheduling Functions

The materials-handling system may be employed as the scheduling mechanism for the entire plant. At the Coventry plant of the Ferguson Tractor Company in England, movement of the entire assembly line is controlled by means of conveyors regulated from a central dispatch office. Although a number of different conveyors are operating at different speeds, they are slowed down or speeded up in proportion to each other by a complicated set of master controls.

FIG. 186. Automatic loading and unloading lower handling costs. *Top*—Trolley hooks are guided into slots of control assemblies. Hooks already loaded are guided around loading station by curved metal piece. (*Minneapolis-Honeywell Regulator Company.*) *Bottom*—Unloading device for removing carrier from trolley conveyor at Remington-Rand, Inc., Elmira, N.Y. (*Electrified Industry.*)

The Western Electric plant at Haverhill, Mass., designed an integrated flow plan, electronically controlled, to overcome problems encountered in small-lot manufacture of 2,000 different types of coils. Routing involves from 2 to 20 operations, changing operation sequence, and an

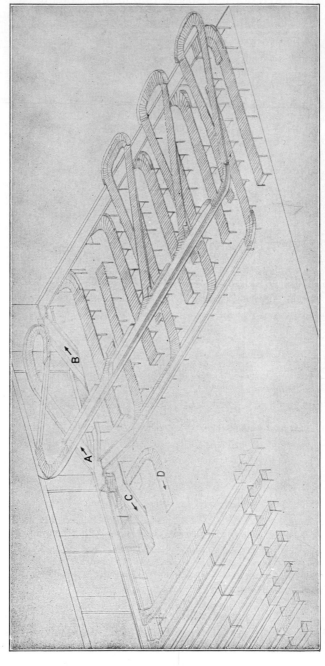

Fig. 187. Isometric drawing of mechanized receiving and marking line placed in operation in 1948 at The Hecht Company, Washington, D.C. (*The Hecht Company.*)

average quantity per order of 20 units. Materials are scheduled for and are delivered to approximately 7,000 operations each week. A power-driven conveyor connects the work groups to the dispatch area. Twenty-seven spurs of roller conveyor hold the work at the individual work areas until the operator is ready to use them. At the completion of the operation,

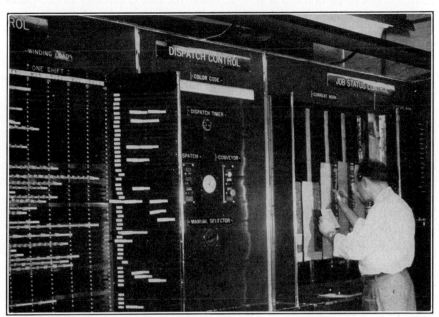

FIG. 188. Controls for the complete handling system of the Western Electric plant at Haverhill, Mass., are located on one control board. The left sections control the winding operation, the center section controls the conveyors and timers, and the right section contains a complete record of each job that is in manufacture. (*Electrified Industry.*)

the work is returned to the dispatch area, where it is then rerouted to the next operation after a record is made of its progress.

The various operations involved in the receiving of merchandise for a department store can also be controlled by the handling system. At the Hecht Company in Washington, D.C., several groups of conveyors not only move the merchandise from the receiving platform on the first floor but carry it through successive operations all under the control of a single dispatcher. This system is shown in Fig. 187.

The merchandise is brought to the second floor by conveyor *B*. By means of solenoid-operated diverters, one of the checkers diverts the merchandise into one of five package-opening lines of the checking section. The merchandise is checked into tote boxes which are supplied as needed from the overhead conveyor lines.

The dispatcher diverts the merchandise to 1 of 15 marking lines. At this time the marking copy and the invoice copy are sent to the ticket office and to the invoice office, respectively, by pneumatic tube. Merchandise not to be marked is sent on conveyor line C directly to the packing section. Other material after marking is accumulated on the belt below the marking line and released at one time by the central dispatcher. The lower run of the main distribution belt carries the goods to the packing section on the first floor. The system was designed by N. P. Greller of N. P. Greller & Associates, Industrial and Management Engineers.

3. Scheduling by Conveyors

From their very nature conveyors provide an ideal mechanism for controlling the flow of production. It has long been possible to decrease or increase the speed of production simply by varying the speed of the conveyor lines. If the conveyor was increased in speed, additional workers would be added to the line to provide the requisite number of assembly man-hours.

The development of various types of electronic controls has increased the automatic selectivity ability of conveyors. For example, on converging lines one will be kept closed while packages move past the critical point on the other line. This may also be accomplished by means of various mechanical devices.

This idea of selectivity has been carried still further in a new conveyor handling system devised to segregate boxes and cartons of various types. With this system, one operator standing at a central control panel can divert boxes or other containers into any number of side channels.

As the box passes the control panel, the operator selects the station or point at which it is to be diverted. He presses a button which sets up an electric path in a relay circuit to record its passage along the main conveyor line. As the box continues, it passes over a series of switches located on this line. Each switch, by means of a relay circuit, automatically records the position of the box. When the box reaches the point where it leaves the main line, the relay circuit has recorded this fact and the box is automatically diverted (Fig. 189).

Photoelectric controls may also be used to sort packages moving along a conveyor. This may be done by a number of different methods. On a conveyor line carrying packages, the beam is set above the short packages and below the top of the tall ones. As the latter pass along the beam, the beam is interrupted, which operates a switch diverting them to another line (Fig. 190a).

A similar method is used to sort packages by width. In this case the light source and the photoelectric tube are mounted so the light beam can

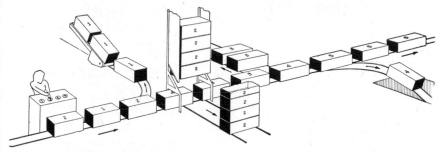

Fig. 189. Boxes are segregated and diverted to five different paths in this segregating system. (*Food Machinery Corporation.*)

pass vertically between the rollers of the conveyor. Cartons to be diverted are placed on the conveyor so that the wide side will break the circuit and actuate the switch (Fig. 190*b*).

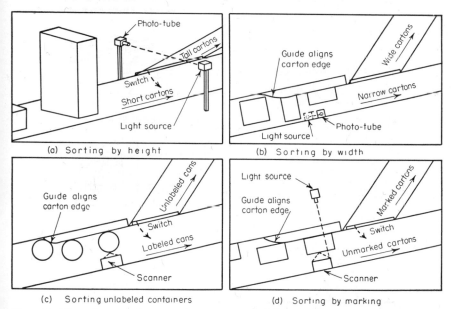

(a) Sorting by height

(b) Sorting by width

(c) Sorting unlabeled containers

(d) Sorting by marking

Fig. 190. Photoelectric relays speed conveyor handling. (*Modern Materials Handling.*)

Sorting may also be done by a scanner which mounts the light source and the photoelectric tube side by side. The light-sensitive element is actuated only when light of a given intensity from the light source is reflected from a foreign surface. It sorts unlabeled cans (Fig. 190*c*) by

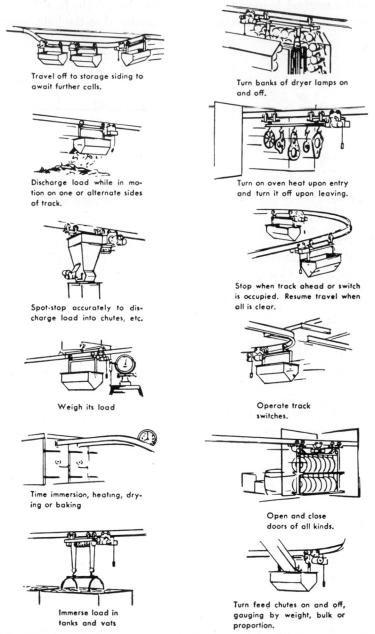

Travel off to storage siding to await further calls.

Discharge load while in motion on one or alternate sides of track.

Spot-stop accurately to discharge load into chutes, etc.

Weigh its load

Time immersion, heating, drying or baking

Immerse load in tanks and vats

Turn banks of dryer lamps on and off.

Turn on oven heat upon entry and turn it off upon leaving.

Stop when track ahead or switch is occupied. Resume travel when all is clear.

Operate track switches.

Open and close doors of all kinds.

Turn feed chutes on and off, gauging by weight, bulk or proportion.

Fig. 191. Functions performed automatically by control system on monorail track. (*The Louden Machinery Company.*)

reflecting the light from the side of the cans as they pass on the conveyor. The labeled cans do not reflect enough light to actuate the diverting unit and thus continue on their way.

The scanner can also be used to sort packages by their markings. The light may be used to hold a line switch open or shut. Unmarked packages reflect enough light to hold the relay open and the switch closed (Fig. 190d). The reflection from a marked carton is less intense and thus permits the switch to open and divert these cartons to another line. An extra light source is used to keep the switch closed when no cartons are passing the scanner.[1]

One overhead monorail conveyor system provides for a wide variety of operations to be performed automatically by the setting of a proper combination or sequence of events on a master control box. This control box has three selector switches with 1,260 possible combinations of switching and destination. Two types of functions are performed.

Internal functions are performed by the drive unit and the control box. These include starting and stopping the drive unit, raising and lowering hoist hooks, opening and closing motor-operated grabs, discharging motor-operated buckets, energizing and de-energizing electromagnets, sounding an electric warning horn, and initiating a function involving timing.

External functions are initiated by the control box but are performed by electrically operated mechanisms mounted in fixed positions in or adjacent to the monorail track. Typical of these external functions are throwing track switches into proper position for the predetermined routing of the load, establishing lockouts and electric baffles to prevent one drive unit from running into another or running off the track through a partly opened switch, controlling a block system to keep drive units a safe distance apart, opening and closing oven doors, building doors and the like, weighing loads automatically, and operating lift or drop sections of monorail track.

4. Scheduling Industrial Truck Equipment

The methods employed in scheduling the operations of industrial truck and mobile-crane equipment will fall within the following classifications: [2]

1. Assigning of materials-handling equipment to definite routes or paths through the shop on a definite schedule.

---

[1] Ernest O. Jellinek, Photo-electric Relays Speed Handling Jobs, *Modern Materials Handling,* February, 1951, p. 31.

[2] Letter from G. L. Thuering, Department of Industrial Engineering, Pennsylvania State College.

2. Assigning equipment to definite areas or departments with (a) central control for entire plant and (b) no central control for the plant.

3. Assigning equipment from a central pool when requested by departments.

As an example of the first type, the Allis Chalmers Corporation of Milwaukee, Wis., has industrial tractor-trailer trains operating on a definite schedule. Eleven collecting stations are scattered over the plant area at which loads are deposited for each department. The tractor following a definite route proceeds from one station to the next, picking up and dropping off trailers en route.

Along with this system other items of equipment such as fork trucks are permanently assigned to definite areas or departments. In still another firm the industrial trucks are operated on a schedule similar to that used at Allis Chalmers. Fork trucks are assigned to specific departments and portable cranes and other auxiliary units are maintained in a central pool. These last items are farmed out or sent out to departments as needed.

A central dispatcher for a fleet of 36 industrial trucks at the plant of the Wagner Electric Corporation in St. Louis eliminated 30 per cent of idle time for trucks and operators. By means of 12 remote substation call boxes, truckers may call the dispatcher when a load is delivered. Jobs are filed by areas, and the first one which that kind of equipment can handle is given to the trucker, thereby eliminating empty hauls.[3]

The new system is paying off three ways:

1. An increased tonnage is being handled with the same fleet of trucks, eliminating the necessity for additional equipment.

2. Production delays caused by breakdowns in the trucking system are minimized.

3. There has been a marked reduction in direct handling cost per unit of product.

5. Means of Dispatching Employed

The size of many modern industrial plants makes it necessary to employ faster means of communication in order to keep equipment operating to capacity and materials flowing smoothly. These systems will range from hand devices involving no extra outlay for equipment through intercommunication systems costing less than $50 to elaborate pneumatic-tube and radio systems.

The main business of a truck terminal is materials handling. Rapid turnover of materials through a loading area restricted in space requires close planning and control. At the Newark Union Motor Truck Terminal,

---

[3] R. H. Hackett, Power Trucks Expedited through Central Control, *Factory Management and Maintenance*, May, 1948, p. 77.

TABLE 7. CHARACTERISTICS OF F.M. TWO-WAY RADIO EQUIPMENT *

Type	Approximate maximum range on level terrain, miles	Weight, pounds	Source of power	Output, watts	Approximate cost, dollars
Hand set (walkie-talkie)	2	10	Self-contained wet- or dry-cell batteries (8-hr. operation time)	Under 1	350
Pack set........	2	20	Same as hand set	1	300–400
Mobile units....	10–25	40–80	Vehicle storage battery or separate driven generator	1–60	400–3,000

* James R. Bright, Radio Control, *Modern Materials Handling*, May, 1951, p. 42.

a   *b*

FIG. 192. Conveyorized handling in the production of rubber shoes at the new mass-production plant of SAIC, Fabrica Argentina de Alpargatas, Buenos Aires. (*a*) Control panels actuate sections of conveyor deflecting arms. (*b*) Deflecting arms guide shoe forms to needed work areas. (*Geo. W. King, Ltd.*)

largest in the world, this control of dispatching is accomplished by means of a pneumatic-tube communicating system, a public address system, a two-way intercommunicating system, and teleregister signaling devices.

Movements of freight and motor trucks are transmitted to the platform control section from the loading dock (Fig. 193) by an electronic signaling device. In the platform control room each movement of the cargo is registered on large boards by means of a system of colored lights (Fig.

FIG. 193. Signaling to platform control section information on disposal of each shipment. (*The Port of New York Authority.*)

194). In the meantime a copy of the truck's manifest is transmitted to the control room by pneumatic tube. Six miles of these tubes in the terminal serve each of the 144 truck bays as well as other points in the terminal.

a. Transmission by Hand. Messenger service for the delivery of messages, blueprints, and equipment or production orders is still a common practice in many factories and offices. One company which had difficulty in keeping reliable teen-age messengers solved the problem by putting them on roller skates. Not only was turnover reduced but the service was speeded up. In other plants where considerable distances are involved, messengers are provided with bicycles, motor scooters, or even automobiles for inter-office communication.

b. Loudspeaker. Where the noise of machines and operating mechanisms is not too loud and the noise of the loudspeaker itself is not overly objectionable, this method provides dispatching of units without undue delay. In one company the fork truck operator is thus notified to call in to the central office for instructions. In another he is simply directed to go to a certain department and that a load is there waiting to be taken to another department.

  c. Intercommunication Systems. By this method also the operator is instructed to contact the central dispatching office. He will generally go

Fig. 194. Platform control room of New York Union Motor Truck Terminal. Operators controlling shipments by use of Teleregister panel board. (*The Port of New York Authority.*)

to the nearest intercom booth or telephone and notify the office that he is waiting instructions for further action. He can also make his own reports when a certain job is delivered and he is free for other work.

  Intercommunication systems are also used to aid in the control of quality as well as the speed at which materials are going through the system. On the continuous pickle line of the Aliquippa, Pa., works of Jones & Laughlin Steel Corporation the operator on the receiving end can talk to the operator on the delivery end more than 250 yards away, who is able to catch deviations from standard immediately.

  d. Radio. At the General Electric plant in Schenectady, N.Y., a two-way radiotelephone system is used to integrate the movement of switching engines. As the plant includes over 300 buildings within a 600-acre area, this integration is extremely important. This is accomplished from a central dispatch office by means of radiotelephones installed in the cabs of all engines and in the automobiles of the yard foremen. This enables the foremen to check quickly on all operations and designate the engine for each job as a move order is received. As all the radios have the same frequency, each engine operator knows where all the other engines are.[4]

Radio control for handling equipment has become an accepted part of

Fig. 195. Two-way radio speeds up service for preventive maintenance and increases the number of service calls which can be made during the day. (*Flow, November, 1950, p.* 36.)

industrial operations. Radio transmitters must be licensed by the Federal Communications Commission and operated according to their rules and regulations. Transmitters operated in the materials-handling field will be licensed under the FCC rules governing the Industrial Radio Services, Part II, Subpart L, the Low Power Industrial Radio Service. In some cases, a particular applicant may be eligible for a license under the Special Industrial Radio Service, Subpart K. Copies of these regulations may be obtained from the Superintendent of Documents.[5]

e. Television. There are many industrial operations which for a number of reasons are difficult to view directly. This may be because of danger,

[4] For a more detailed description, see *Flow*, January, 1951, p. 44.

[5] James R. Bright, Radio Control, *Modern Materials Handling*, May, 1951, p. 40.

distance, heat, height, or other causes. Television can be used to watch these operations.

A large steel manufacturer uses the equipment to watch steel slabs on a conveyor moving into position where they can be transferred to slab treating furnaces.

A coal company uses it to watch for pileups as coal is chuted into a washer in a coal tipple.

A steel mill has substituted a camera for a workman in the hazardous job of watching the flow of liquid steel in a continuous casting process.[6]

f. Telautograph. Written messages are transmitted immediately to one or a large number of points by telautograph. In addition to transmitting the messages simultaneously, it provides a written record automatically both for the sender and the receiver. Also, simultaneous instructions may be sent out to a number of points at the same time.

Such a system is used at The B. F. Goodrich Company in Akron, Ohio. Service tractors and trailers cover an area of 5 million feet of floor space and are capable of handling 235,000 pounds of materials a month. Equipment used consists of 75 lift trucks, 7 fork trucks, 10 locomotive-type tractors, and 3 chisel-type tractors for hauling large rolls, 500 industrial trailers, between 6,000 and 7,000 pallets, and approximately 25,000 skid boards, racks, and other miscellaneous handling equipment. A dispatcher from the department's headquarters is on duty every hour of the day or night and directs operations by means of the telautograph system.

g. Pneumatic-tube System. This system provides not only for the rapid transmission of ordinary messages but with slight adaptation may be used for the transmission of blueprints and other materials which can be put into a proper sized roll. During the Second World War such a pneumatic conveying system provided the main means of communication in the vast Willow Run plant in the production of aircraft.

QUESTIONS

1. What is the relation of production control to materials handling?
2. Describe the importance of the scheduling to materials handling.
3. How can the handling system affect the scheduling of production?
4. In what ways can the handling system simplify the problem of scheduling production?
5. How can conveyors affect the scheduling function?
6. Discuss the scheduling of industrial-truck equipment.
7. Does scheduling of industrial-truck equipment pay? How?

[6] Television, the Next Step in Materials Handling, *Modern Materials Handling,* May, 1951, p. 52.

8. Discuss the means of dispatching commonly used.

9. Describe the operation of the telautograph.

PROJECTS FOR FURTHER STUDY

1. Take a local plant or warehouse as a subject, and prepare a report on the use of various types of dispatching equipment. Explain the reasons for the type recommended (if any).

2. Discuss the places where a radio or intercommunication might be used to advantage in a materials-handling system.

3. Make a study of the means of getting automatic control for flow of materials on conveyors.

CHAPTER 24

OPERATOR TRÀINING AND INSTRUCTION

Materials handling is a philosophy, a way of thinking. It involves an awareness of the importance of moving materials and of the method employed in accomplishing this. There are fundamental principles of movement and accepted practices in handling which should be recognized by all personnel.

Quite often a little thought given to the method of loading, freighting, or packaging, at one point, will save considerable handling later on in the process. An awareness of the potentialities of such savings on the part of operating employees and particularly supervisors is an important asset to any plant.

It has already been seen that materials handling is a very broad field covering a wide variety of industrial activities. Consequently, a large number of people in different trades and in different positions are concerned with handling in one way or another. Each of these individuals should have some kind of instruction and training in the fundamentals of good handling.

1. General Instruction in Handling of Materials

Many times improved handling methods will result when personnel are made aware of handling fundamentals. Quite often a person is preoccupied with the technical requirements of the job he is doing and does not think about the extra movement that may be involved in the method he is using.

While taking a series of time studies of operations in teller's cages in a bank, the author recently had the experience of the worker rearranging some of the elements of his workplace while the study was being made. These changes were made voluntarily by the teller simply because he, for the first time, became aware of the extra distance he was traveling in depositing slips in a deposit box located 6 or 8 feet away from his normal working area. Without prompting, he moved this box to a point 2 or 3 feet away, thus eliminating the steps he had been previously using.[1]

[1] John R. Immer, "Layout Planning Techniques," p. 77, McGraw-Hill Book Company, Inc., New York, 1950.

A few years ago, the RCA Victor Division, in New Jersey, conducted a series of work-simplification training programs for workers in various departments. The company had a suggestion system in effect at the time. It was noted that as each department finished its training program, the number of suggestions from that department skyrocketed. This upsurge in suggestions was attributed to the training program, inasmuch as the workers were being made aware of excess motions.

a. Company Programs. The program of the RCA Victor Company is one of a large number of work-simplification programs which have been sponsored by companies all over the country. These have been developed by company engineers, by industrial engineering consulting firms, or by men outstanding in the field of time and motion study such as Ralph M. Barnes of the University of California at Los Angeles, R. W. Maynard of Methods Engineering Council in Pittsburgh, and A. H. Mogensen of New York City.

Typical of the courses specifically arranged for materials-handling instruction is that of the International Harvester Company of Chicago. The various research engineers in the materials-handling section of the Central Manufacturing Research Division maintain constant instructional work; they provide a special course for training of their foremen in materials handling and packing. This course is designed not only to make them familiar with accepted methods and procedures in materials handling but to make them more aware of the part materials handling plays in production and how closely it is allied to them.

One problem in the instruction of operators of mechanical equipment— that of making the operator feel that rules are important—has been successfully solved by holding an annual "truck rodeo" to emphasize skilled techniques and observance of safety rules and regulations. Such a rodeo has become an annual event at the Buffalo, N.Y., plant of the Westinghouse Electric Corporation. This includes contests in (1) inspection; (2) truck handling; (3) load handling; (4) load judgment; (5) distance judgment; and (6) general rules. A special score card has been devised to be used as a rating sheet in determining the winner of the rodeo.

The following tests are used to determine the rodeo winner: [2]

1. Inspection. [This] is the first phase of the judging. The contestant is told to assume that he is beginning his day's work and to go through his routine prior to starting actual operations. Judges grade him on how well he inspects the items listed on the score card.

[2] Richard B. Milligan, Truck Rodeos Develop Better, Safer Drivers, *Factory Management and Maintenance*, January, 1950, p. 105.

FIG. 196. Handling ability test at Westinghouse truck rodeo requires a well-calculated calm approach by the operator. (*Westinghouse Electric Corporation.*)

FIG. 197. The number of faulty loading practices pointed out here helps determine the operator's score. (*Westinghouse Electric Corporation.*)

2. Truck handling. Ability is judged by the driver's skill in avoiding contact with empty drums so placed that careful manipulation of the truck is necessary (Fig. 196)

3. Load handling. [This] consists of the operator pushing a truck and trailer combination down the aisle and turning 90 degrees between two cans, backing both out into the aisle completing a 180-degree turn, and proceeding down the aisle in the opposite direction.

Fig. 198. The contestant approaches the uprights to see if he has correctly estimated whether or not his truck would pass through. (*Westinghouse Electric Corporation.*)

4. Load judgment. [This] involves the finding of faults of a previously loaded skid. Four unsafe conditions are developed on the skid, and the contestant is asked to look it over. His ability to spot the defects determines the number of points earned (Fig. 197).

5. Distance judgment. [This] is a two-part test of the driver's skill. Two posts are placed along the course so that the space between them approaches the width of the truck. At a given distance from the post, the truck is stopped. The operator is asked to decide whether or not his truck could pass between them. He is judged on the correctness of his answer.

The second part of the distance judgment test is to request the driver to stop 15 feet in front of a crossline in the aisle. His score depends on how close he comes to that distance (Fig. 198).

6. General rules. Observance of aisle markings and signs is the final test given in the rodeo. Operators gain a total of ten points if they follow instructions and warnings posted along the course.

b. Institutes and Training Programs. Although the largest of the conventions and exhibitions held in recent years in this area have been concerned mostly with exhibition of materials-handling equipment, these have been accompanied by a noteworthy program of speakers. For the most part, these speakers have been men with wide experience and training in their specific fields of interest who have made very definite contributions to the dissemination of materials-handling information, both as to methods and to equipment.

In addition, conventions and meetings in general management and industrial-engineering groups have featured speakers on various phases of materials handling. Some of the more outstanding of these are the annual meetings of the American Management Association, the American Society of Mechanical Engineers, the Society for Advancement of Management, and the Time and Motion Study Clinic in Chicago, held by the Industrial Management Society.

Conference reports and booklets have been prepared providing a detailed record of the speeches given at these meetings. In addition, various trade magazines have published summaries of the outstanding talks.

Mention should also be made of the activities of materials-handling associations and societies. The American Materials Handling Society publishes a special section each month in *Modern Materials Handling* magazine. The Society of Industrial Packaging and Materials Handling Engineers with headquarters in Chicago publishes its own journal, *Trends.* Both groups have a large number of individual chapters in the leading industrial cities. In addition, a number of local organizations have been very active. For example, the Minnesota Materials Handling Association in addition to a program of outstanding speakers has made plant visits and detailed case studies of handling problems of its members.

The American Society of Mechanical Engineers has a materials-handling section which has been active in preparation of standards for equipment. The packaging section of the American Management Association has been active since 1931. The International Cargo Handling Co-ordination Association came into being in 1952 with offices in London. It received world-wide support from the beginning and held its first international conference in Rotterdam in May, 1952.

Equipment manufacturers have a central group under the Materials Handling Institute, Inc. In addition there are trade associations for each major (and many minor) classifications of equipment. A recent list of such trade associations included over 400 names of organized groups.

In England, the Institution of Production Engineers has conducted special meetings on materials handling and has published numerous articles on various phases of the subject in its monthly journal. Manufacturers' groups include the Industrial Truck Manufacturers' Association and the Mechanical Handling Engineers' Association. The latter group is composed of crane and conveyor manufacturers. In 1952 the Institute of Materials Handling was formed to represent the interests of consumers in Great Britain. At the same time the School of Materials Handling was established in London, with Douglas R. Woodley as director.

A school for dockworkers is provided by the Department of Vocational Training in Rotterdam. Training is given in three phases: basic training, training of specialists (for tallymen and deckhands), and training of foremen. Theory and practice are combined closely in the program which includes productive work under the supervision of an instructor and practical instruction on a training ship placed at the disposal of the school by the government. Specially prepared manuals for each phase of training, diagrams, photographs, and scale models are used to present effectively the theory of cargo handling to students.

c. *Army and Navy Programs.* As part of the training in port operations, officers and enlisted men at the Transportation School, Fort Eustis, Va., are instructed in principles of cargo planning and documentation pertaining to vessels. Students study the methods and techniques employed in preparing a plan for loading cargo in a vessel. They compute such factors as maintaining stability of the vessel and placing the cargo for maximum utilization of space and methods of storage (Fig. 199).

One army training course for the selection and training of operators of materials-handling equipment includes: [3]

1. Mechanical structure of tractors and fork lift trucks
2. Operation
3. Preventive maintenance procedure
4. Safety rules and precautions
5. Operating faults which lead to damage of equipment
6. Warehousing procedure
7. Stacking methods

The Naval Supply Depot at Bayonne, N.J., very carefully selects candidates to be trained as industrial truck drivers. These candidates are given visual and hearing tests, as well as tests of mechanical aptitude, mental alertness, and physical fitness.

The first training period begins with a general discussion of the principles of palletization and industrial-truck operation. This is followed

[3] "Both Operator Selection and Training: Materials Handling Equipment," War Department Technical Manual 21-302, 1945, p. 11.

by a review of the mechanical characteristics, construction, and operating aspects of the vehicle. Operators are shown how to stop and start the truck and how to drive and steer. They practice doing these things with unloaded trucks in an open area.

The second period is devoted to giving them additional practice in driving in and around obstacles, hollow boxes, driving down narrow aisles, manuevering in tight spots, and turning sharp corners.

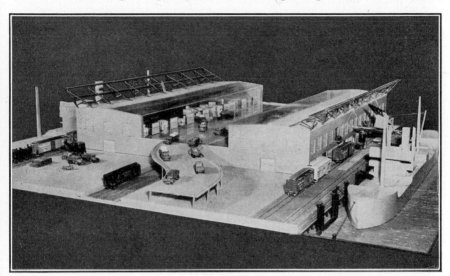

FIG. 199. Scale models of loading docks and buildings are used to instruct in cargo handling, ship loading, and stowage at the Transportation School. (*U.S. Army, Transportation Corps.*)

The third day the operator is taught how to pick up and stow loaded products and how to manipulate the equipment with a pallet load. The fourth period provides further practice in storing and tiering. Instruction and practice is provided for dock operation and loading of ships and rail cars. The operator is also shown how to manuever the truck in difficult places.

At the fifth meeting operators are shown motion pictures of the operation of the fork truck and are given copies of a booklet "Responsibilities of and Rules for Fork Truck Operators." In this session, the operator is required to manipulate the truck in various tight spots and around pallets arranged to represent ship storage, rail, and truck loading problems.

A specific program for the training of civilian personnel in military handling problems is being conducted with the following objectives: [4]

[4] Air Force Letter, June 17, 1948. Similar programs have been outlined by the Department of the Army and the Navy Department.

1. To provide voluntary on-the-job training in Air Force supply methods and procedures for interested personnel in industry.

2. To promote close and continuing cooperation between those elements of industry and the Air Force most directly concerned with the movement, handling, and storage of supplies.

3. To promote the exchange in ideas, plans, and new developments in economy and efficiency of operations, storage and distribution of supplies, with a view toward fostering standardization in fields of mutual interest.

4. To maintain a nucleus of civilian personnel indoctrinated in Air Force supply practices whose assistance may be available during times of emergency.

The training program to be conducted through a 10-day period of a 2-week course includes the following: [5]

1st Day—Registration:
Orientation, including a tour of the installation with particular emphasis on stock control, storage, and issue.
2d Day—Stock Control:
Orientation through stock control:
  Processing of requisitions and shipping orders:
    Control of requisitions in process (requisition number)
    Editing of requisitions for authorization, availability, substitution, interchangeability
    Types of requisitions
  Variations in requisitioning and property accounting (extracting, back ordering, etc.)
  Obtaining supplies other than by means of requisition
3d Day—Stock Control:
Receiving procedure:
  Receiving shipments from Department of Army activities
  Receiving shipment from vendors and miscellaneous sources
  Central receiving, classification, inspection
  Posting to stock records and removing back orders
  Stock control levels:
    Computation and determinations of stock levels
    Training for inventories
    Reports of survey and stock record adjustment procedure
4th Day—Storage:
Factors in space layout
Storage and warehousing methods and procedures:
  Protective storage methods
Inventory procedure:
  Location system

[5] *Ibid.*

5th Day—Storage:
Bulk storage method
Material handling
Stacking
Location system (bulk storage)
6th Day—Packaging:
Cleaning and processing:
  Preservation
Methods:
  Continental limits
  Overseas
7th Day—Receiving Methods:
Traffic procedures:
  Checking
  Inspection
  Delivery
8th Day—Shipping Methods:
Inspection
Packing
Marking
Loading
9th Day—Depot Activity Control:
Supply activity report
Supply cost accounting report
Space utilization report
Other control reports
10th Day—Review and Critique Covering the Two-week Training Tour

2. Study Manuals and Instruction Sheets

Although few commercial companies have prepared as elaborate and detailed training programs and instructions as the various branches of the military, many of them have worked up very presentable manuals particularly applicable to their own operating problems. The General Electric Company received so many requests for copies of the materials-handling manual prepared for use of their engineers that they finally had it printed and issued to the public. A safety bulletin prepared by Dominion Engineering, Ltd., of Toronto, Canada, has safety instructions printed in both French and English.

a. Operation of Equipment. Many manufacturers of materials-handling equipment have prepared detailed instruction booklets and sheets on the operation of their own equipment. Most of these have many illustrations and provide a very clear presentation on the main operating parts and characteristics of the equipment being presented. These manuals will often include detailed instructions for maintenance, lubrication, and other instructions for the care and upkeep of the equipment.

Various users have also prepared booklets on the operation of specific handling equipment within their own plant. A. O. Smith Corp. of Mil-

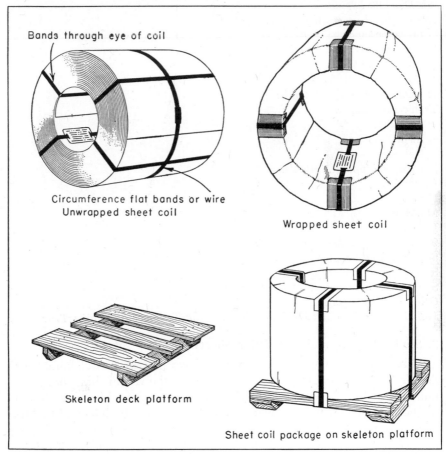

Bands through eye of coil

Circumference flat bands or wire
Unwrapped sheet coil

Wrapped sheet coil

Skeleton deck platform

Sheet coil package on skeleton platform

FIG. 200. Diagrams used to illustrate correct methods for packaging coils of steel for overseas shipment. (*"Packaging, Marking, and Loading Methods for Steel Products for Commercial Overseas Shipments," Simplified Practice Recommendation R237–49, U.S. Department of Commerce.*)

waukee, Wis., for example, has detailed instructions issued to crane men and sling operators. The General Electric Company has weight and size limits posted on each industrial truck.

b. Safety Manuals and Instruction Sheets. Safety instructions on handling methods and materials-handling equipment are made available by various government agencies, insurance companies, equipment manufacturers, and by users themselves. This information is made available in the form of booklets, instruction sheets, posters, and various types of letters.

c. Packaging and Crating. Companies having an extensive packing or crating activity tend to develop their own sets of instruction sheets. International Harvester, for example, issues detailed car-loading patterns for the loading of combines, plows, and other types of farm implements on rail cars and trucks.

The freight loading and container section of the Association of American Railroads has issued detailed instructions for the storage of a wide variety of small, medium, and large irregular objects, particularly where they are handled in less than carload lots. Detailed diagrams are also provided to show the exact method of blocking and tying down various pieces of machinery on flatcars and open cars.[6] In addition the Steel Institute has a manual of detailed instructions for the packaging, crating, and handling of package shipments of steel.

Many of the large merchandising concerns have also been forced to prepare detailed manuals and instruction sheets on the packaging of items for shipment. Montgomery Ward and Company and Sears, Roebuck and Company, for example, both provide such detailed instruction sheets for their packaging workers. In addition, a number of warehouses have developed elaborate folders on specific packaging techniques, particularly for the storage of furniture and other items which are ordinarily difficult to cover.

QUESTIONS

1. Describe the tests given drivers of fork trucks by Westinghouse at their annual truck rodeo.

2. Discuss the training program provided by the Naval Supply Depot at Bayonne for industrial-truck drivers.

3. What major subjects are covered in the program of the Army for training of civilian personnel in materials handling?

4. What types of manuals and instructional booklets are currently available regarding materials handling and packaging?

PROJECTS FOR FURTHER STUDY

1. Prepare a list of instructions for operators of fork lift trucks.

2. Prepare an instruction sheet for the receipt of incoming goods. Base this on a local plant or warehouse.

---

[6] "Rules for the Receipt, Handling, Stowing, Bracing, and Delivery of Less-than-carload Freight," revised October, 1949, Association of American Railroads.

CHAPTER 25

INTEGRATION OF EQUIPMENT

Efficient handling is achieved by effective planning, and this invariably involves the integration of a number of different types of equipment. In fact the test of the materials-handling engineer is his ability to consider a specific materials-handling function and then know what type of equipment to apply to the problem.

1. Characteristic Equipment Combinations

One characteristic of modern handling stands out: one type of equipment will not take care of all the handling needs of a plant. A combination of two or three types at least is necessary to provide adequate facilities. A number of these go together like the proverbial ham and eggs.

a. Hoist and Monorail; Hoist and Crane. The hoist is the most commonly used device for vertical movement of materials. Simple vertical movement is not enough, as there must also be some type of horizontal movement along with it. This is provided by monorail systems (if movement in a straight line is sufficient), or by an overhead traveling crane if lengthwise and crosswise movement is required. Jib cranes will provide coverage for a fan-shaped area.

b. Fork Truck with Tractor Train. It is accepted practice in industry that a fork truck is not economical for the movement of materials for distances in excess of 150 to 200 feet. Longer distances can be served best with an industrial tractor hauling a string of trailers behind it. Thus, in a complete cycle of an unloading operation, the fork truck deposits pallet loads on trailers. The tractor hauls the trailers to the storage area and returns with a string of empties. Meanwhile, a fork truck at the storage area unloads pallets from the trailers and stacks them in tiers.

c. Cranes and Industrial Trucks. This combination is similar to the fork truck and tractor operation referred to above. It is found particularly in cargo-loading operations at ocean docks and terminals. Materials hoisted from the ship are deposited on the dock or on trailers. Larger items such as crates and heavy machinery may be moved by portable cranes.

d. Conveyors; Combination of Various Types. Packaged items are handled on belt, powered roller conveyors where motive power is needed. Gravity wheel and roller conveyors are combined with chutes and slides for utilizing gravity as motive force. On long runs of gravity conveyors, elevation may be gained by the use of short booster units—an elevating

FIG. 201. Heavy rolls of rugs are handled easily with an electric hoist operating on a system of monorail track. (*Cleveland Tramrail.*)

belt conveyor section. Sharp descent is accomplished by spiral chutes or spiral roller conveyors.

2. Integrate Different Types of Equipment

As indicated above, handling in most modern industries involves the use of a large variety of different types of handling equipment. As considered in Chap. 23, production control for materials handling becomes an integral part of the production picture. The effectiveness of this control over the handling system determines the efficiency of the entire production activities of the company.

FIG. 202. Fork truck loads trailers for movement of paper rolls at truck dock. Special clamp grips and lifts roll to trailer bed at Commercial Marine Terminal, Detroit. (*Clark Equipment Company.*)

FIG. 203. This interesting layout of a packing station for oranges combines a straight section of roller conveyor with a flexible section along with a short section of wheel conveyor and a powered belt conveyor. (*Food Machinery Corporation.*)

a. Central Dispatching. A number of firms with widespread manufacturing facilities have been forced to set up central dispatching offices in order to obtain a smooth flow of production. The example of the General Electric Company in Schenectady, N.Y., is typical in this respect. There a central office controls the motion and activity of materials-handling equipment over the entire plant. The Ford Motor Company of Detroit, Mich., was one of the first companies to put into effect a central control agency for the movement of materials. This was accomplished mainly with a conveyor system serving the major manufacturing areas.

3. Materials-handling Systems

Increasingly, the materials-handling engineer is forced to consider not specific types of equipment but various methods or systems of handling which may be applied to the problem at hand. This may involve the use of a wide variety of equipment as discussed above or it may involve the planning of a system around one basic type of equipment.

a. Industrial Tractor and Trailer Trains. Where manufacturing activities are carried on in a single floor or where easy-grade ramps connect manufacturing floors, the trailer train has been found to be an efficient system for movement of materials.

At the new plant of Fisher and Ludlow, Ltd., of Birmingham, England, movement of all materials is based upon such a system. Fork trucks are located in each department to serve a local area and to load and unload the individual trailers.

An adaptation of the same system is found in the truck-tow systems currently being used so successfully for sorting operations in truck and marine terminals. In this instance, the conveyor provides a more rigid control as well as continuous movement for the trailers.

The Cadillac Motor Car Division has operated a trackless train system for a quarter of a century. These trains, operating since 1923, haul 10 trailers. Stations have been established near aisles near assembly or primary processing areas. Every hour, each train driver starts out along a definite route. Two trucks are kept in readiness for rush orders that cannot wait for the regular train. This system takes care of the handling in the plant except for large and bulky items. Automobile frames, sheet steel, bar steel, and rail car loads of coal, pig iron, coke, and limestone have special handling facilities in keeping with their size and volume.[1]

b. Pallet and Fork Trucks. The combination of the pallet and fork truck provides quick movement of unit handling. It achieves the econo-

[1] H. M. Goodhue, Trackless Train Runs on Railroad Schedule, *Factory Management and Maintenance*, February, 1950, p. 88.

Fig. 204. Trailers being loaded with containers filled with pressed shapes at the Birmingham plant of Fisher and Ludlow, Ltd. Trailers are picked up by tractors operating on a fixed route from one department to another. (*Mechanical Handling.*)

Fig. 205. System of palletized handling saves time and increases utilization of cubic space in warehouse at Port Newark. (*The Port of New York Authority.*)

mies of unit handling by eliminating a large number of trips which would be required if items were handled one at a time.

The use of the pallet permits high stacking of materials and consequent utilization of air rights, which formerly were wasted.

c. Skids and Platform Trucks. Skids are used where heavy materials are moved and where it is not generally necessary to stack them on top of

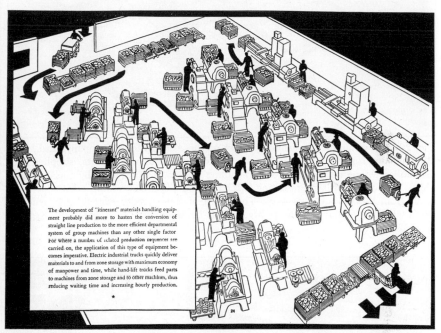

The development of "itinerant" materials handling equipment probably did more to hasten the conversion of straight line production to the more efficient departmental system of group machines than any other single factor. For where a number of related production sequences are carried on, the application of this type of equipment becomes imperative. Electric industrial trucks quickly deliver materials to and from zone storage with maximum economy of manpower and time, while hand-lift trucks feed parts to machines from zone storage and to other machines, thus reducing waiting time and increasing hourly production.

Fig. 206. A system of skid handling which provides temporary storage of materials brought from other departments and the positioning of skids and skid containers at each machine for stock, both before and after each operation. (*Yale & Towne Manufacturing Company.*)

each other. They are found particularly in foundries where a skid container will provide unit handling of parts that are generally heavy and irregular in shape. They are moved by means of hand-operated jack lifts if the skids are of the semilive variety. Hand platform trucks are used for intermittent handling over short distances. Powered trucks, either gasoline or electric, are used where operations are more continuous, loads are heavier, and greater distances are involved.

d. Conveyor Systems. Even before the advent of many of the control devices currently used on conveyors, the nature of the equipment made it adaptable to use as a complete handling system. Its development along

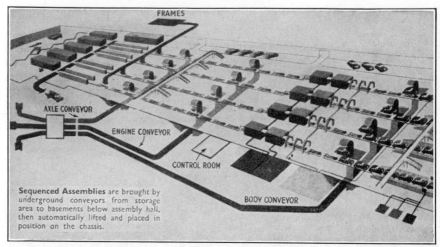

FIG. 207. New automobile assembly plant of the Austin Motor Company, Ltd., near Birmingham, England, utilizes 16 miles of conveyors to move parts, supplies, and assemblies through the plant. This handling system is controlled by business machines. Punched cards representing machines and parts control the release of these items from the storage conveyors. The speed of these feeder conveyors is synchronized with that of the main assembly lines. [*The Machinist* (*London*), Sept. 8, 1951, p. 1339.]

FIG. 208. A system of gravity roller conveyors and live roller conveyors provides continuous supply to and from unloading from the delivery trucks in this beverage bottling plant. (*The Alvey-Ferguson Company.*)

with the growth of mass-production techniques, as exemplified in the automobile industry, made it one of the first types of equipment to be used to serve this function.

The handling of bulk materials or materials to be chemically processed naturally involves the use of conveyor equipment. Because of the fact that the flow of the product was an integral part of the productive process, the now commonly accepted principles of straight-line and continuous flow

Fig. 209. These 5-ton cab-controlled cranes provided a complete handling system for the assembly area in a large Middle Western airplane plant during the Second World War. (*The Louden Machinery Company.*)

found their first application and development in these industries. It is no mere coincidence that the modern conveyor found its first application in such a process industry.

e. Cranes. Overhead traveling bridge cranes provide for complete coverage of a manufacturing area. Where exceptionally heavy components or finished parts must be handled, cranes provide the ideal method of movement.

The complete adaptability of the crane combined with the various attachments to it make it an ideal type of equipment where a wide variety of handling problems is encountered. Outdoor systems may be of the typical traveling bridge type, or the bridge unit may be mounted on gantry legs which run on rails. They may be of the full gantry type or of a single-leg gantry with the short leg running on a raised track section.

Portable cranes are commonly used for outdoor operations, both in the handling of nonregulated items such as coal, iron ore, and gravel, and large heavy units such as industrial machinery. Again, a wide variety of attachments makes cranes a versatile and efficient handling unit.

4. Specific Processes

With the increasing integration and control over modern materials-handling systems, industries, even with a job-lot type of operation, may approximate a flow of materials similar in many instances to that of a modern chemical plant. Where larger quantities of a single product are produced, this ideal of continued flow is even easier to attain.

a. Preparation of Quartzite for Roofing Granules. At the Wausau, Wis., plant of the Minnesota Mining & Manufacturing Company, the rock for roofing granules is blasted from the quarry and oversize blocks are reduced to 2-foot pieces. The material is loaded by two 2-yard and one 2½-yard shovels into the ten 14-ton-capacity trucks which carry the rock 4½ miles to the plant. Here it is dumped onto a conveyor which regulates the feed into a jaw crusher.

The material drops to a vibrating screen which separates the pieces larger than 1 inch in diameter. These are carried on another conveyor to a gyratory crusher for further reduction. Other conveyors carry it through later drying, screening, and crushing operations. At some places the rock is transported at a temperature of 350°F. The abrasive nature of the quartz also adds to the difficulty in handling.

The materials are carried on a belt conveyor over a Merrick Weigho-meter which weighs the materials while in transit. They are then dumped into storage bins of 55-ton capacity. Final blending of colors is accomplished by releasing a regulated amount of each color from the respective bins onto a conveyor belt going to the final storage bins. It is later packaged or shipped in paper-lined boxcars (Fig. 210).

b. Sugar Refining. An interesting example of the flow of a bulk commodity, both as a bulk material and in bags, is provided by the operations of the California and Hawaiian Sugar Refining Corporation, Ltd., located at Crockett, Calif. This plant processes 750,000 tons of sugar each year. Raw sugar arrives by ship, both in bulk and in bags. It is unloaded by a belt conveyor, where it enters the refining process.

While in a fluid state, the sugar is transported through process by pipes and chutes; dry sugar is moved by chutes and elevator conveyors and the packaged sugar by chutes and belt conveyors to the shipping department.[2]

[2] Andrew R. Boone, 750 Million Lumps of Sugar Every Day, *Popular Science,* March, 1950, p. 146.

c. Cold Rolling Mill. The new nonferrous rolling mill recently opened by the Scovill Manufacturing Company in Waterbury, Conn., is considered the last word in continuous strip-mill operation. In this $10 million

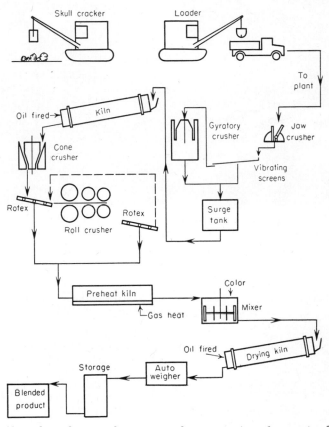

Fɪɢ. 210. Flow chart showing the steps in the preparation of quartzite for roofing granules. (*Minnesota Mining and Manufacturing Company.*)

plant, the handling of strip and coil stock between successive rolling operations is accomplished by means of an elaborate system of conveyors and control devices.

The mill performs the first series of rolling operations on the conversion of nonferrous bars to sheets, reducing them from 2½ inches in thickness to a gauge of 0.400 inch. These bars weighing 2,000 pounds must be kept moving in a continuous stream and yet storage must be provided also.

FIG. 211. Due to the weight (a ton or more) and size of cold-rolled bars of brass, it is necessary to eliminate all manual handling of the material. This roller-conveyor system enables a moving inventory to be carried at all principal processing points in the mill. (*Scovill Manufacturing Company.*)

FIG. 212. A vacuum-cup system is used to transfer the individual bars of brass to the mill entry tables where they are entered into the rolls by a hydraulic pusher or a power feed entry table. (*Scovill Manufacturing Company.*)

Vacuum-cup transfer devices are used to switch the bars from one conveyor to another.

Roller conveyors carry the bars through roller hearth furnaces with temperatures of 800°C. After the first rolling operation, any rough spots on the bars are removed by milling machines. From here, after a rigid

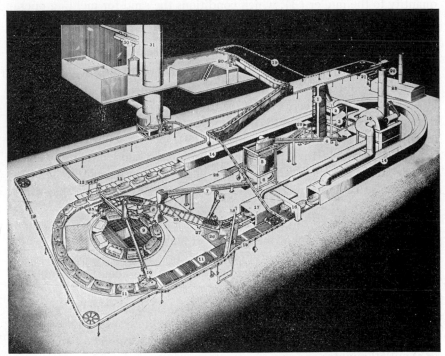

FIG. 213. Diagram of mechanized foundry. See text for explanation of numbers. (*Mechanical Handling Systems, Inc.*)

inspection, they go to the 4-Hi cold-rolling mills. At the end of the first operation, they are $\frac{5}{16}$ inch in thickness and are coiled.

The coiling machine is built on the discharge conveyor which carries the coils to a troughed roller unit and thence to an upender. A heavy-duty crane carries the coils to edge-trimming operations, after which they are annealed, pickled, and taken by crane to shipping-point facilities.

d. Mechanized Foundry. The General Foundry and Manufacturing Company of Flint, Mich., manufacturers of heavy cast-iron brake drums and shoes, pours 120,000 pounds of metal a day. A record production of two castings a minute with an average crew of 26 men has been attained with their new mechanized layout. The heart of the system is a carrousel-type molding conveyor. This forms a loop, 32 feet wide by 127 feet long, which contains within it all but three operations.

The diagram of this system in Fig. 213 illustrates how this high production rate is accomplished. A bucket elevator (1) carries the sand to a 5-ton-capacity storage hopper (2). It is released in batches of exact quantity to the muller (3), which conditions the sand for molding operations. The muller, operating on a 70-second cycle, discharges automatically to an inclined trough-type belt conveyor (4), which carries it at the rate of 37 tons per hour to a 25-ton storage hopper (5). It is then released in a continuous stream through a rotary-plate feeder (6) to provide a steady feed to the sand slinger. To ensure this, the sand is carried by another inclined trough-belt conveyor (7) to another hopper (8). It passes through a screen and is fed to the sand slinger where it will be discharged into the pattern molds on the turntable (9).

At this turntable the sand slinger throws the sand into the pattern sections, with the excess sand falling through the gratings on the floor. An arm sweeps this sand onto the main sand-return belt conveyor (28), which returns it to the starting point.

When both the cope (large top mold) and the drag (small bottom mold) have been rammed, the drag is lifted by the jib crane (10) and placed on the mold conveyor (11). The cope is then placed over the drag and the two are bolted together to form the completed mold for two castings, weighing 1,600 pounds.

The mold conveyor consists of 56 pallets, 32 by 54 inches each, on 64-inch centers. Each pallet is mounted on double tracks. The conveyor is chain driven at a rate of 6 feet per minute which completes the circuit in about 50 minutes.

A pouring ladle brings molten metal from the cupola on an overhead monorail loop (12). To pour the metal, the operator steps on a floor-level slat conveyor (13) which is synchronized to run at the same speed as the mold conveyor. After pouring, the molds are carried through a cooling tunnel (14) to an automatic air-operated pusher unit (16). This pushes the molds onto a gravity roll bed inside the mold conveyor loop. They are then pushed onto a motor-driven shakeout unit which removes the sand from the castings.

From this point, the hot sand from the shakeout unit drops down on a heavy-duty, leakproof metal apron conveyor (26), built to withstand the impact of 13 cubic feet of sand dumped at one time from a mold. The sand is then conveyed on a crossbelt conveyor (27) to the main sand-return conveyor (28). All of the sand is elevated to the main return conveyor and discharged over a magnetic pulley (29) to remove any tramp iron. The sand falls into a 36- by 54-inch vibrating screen equipped with a lump breaker, and is fed by a bucket elevator back to the main storage hopper.

Returning to the shakeout unit, the castings and cope and drag are moved along the gravity roller conveyor (25). The jib crane (24) separates the cope and drag after which they are rolled alongside the turntable for re-use.

The castings are picked up by another jib crane, which places them on a continuous overhead trolley conveyor (19) which carries them (and at the same time cools them) above the work area to the furnace-charging floor (20) above the cupola. Here the gates, risers, and sprues are knocked from the castings and remelted. The same trolley conveyor delivers the castings to the shot-blast room for cleaning. The castings are removed by a crane (21) to another trolley conveyor which carries them through the shot-blast booth, after which they are ready for inspection and grinding.

QUESTIONS

1. What are some of the combinations of materials-handling equipment most frequently used?
2. What is meant by a materials-handling system?
3. Describe the operation of a tractor and trailer-train system.
4. Discuss the use of industrial trucks with skids and pallets.
5. What are the operating characteristics of a conveyor system?
6. Describe the uses of a crane handling system.
7. Outline the method of handling employed for the movement of roofing granules in the quarry.
8. What types of handling equipment are used for movement of sugar through the various processing steps?
9. Describe the handling of strip and coil stock in cold-rolling operations.
10. Trace the flow of materials in the example of a mechanized foundry given in the text.

PROJECTS FOR FURTHER STUDY

1. Prepare flow charts for the movement of sand and castings, as described in the example of the mechanized foundry given in the text.
2. Write a report on combinations of different types of equipment other than those listed in this chapter.
3. Taking a typical magazine article on the handling of steel, prepare a flow chart and diagram.

4. Compare the emphasis given to the movement of materials in four different articles written describing the opening of the rolling mill of the Scovill Manufacturing Company. These references can be obtained from the Engineering Index for 1949.

CHAPTER 26

MAINTENANCE

The ability of mechanical equipment to provide reliable and economical performance over a long period of time is dependent upon proper operation and maintenance. This involves regular lubrication and inspection of all working parts, which is accomplished most effectively by following an established system.

1. Organization

Only in the larger companies will the maintenance of materials-handling equipment be the function of a separate group; even in many of these, it is regarded as a specialized part of the general maintenance function for the entire plant. Hence all the considerations applicable to the general maintenance program of a plant will also apply to materials-handling equipment. In addition, certain special conditions and requirements will be noted.

Quite often, down time of materials-handling equipment must be considered not in terms of rate per hour for the time lost for that one piece of equipment but in terms of production lost. One manufacturer accepted a large order on the basis of putting on a second shift to cover the order. Because of faulty maintenance 60 per cent of his trucks were in the repair shop, and he was unable to fulfill his promise in the required time.

Where the operations of a department are tied to a specific system of handling, failure of that system may stop production completely or seriously cripple it until the handling system is made operative again. A firm in Chicago had operations in its five-story plant paced by an overhead trolley conveyor system. A breakdown for one day brought back into use small four-wheel wagons formerly used, and additional wagons were hurriedly purchased in order to keep production going. In another case, failure of an overhead traveling bridge crane forced the company to pay a penalty for late delivery.

Organization of maintenance depends upon the size of the company and the number of pieces to be serviced. The function should be delegated to the plant engineer. In medium-sized firms a clerk is necessary to perform the proper control function.

At the steel and tube division of the Timken Roller Bearing Company maintenance of handling equipment comes under the supervision of the materials-handling department of the division. This centralization of responsibility for materials-handling equipment is often found in plants of this size. The alternative usually is to have a section of the maintenance department specializing on this type of equipment.

2. Information Needed for Maintenance

A survey of materials-handling operations in 120 plants was recently made by *Industry and Power* magazine. Executives and engineers of almost 50 per cent of the industries contacted felt they lacked sufficient information to establish an ideal procedure for inspection and maintenance. Only 14 per cent of the companies were found to follow some sort of procedure.

Yet the first step in ensuring adequate inspection and maintenance is having adequate equipment records and information. This requirement was recently emphasized in an article [1] in which the following points were stated:

1. Before you buy equipment, determine what work you want it to do and find out whether or not it is fitted for those jobs.

2. Before you buy, ask what the probable maintenance costs will be.

3. When you buy, obtain full preventive maintenance instructions.

4. Embody these instructions in standing procedures, and make sure they are complied with both by shopmen and equipment operators.

5. Schedule your preventive maintenance.

6. Select your shopmen carefully.

7. Train shopmen and equipment operators in preventive maintenance procedures.

8. Make sure the equipment is not used under circumstances where it might be damaged easily.

9. Keep records on maintenance work which has been done on each machine.

10. Keep records of maintenance costs.

3. Record Keeping and Reports

Complete control over the inspection and maintenance of materials-handling equipment is dependent upon a proper and adequate system of records and reports. These should be kept as simple and easy to fill out as consistent with requisite information. Reports should be of the checklist type, which requires the operator or inspector to consider and check each item.

[1] John D. Sheahan, Maintaining Handling Equipment, *Distribution Age*, December, 1946, p. 52.

a. Daily Operating Reports. These are generally filled out by the operator of the equipment and are used particularly for cranes and industrial trucks. The driver may check off each item as he inspects his machine before starting his day's work or he may make out the report at

MANUFACTURING RESEARCH DEPARTMENT

DAILY LIFT TRUCK REPORT

Works_____ Truck No._____ Date_____

Engine Running Time Per Day_____ Hours_____ Minutes

TOTAL

Cost of Gasoline_____Gallons per day at_____ cents per gal. $ _____

Cost of Oil_____ Quarts per day at_____ cents per quart   _____

Cost of Battery Charge KW hrs. per day at_____ cents per hr.   _____

Cost of Labor for Truck repairs _____hrs. per day at $_____per hr. Chassis _____

_____hrs. per day at $_____ per hr. Power

Unit _____

Cost of Parts for Truck repairs_____ Chassis   _____

_____Power Unit   _____

Cost of Labor for Servicing_____ hrs. per day at $_____per hour-Chassis_____

_____ hrs. per day at $_____per hr.-Power Unit_____

(Remarks on performance, adaptability, breakage, reason major repairs were necessary, etc.)

(List all major repair parts)

(Use other side of sheet if necessary)

Fig. 214. Truck operator's reports serve as the basis of the daily operating cost record. (*International Harvester Company.*)

the end of the shift. In either case he will note any repairs needed or anything else that should receive additional attention.

b. Periodic Inspection Reports. These are necessary to ensure that inspections are made as scheduled. The results of each inspection should be posted to the card which holds the record for that piece of equipment. These will vary according to the type of equipment and the operating requirements.

Particular note should be made of anything that should receive extra

MANUFACTURING RESEARCH DEPT
MONTHLY SUMMARY OF DAILY LIFT TRUCK REPORT

WORKS ______ TRUCK NO. ______ DATE ______ MAKE & MODEL ______

Date	Engine Running Time Per Day		Gas Consumption		Oil Consumption		Kw. Hour Consumption		Chassis Repair			Power Unit Repair			Service Parts		Chassis Service			Power Unit Service		
									Labor			Labor					Labor			Labor		
	Hours	Min.	Gals.	Cost	Qts.	Cost	Kw-Hrs.	Cost	Hrs.	Min.	Cost	Hrs.	Min.	Cost	Parts	Cost	Hrs.	Min.	Cost	Hrs.	Min.	Cost
1																						
2																						
3																						
29																						
30																						
31																						
TOTAL																						

APPROVED ______ Works Auditor ______ DATE ______

FIG. 215. Daily Operating Cost Record for industrial truck. (*International Harvester Company.*)

attention, such as minor repairs, adjustments, needed cleaning, or replacement of worn parts. Repairs made in the early stages can be done at less cost and with less inconvenience and danger than if allowed to become more serious.

At the Belden Manufacturing Company, Richmond, Ind., 382 pieces of operating equipment are scheduled for inspection on a monthly or semi-

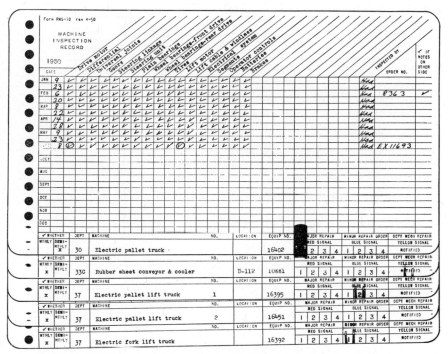

Fig. 216. Machine inspection record. (*Belden Manufacturing Company.*)

monthly basis, depending on the potential frequency and severity of repairs. The maintenance engineer responsible for carrying out this program checks each potential trouble point on a machine inspection record (Fig. 216). These record sheets (one for each piece of equipment) are kept in a loose-leaf visible binder.

As the maintenance engineer makes his inspection, he marks the potential trouble-point headings as follows:

1. Points OK ($\vee$) with black pencil.

2. Machine adjustment by the department mechanic ($\times$) with black pencil.

3. Points in poor condition but not requiring immediate repair ($\vee$) with blue pencil.

4. Points requiring repair (√) with red pencil.

5. Repairs for points which are classed as emergency in order to prevent breakdown or which present safety hazards are encircled with black pencil.

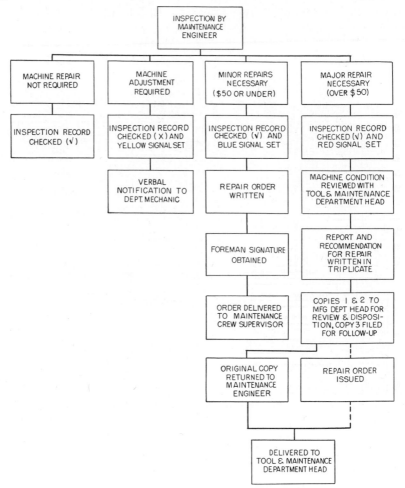

Fig. 217. Diagram of preventive maintenance procedure at the Richmond, Ind., plant. (*Belden Manufacturing Company.*)

Control for the system is provided by visible portions of the form. Colored celluloid signals set in the lower right-hand corner indicate the type of action required, as outlined in Fig. 217. The position of these signals over box 1, 2, 3, or 4 indicates the number of inspections that have been made without the reported repair having been taken care of.

At the time of the inspection, the maintenance engineer makes out a repair order when minor repairs costing $50 or less are required. These are authorized by the department foreman before the inspector leaves the department. For major repairs costing $50 or more, the engineer reviews the condition of the machine with the head of the tool and maintenance department. The results of this interview are written up in a report (Fig.

MAINTENANCE ENGINEER'S REPORT TO DEPT HEAD OF MACHINE CONDITION & RECOMMENDATION FOR REPAIR

TO DEPARTMENT HEAD: R Spade — DEPT 30
MACHINE NAME & NO.: Electric pallet truck — EQUIP NO. 16402
SIGNED, MAINTENANCE ENGINEER: H Alter — DATE 6-8-50

ITEM NO.	MACHINE CONDITION REPORT	CORRECTION	SAFETY	EMERGENCY REPAIR	ENGR RECOMMENDN
1	Drive motor needs complete overhaul	Rebuild completely; replace bearings, brushes, turn down commutator and clean			✓
2	Lift motor needs to be overhauled	Rebuild completely as above	✓		✓
3	Cable is frayed	Replace cable on windlass		✓	✓
4	Universal joints worn	Replace			✓
5	Brakes insufficient	Reline	✓		✓
6	1 tire damaged	Replace			
7	Wheel bearings	Repack with grease			✓
8	Battery power low	Replace			✓

ENGINEER'S REMARKS: All mechanical and electrical parts should be removed, cleaned, and replaced as required.
Item 6 – Tire damage not serious enough to warrant replacement at this time.
Truck should be painted.

ESTIMATED REPAIR COSTS

COST DISTRIBUTION	TOTAL ITEM COSTS ALL LISTED		RECOMMENDED	
MATERIAL	$290	50	$ 260	50
LABOR	150	75	125	75
OVERHEAD	129	65	108	15
TOTAL	570	90	494	40

DEPARTMENT HEAD DISPOSITION

		REMARKS
APPROVED ITEM REPAIRS ✓		
ALL	✓	Overhaul beginning
SAFETY		weekend 6-23.
EMERGENCY REPAIR		
ENGINEER'S RECOMMENDATION		
OTHER (SEE REMARKS)	✓	
NONE (SEE REMARKS)		
REPAIR ORDER ISSUED	✓	SIGNATURE R Spade — DATE 6-9-50

INSTRUCTIONS: MAINTENANCE ENGINEER send copies 1 & 2 to head of dept where machine is located. Retain copy 3 for follow-up file. Refer to Ind Eng Procedure, filed under - Machine Shop, number 7, for instructions. DEPT HEAD indicate approved repairs in check boxes. Use Remarks box to request additional information, instructions, etc. Return original copy to Maintenance Engineer, with repair order, if issued.
Form RMS-9 rev 9-49

FIG. 218. Repair order form used for major repairs. (*Belden Manufacturing Company.*)

218) made out in triplicate. Copies 1 and 2 go to the head of the manufacturing department in which the machine is located and copy 3 is put in a follow-up file. The department head decides whether to repair or replace the piece of equipment and returns the form to the maintenance department with comments on the action he has taken.

c. Job-order Tickets. Complete primary documentation on all costs and charges to materials-handling equipment is necessary for the determination of handling costs. Even minor repairs and adjustments are thus recorded and added to the record to that machine.

Approval of job orders is set up on a sliding scale, with the maintenance foreman approving all orders up to a certain size. Within the next cost group, the maintenance superintendent or the materials-handling superintendent may be required to approve them. Beyond this maximum, it becomes a matter of general factory concern, requiring approval of the production superintendent or factory manager.

d. *Equipment Cost Records.* The final step in control is the posting of the job-order tickets to the equipment cost records. This will often show whether the particular type of equipment being used is the one best suited to that particular task. In one farm implement plant, excessive repair costs on one type of industrial truck resulted in a change to another type, after which these costs became practically negligible.

4. Maintenance Services

The increased use of materials-handling equipment by small firms raises problems of servicing and preventive maintenance which are not encountered in larger plants. In the latter, which have a large number of units of equipment of various types, there is a regular maintenance department or in any case an individual to perform this service. The small company using perhaps only one or two pieces of equipment is able to afford this specialization. Therefore, quite often little or no maintenance occurs. Machines are not lubricated, are not given periodic inspections, and even minor repairs are not made until they result in a breakdown of the unit.

To overcome this difficulty and to lessen the complaints on the use of their equipment, some manufacturers have established maintenance and repair centers in the larger cities such as New York, Chicago, and San Francisco. In other instances the independent distributors will maintain this service as part of a sales program.[2]

5. Automatic Lubrication

Because of high-temperature processes through which trolley conveyors may be drawn, lubrication sometimes requires special consideration. Powdered graphite is often used in this application. Graphitar, a carbon-graphite composition, provides a satisfactory bushing (operated either dry or lubricated with kerosene, water, or alcohol) for trolley wheels.

Trolley wheels may be lubricated automatically with a special star-shaped cam. A lubricating arm is positioned on the grease cap of the wheel and a measured amount of grease is injected as the wheel passes by. This unit can handle heavy grease and does not require air pressure for

[2] For an interesting discussion regarding the payment for the maintenance of such handling equipment and what the charges should be, refer to Matthew W. Potts, Servicing Handling Equipment, *Distribution Age*, April, 1948, p. 27.

its operation. Still another device oils trolleys and chains as they pass underneath the unit.

6. Schedules and Programs

Effective preventive maintenance is dependent upon a definite program maintained and nurtured by a rigid schedule. Handling equipment is generally closely tied to production. Advance planning is required to permit its removal from the production stream. Pressure of work too often results in inspections being delayed or omitted entirely. This is especially true in small firms where schedules may not be so rigidly established and no one person is made responsible for this job.

The frequency of checks generally depends upon the conditions under which the equipment is operated. Otherwise the manufacturers' recommendations will govern. In one recent survey the following basic servicing periods for industrial lift trucks were recommended: [3]

a. 8-hour Inspections. In addition to the normal preparation for daily work routine the driver should warm up the engine and test steering gear, brakes, hoisting mechanism, controllers, tires, and other visible parts. Any defects noted should be reported immediately.

b. 40- to 60-hour Servicing. This includes washing and cleaning thoroughly and complete lubrication as recommended by manufacturer. Minor adjustments should be made to the engine as well as a check of water or oil leaks and general testing of machine.

c. 300-hour Tune-ups. Carbon removal and replacement of worn parts.

d. Semiannual Checkups. Wheel bearings should be repacked. Chains on hoisting devices should be cleaned and inspected. Brake linings should be examined. Other parts to be checked include the steering gears, universal drive joints, axles, wheels, pins, yokes, and ball connections. Also, crankcase and transmission oils and greases should be changed.

7. Equipment Instructions

Most manufacturers of equipment provide complete instructions for the care and maintenance of their product. This includes directions for thorough lubrication and greasing, charts showing the location of greasing points, and special instructions as to extra attention to be given the equipment. Such manuals are an invaluable guide to the care of the equipment.

a. Conveyors. Inspection and lubrication of conveyors fall into two parts: (1) attention given to motive-powered devices and (2) attention given to track or rolling facilities.

[3] W. E. Poole, Planned Care Results in Less Lift-truck Wear, *Industry and Power,* May, 1948, p. 94.

Inasmuch as most conveyors are powered by an electric motor, this may come under the duties of the plant electrical inspector. In very large plants, an electrical inspector may be assigned to motors and controls on

SHEPARD NILES CRANE & HOIST CORPORATION

CRANE INSPECTION REPORT

Crane No. .... Type .... Hoist Serial ....

Inspected by .... Date ....

KEY WORDS — OK; G=Good; F=Fair; W=Worn; A=Need Attention; C=Need Cleaning; T=Too Tight.

RUNWAY and CONDUCTORS

Track Alinement .... Spread .... Fastenings ....

Line Conductors .... Conductor Supports ....

TRUCKS and MAIN COLLECTORS

Truck Wheels, Flat Spots? .... Flanges .... End Play ....

Axle Bearings .... Lubrication ....

Truck Drive Bearings .... Lubrication .... Gears ....

Gear Screws .... Pinion .... Key .... Collectors ....

GIRDERS and DRIVE

Drive Shaft .... Couplings .... Bearings .... Lubrication ....

Foot Brake Shaft .... Couplings .... Bearings .... Lubrication ....

Bridge Brake Case .... Adjustment .... Lubrication ....

Walkway .... Railing .... Ladder ....

Bridge Motor Support .... Shaft Extension .... Couplings ....

Bridge Drive Gear Case .... Gears .... Lubrication ....

MOTORS

Location	Armature or Rotor	Commutator or Slip Rings	Brushes	Brush Holders	Bearings	Lubrication
Bridge						
Hoist						
Aux. Hoist						
Trolley						

Trolley Wheels .... Trolley Wheel Bearings .... Lubrication ....

Trolley Gear Case .... Case Support .... Gears .... Lubrication ....

Hoist Gear Case .... Main Gear Train.......... Comp. Train .... Lubrication ....

Mech. Brake .... Drift* .... Elec. Brake .... Adjustment .... Lubrication ....

Drum .... Cable .... Cable Pin .... Limit Switch ....

Limit Switch Adjustment .... Hook..........Sheaves .... Lubrication ....

Trolley Conductors .... Trolley Collectors .... Cage Roof ....

Door .... Windows .... Foot Brake Treadle .... Cont. Levers ....

CONTROLLERS

	Brushes	Brush Holders	Contacts	Wiring	Springs	Resistance	Screws Tight
Bridge							
Hoist							
Aux. Hoist							
Trolley							

* The load should come to rest, from full speed lowering, almost instantly when the controller is centered.

FIG. 219. Recommended crane inspection report. (*Shepard Niles Crane and Hoist Corporation.*)

conveyors and elevators exclusively. Transmission and drive units may be inspected as part of the drive mechanism.

The condition of trolley wheels should be noted at stated intervals. These should be kept properly lubricated to avoid excessive wear. If possible, automatic lubricating means should be employed. Condition of track joints and of the rail upon which the wheels run should be noted and checked.

b. Industrial Trucks. During a recent survey,[4] plants found to have the best maintenance programs were those with well-equipped repair garages.

In these companies the trucks were brought to a central location at the end of each work period and given proper care.

Sections 2 and 3 of this chapter apply particularly to the maintenance of industrial trucks. A schedule for inspections must be set up with specific items being checked each time. Complete cost records of operating expense as well as all repairs and replacements are needed to complete the picture.

c. Cranes. The amount of attention a crane should receive for lubrication depends wholly upon the degree of service and temperature condition. A hard-worked sleeve-bearing crane should receive daily care, while a roller-bearing crane should require not more than weekly attention.

A recommended form for the regular inspection report is shown in Fig. 219. These reports will be used as the basis of work orders for any repairs that may be needed. They will be filed to form part of the permanent record of that piece of equipment.

QUESTIONS

1. Discuss the organization needed for maintenance.

2. What is the first step in ensuring adequate inspection and maintenance? Explain your answer.

3. What information is needed for setting up adequate maintenance procedures?

4. Discuss the records and reports necessary to adequate control of maintenance.

5. Describe the maintenance program of the Belden Manufacturing Company.

6. Discuss the problem of preventive maintenance of handling equipment in the small plant.

7. What is meant by automatic lubrication?

8. Outline an inspection program for industrial trucks.

9. Discuss the maintenance requirements of the major types of handling equipment.

PROJECTS FOR FURTHER STUDY

1. Make a study of the maintenance programs of three companies manufacturing industrial fork trucks. (See local representatives of these firms.)

2. Develop a maintenance program for a company operating six gasoline fork trucks on a five-day week with a two-shift schedule (8 hours per shift). Outline a schedule of inspection for a six-month period.

[4] *Ibid.*

CHAPTER 27

SAFETY

Safety in materials handling is dependent upon the same rules and principles as safety programs in general. They are generally a part of this larger program. In some companies, because of the nature of operations, increased emphasis will be placed upon various phases of handling.

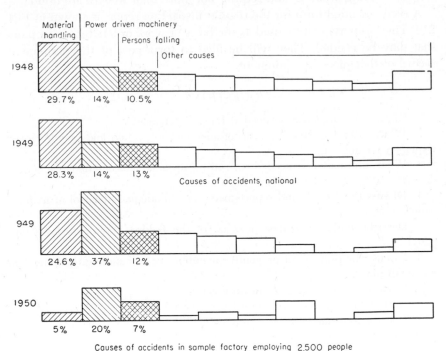

FIG. 220. Reduction in materials-handling accidents in a selected firm compared to the national average (British). (*Mechanical Handling.*)

The cost of industrial accidents in this country is staggering. The National Safety Council estimated this cost in 1940 to be over $2 billion. This figure includes only the accidents reported to management. For each reported accident, there are probably 10 unreported ones involving the waste of time, machines, material, and men. It has also been estimated that for every dollar of waste spent on accidents actually reported, there are probably $10 which may be attributed to indirect causes of waste which do not appear in the cost figures. These accident costs are added to the price paid by the consumer for the goods manufactured, thus raising the cost of living by this amount. In the long run, the consumer pays for these accidents.

A good example of the extent to which mechanized handling and a good safety program can reduce accidents was recently provided by a plant in England employing 2,500 people. This company investigated handling accidents and undertook a methods-improvement program. Although total production increased by 25 per cent in the plant during this period, the accidents caused by handling were reduced, as shown in Fig. 220.[1]

1. General Considerations

Safety, whether it be for materials handling or for machine operations, is dependent upon advanced planning to eliminate the causes of accidents and to instruct workers so that accidents will not occur.

An over-all safety program must have the complete backing of top management and be administered by someone who has the specific responsibility for its functioning.

The records of many companies that have gone for a million or more man-hours without a serious lost-time accident show that it is possible to attain the goal of accident-free operation. Such a result, however, does not just happen. It requires a very definite program of accident prevention and of safety instruction for all the workers of the plant and for all people designing machinery or locating equipment within the plant.

Causes of accidents have been defined as falling into two main classes, unsafe conditions and unsafe acts of persons. According to Lippert, these causes are as follows: [2]

UNSAFE CONDITIONS—ENVIRONMENTAL CAUSES
1. Inadequately guarded
2. Unguarded
3. Defective condition
4. Unsafe design or construction
5. Hazardous arrangement or process
6. Unsafe illumination

[1] W. J. Dimmock, Mechanical Handling in Industry and Its Effect on Costs, *Mechanical Handling*, June, 1951, p. 243.

[2] F. G. Lippert, "Accident Prevention Administration," p. 4, McGraw-Hill Book Company, Inc., New York, 1947.

7. Unsafe ventilation

8. Dress or apparel

UNSAFE ACTS OF PERSONS

1. Operating without authority
2. Operating or working at unsafe speed
3. Making safety devices inoperative
4. Using unsafe equipment, hands instead of equipment, or equipment unsafely
5. Unsafe loading, placing, mixing, or combining, etc.
6. Taking unsafe position or posture
7. Working on moving or dangerous equipment
8. Distracting, teasing, abusing, or startling
9. Failure to use safety attire or personal protective devices

W. D. Keefer in Blake's "Industrial Safety" adds a third class: [3]

UNSAFE PERSONAL CAUSES

1. Improper attitude (deliberate chance taking, disregard of instructions, injured man knew how to do his job safely but he failed to follow safe procedure, absent-minded, etc.)
2. Lack of knowledge or skill (injured man did not know how to do his job safely, too new on the job, unpracticed, unskilled, etc.)
3. Physical or mental defects (one arm, deaf, epilepsy, partially blind, etc.)

a. Good Housekeeping. An orderly layout is a necessary aspect of safe premises. A disorderly arrangement of materials and storage of materials in aisles extending out into areas where traffic may be heavy are conducive to a high accident rate. Many companies have discovered that a good housekeeping program will contribute a great deal toward reducing accidents. It also tends to have a salutary effect upon morale.

At the Caterpillar Tractor Company, Peoria, Ill., the problem of keeping clean 7 million square feet of factory aisle space is helped by the use of mechanical 16-inch scarifiers which not only clean the aisles but also have a smoothing effect on the floors. These are followed by 36-inch power sweepers which pick up the loosened dirt of the scarifiers as well as pick up factory dust. Schedules are elastic and machines are quickly dispatched to areas where most needed. In order to interfere as little as possible with production, cleaning crews are generally scheduled to areas when machinery is idle.[4]

[3] W. D. Keefer, in R. P. Blake's "Industrial Safety," Prentice-Hall, Inc., New York, 1943.

[4] H. S. Simpson, We Licked Dirty Aisle Dangers, *Factory Management and Maintenance,* February, 1950, p. 90.

b. Use of Mechanical Handling. Handling and lifting devices now available in wide range speed up production and relieve the worker from the danger of back strain and hernia frequently caused by heavy lifting.

The causes of weight-lifting injuries are known. Their importance will vary from one plant to another. Generally, the less highly mechanized plant will have a larger number of injuries of this type than one more fully mechanized (Fig. 221).

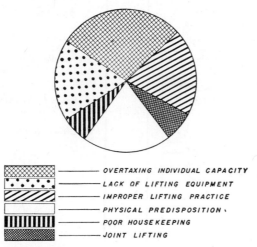

OVERTAXING INDIVIDUAL CAPACITY

LACK OF LIFTING EQUIPMENT

IMPROPER LIFTING PRACTICE

PHYSICAL PREDISPOSITION

POOR HOUSEKEEPING

JOINT LIFTING

FIG. 221. Causes of weight-lifting injuries—strains, sprains, and hernia. (*"A Guide to the Prevention of Weight-lifting Injuries," Special Bulletin* 11, *U.S. Department of Labor,* 1943.)

Typical of the educational efforts of industrial insurance companies are the instructions on lifting distributed by the Employers Mutual of Wausau, Wis. (Fig. 222).

c. Storage Facilities Provided as Needed. Storage space should be designed to accommodate the different types of materials, and each item should be kept in a specific place. Many accidents are caused by failure to provide proper facilities of special types of materials being stored. Irregular-shaped items such as long lengths, sheet steel, etc., present particular difficulties unless special arrangements are made.

d. Orderly Flow of Materials. Interruptions in the flow of production tend to throw storage arrangements out of balance and increase the problem of caring for and handling these materials. Proper planning helps to control the flow of production and minimizes the difficulty of storing unusual quantities.

e. Adequate Aisle and Storage Space. Aisle areas must be clearly marked and nothing permitted to be left or stored within the aisle line.

The width of the aisle should be adequate for safety. Where two-way traffic is permitted, it should be at least 3 feet wider than the combined width of the widest vehicles used. For one-way traffic, the aisle should be at least 2 feet wider than the widest vehicle used. Aisles should be adequately lighted at all times; also, warning signs and mirrors should be provided at corners and intersections. All storage areas should be clearly

FIG. 222. Safety instruction cards issued by National Safety Council. ("*Handling Materials and Objects,*" *National Safety Council.*)

identified and set aside for that specific purpose. Adequate storage area should be provided for vehicles so that they will not obstruct aisles when not in use.[5]

f. Approved Operating Methods and Training Programs. Much can be done by management to eliminate operating hazards and conditions which might result in accidents. However, this can go only so far. The human element must also be considered. Workers must have proper instruction and be made aware of the danger of certain operations and certain situations. This safety instruction then becomes a very important part of the program. The regular safety program should include instruction in methods of handling, storage and stacking of materials.

[5] C. S. Ziolkowski, The Useful Power Truck, *National Safety News,* January, 1948, p. 22.

The human element is one of the greatest problems in a safety program. Selection of workers should be based on their physical, mental, and nervous make-up and previous safety record. An applicant for the job of operating any power equipment should be able to pass satisfactorily some of the proved automobile driver's tests, such as reaction time, color, field and distance vision, distance judgment, hand and eye coordination, and hearing.

Arousing the interest of employees in safety aids in accident prevention. Some methods that may be used are posters, booklets, motion pictures, rule books, contests, safety committees, suggestion boxes, meetings, and employee magazines. Being safety conscious is one of a worker's greatest assets.

Unions can also participate in the safety program. It is advantageous to both management and unions, because unions gain in prestige from the safety measures they help put through and management gains in efficiency. Experience shows that unions can help best by attending accident hearings, participating in inspections, and distributing educational material. They can lend a hand in the support of certain activities such as eye protection, safety shoes, proper lifting, and the use of respirators. They can also assist management in enforcing safety regulations.

In addition to company-sponsored training programs, assistance will be given by governmental agencies and by insurance companies. State safety commissions, for example, have safety inspectors who visit firms and point out violations of safety rules. They aid the company in presenting an effective program that will emphasize the value of safety methods and procedures to workers. With such services available, there is no excuse for any manufacturer to be unaware of safe handling practices or to operate under conditions which make accidents possible or likely to happen.

Insurance companies also have a full-time program designed to reduce industrial accidents. This applies to materials handling as well as to other aspects of safety. In fact, one company has drawn up a complete safety program based upon the analysis of handling methods in individual companies. These surveys have produced impressive results where they have been used.

g. *Floor Surfaces.* The floor surface over which the equipment travels should be even, free from holes, pits, and sudden changes in elevation. Such conditions cause loads to fall and also cause the operator to lose control of his vehicle. The life of the equipment is also shortened when these conditions are present. Hard-surface floors should be used, even though they may cause more wear on the wheels of the power equipment. It is easier to repair or replace wheels than to renew worn floor surfaces.

2. General Equipment Considerations

In addition to certain instructions applicable to individual types of equipment, there are other considerations which apply to equipment in general.

a. Proper Type of Equipment for Each Task. The value of a specific type of materials-handling equipment is its ability to perform a certain

```
                                    1   2   3        Form MA117
                                  ┌───┬───┬───┐
                                  │   │   │   │
                                  └───┴───┴───┘
                                      SHIFT
                     ALLIS-CHALMERS MANUFACTURING CO.
                       DAILY REPORT OF CRANE OPERATOR
                  Crane No.............Dept...........Date.............194....
                    General Condition of Crane at Quitting Time

                  Fuses........................Limit Switch...............
                  Foot Gong..................Hoist Cable..............
                                              Trolley Wires
                  Controller..................and Collectors..........
                                              Truck Wheel
                  Foot Brakes................Bumpers...................
                  Magnet Brakes............Operator's Cage.........
                  Load Brakes................Guards.....................
                  Truck Wheels..............Safety Lights............
                  Rails..........................Safety Flags.............
                  Light or Heavy            Light or Heavy
                  Grade Oil...................Grade Grease..............
                  Are Grease Containers Covered..........................

                  Repairs to be made:.................................
                  ..............................................................
                  ..............................................................
                  ..............................................................

                  Repairs made during shift:.........................
                  ..............................................................
                  ..............................................................
                  ..............................................................

                  ...........................OPERATOR...............
                  Operator to state fully exact condition of above parts,
                  together with any information he may deem necessary
                  to make full report.
```

FIG. 223. Daily report of crane operator. (*Allis-Chalmers Manufacturing Company.*)

task. It is necessary to know the capabilities and limitations of each type of equipment and to select the proper type for the job at hand. Failure to do this may result in purchasing more equipment than is actually needed, with consequent excess costs. Or, if the equipment is unable to satisfy the demands made upon it, the result may be a serious accident to the operator or to other workers standing nearby.

b. Proper Maintenance, Preventive Maintenance. A definite plan of maintenance to ensure that the equipment is at all times in safe mechanical condition is an important factor in its safe operation. The operator of the equipment should be furnished with a list of items for a daily checkup before he starts to use the equipment. In addition to a daily checkup, a program of preventive inspection and repair by a maintenance department should be put into effect. Records of the inspection and repairs made on each item should be kept to ensure that nothing is overlooked. This information also provides a history of the service, maintenance cost, and useful life of each item as a guide for determining future purchases.

c. Inspection Procedures. Materials-handling equipment should be subjected periodically to a complete examination of working parts. This is particularly important for cranes, rope slings, and other lifting devices which are used in connection with the handling of heavy materials. These procedures will have to be set up on a definite schedule. In one company, one inspector is kept busy just examining all cranes and materials-handling equipment of the company. A complete form is filled out for each item of equipment inspected, and the forms are filed in a central office. Any repairs suggested or possible defects in the equipment are noted on the form, and steps are taken immediately to remedy the situation. This not only prevents accidents but adds to the life of the equipment.

A program of preventive maintenance will not only ensure that equipment is kept in service and in operation at all times but will go a long way to reduce accidents in the plant. Many accidents caused by equipment defects could be prevented if periodic check were made.

3. Specific Equipment Consideration

Rules and instructions for the safe operation of specific types of handling equipment may be obtained from the manufacturers of the equipment, from insurance companies (especially those specializing on industrial accident insurance), the National Safety Council, or from various state industrial safety boards and commissions. In addition, many companies have printed detailed instructions for various types of handling jobs with which they are concerned.

a. Hand Trucks. Hand trucks and wheelbarrows of various types are used in practically every industry. Many accidents occur because the wrong type of truck or wheelbarrow is used for handling certain materials; others arise from the fact that the equipment is of weak construction or in poor repair; some others are the result of poor floor conditions and insufficient aisle space; while many others are the result of careless loading and unloading practices. One insurance company [6] has developed the following rules for handling this type of equipment:

[6] Employers Mutual Liability Insurance Company of Wisconsin.

General

1. Trucks are intended for moving material, not passengers. No riders should be allowed.

2. Always load a truck in such a manner that material will not slide or roll off.

3. When the load is too heavy to move or if the truck is one of the larger type and unwieldy, ask for help. Do not strain yourself.

4. It is dangerous to use an empty truck of any kind as a "scooter" by racing it and hopping on for a ride. Avoid "horse play."

5. Wear safety shoes.

6. Whenever a truck is not in use, see that it is placed clear of passageways even if out of service for only a short period of time.

7. Give ample warning when you approach blind corners.

8. Do not use a truck with broken wheels or damaged handles. Inspect your truck before using it.

9. Keep the axles greased.

10. Never replace a cotter pin in an axle with a nail. You may be the one to strike your leg or ankle against it.

11. When trucking in close quarters, keep a close watch to see that your knuckles do not get scraped.

12. Trucks should not be overloaded. Limit the load to the safe capacity of the truck. Use the correct type of truck for the job.

Four-wheel Push Trucks

1. Get the habit of keeping your feet out from under the wheels and casters while loading and shifting position of trucks.

2. Except in the use of trucks designed to be pulled, keep the truck in front of you and push. If two men are required to handle the load, one should push the truck and the other pull. Lift trucks are made to be pulled.

3. Never load a truck so high you can't look over it to see where you are pushing it.

4. Get the habit of placing your hands for pushing where your fingers will not be crushed if the truck runs close to or bumps into a stationary object.

5. When a truck is not in use, the handle should be kept in upright position so as not to present a tripping and stumbling hazard.

Two-wheel Hand Trucks

1. The first and most important part of safe trucking is to learn to balance the load and to so place it that it will stay put on the truck. If you do not balance the load over the wheels, you are more likely to strain your muscles.

2. Look out for broken, cracked, or splintered handles.

3. Never leave a truck where it can fall over and obstruct a passageway.

4. Never go ahead of your truck down a ramp.

5. Never run a truck over a trucking plate or skid that is not fastened in place securely.

Wheelbarrows

1. Never run with a wheelbarrow with the handles in an upright position. It is best never to run with a wheelbarrow at any time.

2. When wheeling a heavy load, keep your back upright, and lift with your legs to avoid back strain.

3. Balance all heavy loads and they'll not be apt to throw you.

4. When handling heavy loads, stay as clear of the handles as possible in case the load tips.

5. Watch for insufficient clearances. Better still, protect your knuckles with leather, wood, or metal knuckle guards on the handles.

6. Avoid using wheelbarrows with cracked or broken handles, damaged wheels, loose legs, and ragged edges.

7. See that all wheeling planks are well supported and not apt to shift out of place.

b. Power Industrial Trucks. These trucks generally operate in aisles and working areas along with other factory personnel, including workers preoccupied with their regular duties. This puts a great responsibility upon the driver of the unit and requires a rigid adherence to safety rules.

With the increased use of power industrial trucks in specialized applications, many companies have developed their own sets of safety rules. The following are offered as general rules which should be incorporated in bulletins for a specific company.

RULES FOR THE SAFE OPERATION OF POWER INDUSTRIAL TRUCKS [7]

1. *Move control levers firmly from one speed to another and without hesitation.* This is to prevent arcing, which pits the contact surfaces of the switch. If you allow these contacts to become damaged you may fail to get the expected response from your control lever at a time when you want it very much.

2. *Keep your load as low as possible when moving.* There is less danger of tipping a load carried at a low level. Keep it low enough so that you can see over it.

3. *Keep your truck behind the load.* If you should get off suddenly, or fall off, then the load will be moving away from you. When going up steep

inclines, it is sometimes better to reverse this position and have the truck pull the load, depending upon the type of truck.

4. *Avoid making quick or jerky stops.* The momentum of the load may play tricks on you. Be especially careful about stops when you have a load elevated for tiering or stacking.

5. *If your truck has a tilting device, use it.* By tilting the upright toward you the weight of the load is brought back slightly and the balance is improved. This slight tilt of 10 to 15 degrees will avoid spilling the load when rounding corners.

6. *Go easy when approaching danger points.* These are elevator gates,

[7] The Elwell-Parker Electric Company.

pits, bridges, inclines, tunnels, and tracks. Get the habit of crossing tracks diagonally instead of at right angles.

7. *Take a good look at your load before you pick it up.* If you have to move a doubtful load, *slow down.* A properly loaded truck is easier and safer to unload. Know how much your truck is supposed to carry and do not permit it to be overloaded.

8. *Be sure to pick up every load squarely.* Then there is less danger of the load shifting due to offside loading, while traveling. When small boxes in pallet or skid lots are raised above the uprights, be sure that those on the back corners have not shifted to fall on you. Insist on wide load back rests.

9. *Report rubbish on floors to your foreman.* You and your truck are safer on clean runways. Be especially careful of rubbish, water, oil, or grease on all ramps over which your truck must travel. Avoid running truck through scrap from punch presses and lathes.

10. *Don't cut corners.* You are in danger of having to stop quickly—lose the load, hurt someone, or damage the goods.

11. *Keep your truck clean.* Dirt and rubbish make your footing uncertain and may cause trouble if obstructions lodge somewhere in the mechanism.

12. *Don't carry passengers.* You need all the room you have, for perfect control of your truck.

13. *Don't allow others to operate your truck.* They may injure someone, or damage the truck or tires. It takes time to secure and install spare parts.

14. *Report need for repairs immediately.* Repairs take the least time when they are made soon enough to avoid strains on other parts.

15. *Report materials or obstructions left in aisles.* You may be able to drive around an obstruction once, but the next time it may be a hazard. Both your personal safety and that of your fellow workers need to be considered.

16. *Observe traffic rules.* Keep to the right, and do not travel in the wrong direction on one-way lanes.

17. *Do not drive with wet or greasy hands.* If necessary, keep a towel or wiping rag where you can reach it easily to dry hands for taking hold of controls.

18. *Slow down before opening doors by remote control.* Be prepared to stop easily if you find that the way is not clear beyond the door.

19. *Watch low clearance signals.* When it is necessary to drive through low clearance passages, make sure of the height of your load in relation to the clearance. Don't guess.

20. *Observe fire-prevention rules.* If your truck carries a fire extinguisher, make sure that it is in good condition and that you know how to use it.

21. *Avoid sudden stops, starts, and changes in pace when transporting bulk materials, especially liquids.* This is to prevent slopping material over onto the floor or onto the truck. If baffle rings are available to prevent slopping over, insist on using them.

22. *Approach swinging doors squarely, and in the center.* To avoid breaking hinges.

23. *Use your horn.* Don't abuse it. Signal when approaching intersecting aisles, blind corners, or swinging doors. Several short blasts are better

than one long blast. Signal and slow down when approaching a pedestrian who is walking away from you. Avoid startling others with loud blasts. Your horn can be a hazard if used improperly. Remember that sounding horn does not give you the right of way.

24. *Keep in the clear.* If other trucks are operating, keep at least 15 feet behind the truck ahead of you. Do not travel two abreast.

25. *Park safely.* Your truck should not be left where it will block aisles, loading platforms, or doorways.

26. *Look before you start.* Be sure that there is no person or object in the path of your truck, not only at leg level, but also at head level, particularly before backing. Take a look before backing out from under a load.

27. *Report every collision to your foreman.* Even if no damage is done, the causes of all collisions with other trucks, with persons, or with other objects should be determined and corrected.

28. *Avoid crowds.* Keep away from congested areas during shift changes and lunch periods.

29. *Allow no fooling around your truck.* Report all offenders to this rule. They are a hazard to you.

30. *Handle hoists carefully.* Do not raise or lower them when traveling. Keep hands off hoist tracks. Do not drive with hoist higher than necessary when loaded. Lower hoist when empty.

31. *Never haul inflammable liquids or acids except in approved containers.*

32. *Don't drive in the dark.* Make a prompt report whenever you find runways or aisles poorly lighted.

33. *Dress safely.* Wear shoes that are suitable.

34. *On elevators* shut off power and set brakes.

QUESTIONS

1. Discuss the annual cost of industrial accidents.
2. Outline the major causes of accidents.
3. How does good housekeeping affect safety in a plant?
4. What are the major general considerations of a safety program?
5. Discuss the importance of aisles and proper storage spaces to safety.
6. What conditions are necessary for the successful operation of a safety program?
7. What specific rules apply to the safe operation of handling equipment?
8. Explain the part played by inspection procedures in ensuring safety in a plant.

PROJECTS FOR FURTHER STUDY

1. Make a list of injuries which may result from lifting heavy objects.
2. Prepare a report on the work of accident insurance companies on accident prevention.
3. Examine the following types of equipment (preferably while in operation), and prepare a brief report of safety hazards and recommendations for their safe operation: (*a*) industrial fork trucks, (*b*) mobile cranes, (*c*) portable elevators, and (*d*) overhead traveling cranes.

PART VII

SPECIAL HANDLING PROBLEMS

CHAPTER 28

MACHINE OPERATIONS

1. Handling of Heavy Materials

For purposes of identification heavy materials are interpreted as those materials involved in production processes which definitely require the aid of mechanical devices in positioning to the machine. Where this type of handling is involved, there is a problem not only of movement from one operation to the next but also of providing some type of overhead mechanical device for positioning on the machine bed itself.

In such industries the cost of handling may exceed as much as by ten times the amount expended in direct machining labor. A study in one steel plant revealed that for every ton of finished product, more than 80 tons had been moved in the process. Other plants normally figure 200 to 400 per cent overhead or more for handling and between-operation expenses.

In the fabricating of steel structural sections, for example, extensive mechanical-handling equipment must be available for movement of the materials. At the same time the operations themselves are often of short duration. In order to get a continuous flow of production through the plant, it is necessary to move these structural sections from one work position to the next. The orderly progression of these materials through the shop in this manner is necessary for economical operation of this type of metal fabrication.

The main factors affecting the selection of specific types of equipment for the performance of this handling function are:

1. Weight, size, and shape of the item to be moved.
2. Frequency of movement.
3. Area to be covered by the equipment. For example, if vertical movement only is required a simple hoist may be sufficient. If, in addition to this, horizontal movement in one plane is also needed, a monorail system may be the answer. For movement within a definite area, a jib crane is used. Gantry cranes may be used inside the plant for full coverage of an area, both forward and sideways. Finally, where it is necessary to move heavy objects over the entire manufacturing area, it will probably be necessary to utilize an overhead traveling bridge crane.

a. Hoists. Where a simple job of lifting or lowering heavy items is involved, the hoist will be employed. The type most commonly used in industry today is the electrically powered unit (Fig. 224). This may be of a standard make or of a special underslung type to conserve head room. If operation of the lifting device is intermittent and the height lifted is

Fig. 224. Electric hoist is used to load counterweight of fork truck to radial drill. (*Yale & Towne Manufacturing Company.*)

within certain limits, air hoists may be used advantageously. In smaller installations where the frequency of movement does not justify the in-installation of power equipment, a hand chain-operated hoist will be employed. These will be used for weights up to 1,000 or 1,500 pounds. Vertical movement of materials, however, is seldom sufficient and the hoist is generally found employed with other types of handling equipment.

The installation of an inexpensive electric hoist in the tool and die department of the Fairmount Tool and Forging Company of Cleveland,

Ohio, increased production and saved time of workers. This crane is used for the lifting of heavy forging dies in and out of machine tools used in their fabrication and has considerably cut the time normally required for the handling of these heavy pieces (Fig. 225).

b. Monorail Systems. Where horizontal movement of the material is needed along a single line, the monorail or trolley system is employed. In the simplest installations, the hand-operated hoist is pushed along the

Fig. 225. Hand-propelled bridge crane speeds up handling and makes the job easier in the tool and die department of the Fairmount Tool and Forging Company, Cleveland. (*Cleveland Tramrail.*)

monorail track, also by hand, to the desired location. In more elaborate installations, the hoists themselves are electrificd, and movement may again be by hand pushing or by an electrically operated motor attached to the hoist itself (Fig. 226).

An overhead monorail system with a chain hoist is used in a maintenance shop of the central Greyhound Lines, Inc., of New York. This shop is responsible for the upkeep of 100 modern Greyhound coaches. A simple hand-propelled system is provided for the handling of engines and other heavy parts in and out of the coaches and in the machine shop. This monorail system connects to a traveling bridge crane which covers the area in which the coaches are serviced (Fig. 227).

The location of columns in old plants often requires a considerable amount of ingenuity for the installation of overhead handling systems.

Fig. 226. Loading sheet steel to machine is simplified with electric hoist on monorail track. This hoist is shown passing through the curve of an electrified sliding switch. (*The Louden Machinery Company.*)

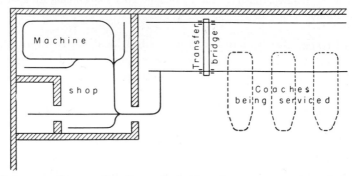

Fig. 227. Layout of monorail and transfer bridge of maintenance shop of the central Greyhound Lines, Inc., of New York. (*Cleveland Tramrail.*)

This was solved by the Seagrave Corporation of Columbus, Ohio, by a transfer bridge crane in each bay. Transfer of the 12-cylinder motor blocks for fire engines is made from one bridge crane to another by means of short stationary rails. Carriers can also be transferred to the tram rail system which provides handling coverage for nearly the entire factory. Thus the engines can be delivered directly from the transfer bridges to all parts of the shop.

c. Jib Cranes. Jib cranes are ideally suited to handling of heavy objects around a specific machine. The fan-shaped area covered by this unit is generally sufficient for the average machine operation. The most commonly used type of jib is the wall or column type which is attached to an upright structural section of the building. The limit of the lift will then be defined by the lifting capacity of the hoist, the strength of the horizontal bar and supporting member, and the ability of the structural member to take the stress imposed by the weight of the jib and its load.

Where structural members are not strong enough to take the additional stress of a jib crane, a column-type jib may be installed. It is quite common to look down the line of machine tools in a large machine department and see some type of jib crane serving each and every machine. A portable type mounted on a swivel base moves on rails and is used in heavy machine-shop work.

d. Gantry Cranes. Within the enclosed area of the shop, the single-leg gantry is commonly seen. The short leg of the gantry will generally be mounted upon a raised channel track while the outer gantry leg will be mounted upon the customary rail track installed in the floor. These units have the advantage of serving not just a fan-shaped area like the jib crane but a complete area within the limits of the movement of the crane. The main advantage of this type of equipment is that it provides complete coverage of the machine area and yet does not interfere with the operation of the bridge crane overhead. This takes a great deal of the handling load off the bridge crane and makes it possible to reserve the heavier equipment for the movement of larger pieces (Fig. 228).

The use of single-leg gantries to serve local areas in a machine shop has boosted production and cut handling costs. Because of the lower height of these units, they do not interfere with the operation of a larger overhead bridge crane covering the entire bay.

The use of these cranes provides increased flexibility for the overhead handling system. It relieves pressure on the larger traveling bridge unit which then can be used for heavier work. It is general practice to have a number of single-leg gantries in a shop bay, each gantry serving a localized area.

e. Bridge Cranes. In ordinary factory assembly operations, the overhead traveling bridge crane provides the ultimate in coverage and flexibility. It is generally on runways high enough to clear all pieces of machinery and has access to the entire machine area. Individual trolleys may have a capacity of 75 to 100 tons. For heavier lifts, two or more bridge cranes may be combined.

FIG. 228. Four motor-driven push-button-controlled single-leg gantries work under a heavy overhead crane in the heavy-duty turret lathe assembly department of Warner & Swasey Company. (*Cleveland Tramrail.*)

Thus, in the operations of the A. O. Smith Corporation of Milwaukee, Wis., crane lifts of 125 tons are handled with two and three cranes operating in tandem. A special drawbar lift mechanism has been devised to permit such lifts.

A slightly different approach to the problem of moving heavy materials between forging machines was used in the Los Angeles forging shop of the Allegheny-Ludlum Steel Corporation. This included an arrangement of four tram-rail runways, each with one or two hand-propelled cranes serving four furnaces located in the center of the building. This not only provides for complete coverage of the working area but permits each hammer to be served by two cranes. One interesting aspect of the problem was the provision for taking up the severe strains transmitted to the cranes by the crushing action of the hammers (Fig. 230).

The manufacturer of machine tools requires the handling of many heavy parts. The Monarch Machine Tool Company of Sidney, Ohio, utilizes a complete system of overhead handling to ease the burden of heavier lifting. This system of hand-propelled overhead bridge cranes offers complete coverage for the machine working area. Electrically operated hoists provide for fast lifting of parts with no effort on the part of the

FIG. 229. At the National Acme Company of Cleveland, Ohio, a 2-ton crane with electric hoist is used for handling parts into and out of this Ingersoll planer. (*Cleveland Tramrail.*)

operator. This feature is particularly helpful for the older workers of the shop whose long years of experience can thus still be utilized (Fig. 231).

f. Mobile Cranes. These units, which are more commonly used in outdoor installations where greater flexibility of movement is required, provide a complete coverage of an extensive storage area without the extra expense of the overhead units, such as the gantry and the bridge cranes involve. Some of the motor-truck types are operated in connection with a flat bed attached to the vehicle; thus the single unit serves as a transporting and a lifting medium. In other instances these portable crane units are used to pull around a string of trailers. They are then able to load the trailers themselves and proceed on their way without the aid of any additional equipment (see Chap. 10).

g. Machine Positioning Devices. The positioning of materials to a machine or the holding of materials while machine operations are performed sometimes requires considerable ingenuity and a wide knowledge of the types of equipment which may be used for this purpose. Fixed hydraulic lifts may be used for heavy lifts at a fixed position. Portable tables or lifts are more commonly used and have more flexibility in

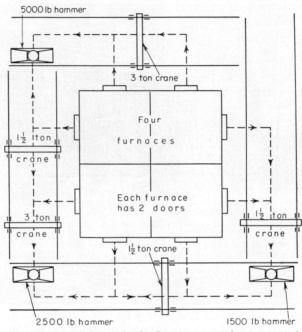

Fig. 230. Layout of system of transfer bridge cranes in the Los Angeles forge shop of the Allegheny-Ludlum Steel Corporation. (*Cleveland Tramrail.*)

addition to permitting limited horizontal movement. They may be used to remove heavy dies from machines or to hold heavy stock. By means of sheet feeding tables the top of a pile of sheets may be kept at feed-line height (Fig. 32).

Welding positioners provide for the adjustment of working height and angle of large unwieldy assemblies for welding together. Universal-type positioners position materials so they can be rotated around three axes and provide positive control in any position. Another type of positioner consists of two platforms to hold a large number of small parts at working heights. They may be raised and depressed by springs or counterbalancing.

FIG. 231. Electric hoists on overhead transfer bridge cranes do the heavy lifting at Monarch Machine Tool Company. (*Cleveland Tramrail.*)

2. Handling between Operations

Although the cost of handling materials other than the heavy materials referred to above is not as great, it is still a very important consideration in the total processing costs of the materials.

a. Trolley Conveyors. Materials are moved through processing operations such as paint spraying, bonderizing, enameling, or drying by means of a continuous type of conveyor. The overhead trolley conveyor serves this purpose. Labor is required to put the object on the conveyor and to take it off and no other handling is required.

In the Indianapolis truck-engine plant of the International Harvester Company there are 8,000 lineal feet of trolley conveyor carrying 3,000 hooks. One stock conveyor extending for a little less than ½ mile has flat trays for carrying cartons and boxes. Based on the plant's capacity of 680 machines daily, this stock conveyor delivers about 75 tons of stock daily to the two assembly lines.[1]

b. Monorail and Traveling-bridge-crane Systems. Where materials are moved a short distance between operations and it is desirable to keep

[1] Modern Production Methods at the New International Harvester Truck Engine Plant, *Mill & Factory,* November, 1938, p. 54.

them at a regular working height the monorail system will be considered. This system, like the trolley conveyor, keeps the material off the floor and also keeps it moving on an established line. It does not have the control element in time the trolley conveyor has, but in some types of machine operations this serves as an advantage rather than a disadvantage.

A number of problems in the handling of diesel engine crankshafts were solved by an overhead monorail system with the use of special racks

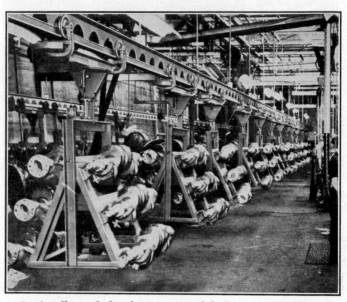

Fig. 232. The handling of diesel engine crankshafts was solved by an overhead monorail system with special racks designed to hold six crankshafts. (*Cleveland Tramrail.*)

designed to hold six crankshafts. All materials in process are kept off the floor and yet are made available to the workers. Work is now made available to the individual machine operators at working height; hence, bending over to pick pieces off the floor or from skids has been eliminated. Also, the tugging of heavy skid loads of shafts from machine to machine was eliminated as well as the space formerly required for these skid loads. Machine operations are performed in logical sequence. The materials are moved from one operating area to the next by being pushed by hand. This layout, involving a complete reorganization of the department, stepped up production and cut handling costs (Fig. 232).

The use of overhead handling made possible a saving of one-half the space required for the installation of 380 screw machines in one department. The complete elimination of floor movement of material in the department made it possible to put these machines into an area of only 75,000 square feet instead of 150,000 square feet formerly required.

Machines are closely arranged in rows with just enough room between the operators to enable them to work comfortably. All rod stock is carried to the racks provided for each machine by an overhead double-beam transfer-bridge system.

Fig. 233. Overhead loading of screw machines. Light by each machine notifies crane operator when more stock is needed. (*Cleveland Tramrail.*)

The operator working in the overhead cab lowers bundles of rod into the racks quickly and without assistance from persons on the floor. A transfer bridge at the end of the building makes it possible to run the carrier onto any of the several tracks over the machines. Figure 233 shows the complete coverage of the system.

The carrier travels on two rails and the grab has a three-point rope suspension permitting it to be raised or lowered with ample stability. Two pairs of arms of the grab are opened and closed by a motor-driven crank. The operator may deposit one or several bundles of rod in a rack by manipulation of controllers in his cab.

A monorail system was used to increase production for a screw-machine department of the General Motors Corporation in their Frigidaire Division at Dayton, Ohio. Materials-handling personnel was cut by 62 per cent. The new system supplies approximately 13 tons of bar stock per day to 127 machines. It also removes 3 tons of chips per day to a centrifuge operation for oil removal.[2]

c. Gravity Roller Conveyor. This is one of the more commonly used types of equipment for the movement of materials between operations, particularly where an over-all system for handling is desired. Materials to be machined may be moved to the next work position by means of gravity or by power. In the case of the latter, cutoff devices are often

Fig. 234. Gravity roller conveyor aids in moving materials into and out of large press. (*A. O. Smith Corporation.*)

used to shunt the material into the proper machine place. This method also makes it possible to provide a large amount of the type of storage space often referred to as live storage. An adequate bank can thus be maintained for each and every machine without extra handling required to put the material into motion again.

Short sections of gravity roller conveyor built in on each side of a large press at the A. O. Smith Corporation in Milwaukee speeded up the operation and eliminated a hazard for the operators in loading heavy materials to the machine. Such sections may connect to a roller-conveyor system for transport to the next operation or may be used just as a positioning aid to the individual machine (Fig. 234).

In the Flint, Mich., plant of Buick Motors, airplane engines were moved from one machine operation to another on roller conveyors. These were

[2] M. M. Roberts, Monorail Raises Production of Screw Machines, *Factory Management and Maintenance*, April, 1948, p. 75.

at machine bed height so engine blocks could be rolled easily into and out of each machine without any lifting required.

d. Elevating Conveyor. Quite often it is necessary to elevate materials to a position higher than that in which they come out of the previous machine. A common arrangement is to have the material ejected from the machine sliding down a chute into the lower receiving end of the elevating conveyor. This unit elevates it to a bin or hopper arrangement on

Fig. 235. Elevating conveyors raise parts to feeding bin of next machine. (*The E. W. Buschman Company.*)

the top of the next machine from which it is fed by gravity to the work position or the work area (Fig. 235).

e. Portable Conveyor Units. With flexibility as the modern keynote in machine operations, machines and auxiliary equipment have to be designed and planned to provide this element. Machines themselves may be mounted on various types of rollers or casters or may have side fixtures or devices to enable them to be pulled easily from one position to the other. The handling systems used in connection with them must be as flexible. These for the most part will consist of small chutes, passing boards, elevating conveyors, or single sections of gravity roller or wheel conveyors.

f. Chutes. Although in most instances it is necessary for the worker to position the piece to the machine, with all the mechanical equipment now available it is certainly not necessary for him to take it out. This may be done automatically by means of ejection pins or air ejection methods. Either of these can force the material out of the machine itself into a chute where it proceeds by gravity to a container located at the side of the machine and out of the immediate working area.

Fig. 236. Platform truck delivers a load of machined parts to the "In" area of Bullard department in general machine shop. High-lift powered hand truck moves skid containers from temporary storage within the department to one of the Mult-au-matics. (*Yale & Towne Manufacturing Company.*)

g. *Industrial Trucks.* The other types of equipment used for the movement of materials between machine operations involve some degree of continuity of operations or of a fixed sequence. Yet a majority of machine-shop operations today do not permit that type of operation because of a wide variety of products being machined, small-lot orders, or of wide variation in time of successive machine operations. This need for flexibility is answered by the industrial truck.

Small castings are commonly handled in skid or pallet containers which are moved from one machine to another for successive operations. Later they may be stacked on pallets with dividing platforms to protect the upper layers. In the small shop various types of hand trucks may be used to move these loads. If the loads are heavier and longer distances are involved, a powered walking-type fork or platform truck may be used. As the amount of handling increases by weight, frequency of move, and the distances involved, it will be more advisable to use an operator-riding type of powered vehicle.

The new Philadelphia plant of the Yale & Towne Manufacturing Company, completed in the winter of 1948, embodies the latest handling

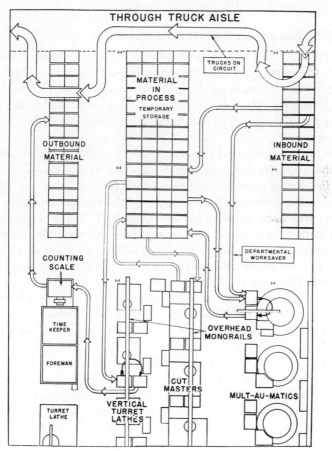

FIG. 237. Layout of truck circuit system designed to speed up movement of materials from one department to another. (*Yale & Towne Manufacturing Company.*)

methods to be expected of a manufacturer of handling equipment. Portable carriers and containers were designed for specific materials. Skids were provided for structural materials; skid bins for rough castings and forgings. Inserts and stacking-type wood trays were provided to protect the finish of finished parts.

A handling system to permit a small number of truckers to keep materials on the move involved the creation of special "In" and "Out" areas (Fig. 236). A circuit was set up, including a group of departments between which there was a heavy flow of materials. A truck with a load would go immediately to the department to which the load was routed and deposit it in the "In" area. If there was no outbound material from the "Out" area of that department, it would proceed to the next department on the circuit until it got a load (Fig. 237).[3]

3. Handling Equipment Built into Machines

As the quantity of a unit to be produced increases, the opportunity and feasibility of designing special handling features increase. These integral handling devices increase safety, prevent accidents for the workers, provide rigid control on the movement of materials while within the machine, and, once put into operating condition, require no extra labor to perform their function.

a. Transfer Machines and Automatic Machines. The turret lathe, automatic lathe, or Bullard automatic are included in this classification. Each of them involves a repositioning or an indexing of either the part being machined or the cutting tools. In each case the manual handling between operations has been eliminated or diminished. Transfer machines are simply a battery or combination of regular machine tools adapted to a group purpose. The machine units are fastened to a common base, and conveyor devices index and move the materials from one work position to the next. This was particularly successful in the machining of high-production items such as automobile cylinder blocks and airplane cylinder blocks during the Second World War. The initial investment and original engineering time is quite high but once set into operation the production rate is as high.

b. Fingers for Automatic Positioning. Automatic fingers have been devised to perform much of the dangerous work of positioning work to a machine or working area. At the Ford Motor Company, for example, a large 50-ton press is served by a set of such fingers. As the press operation is completed, these arms draw the finished piece from the machine and deposit it on an automatic conveyor which carries it to the next operation. Another set of fingers at the same time automatically inserts another sheet (Fig. 238).

Quite often when progressive dies are used, automatic finger or ejection devices will move the materials from one operation to the next position. This is done automatically and without any danger to the fingers of the operator.

c. Progressive Dies and Automatic Indexing. Where a number of successive stamping or press operations must be performed on a small metal

---

[3] A more detailed description of the system will be found in *Modern Materials Handling*, August, 1949, p. 17.

part and the quantity desired is exceedingly large, it is quite often economical to devise even very complicated progressive dies. These dies have automatic fingers or small metal devices to push the material into the next work position.

Automatic indexing is a feature of the machines already referred to. In this operation, the cutting tools are released, the material transferred

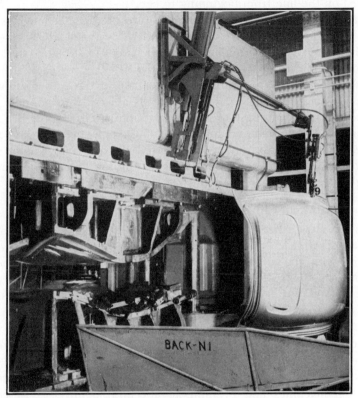

Fig. 238. Large metal sheets are withdrawn from press by metal arms which deposit them on nearby conveyor for movement to next operation. (*Sahlin Engineering Company.*)

from one work position to the next work position, and the cutting tools again brought to bear for the succeeding operation.

d. Special-purpose Machines with Handling Built into Them. A small number of mechanical devices or complicated machine setups have been devised which will carry materials through a more or less complete process without any manual handling. Recently, a British inventor announced that he had devised a machine which would turn out a complete radio set without any handling required in the assembly process.

Long before this, however, in fact starting in 1920, the A. O. Smith Corporation of Milwaukee, Wis., devised what was then termed a wonder of the mechanical age. This was simply a production line for the fabrication and assembly of automobile frames. With a capacity of 10,000 frames per day, it moved the component through a wide assortment of operations by means of mechanical conveying devices. No manual handling was required on the line from beginning to end.[4]

e. Handling Rivets. A noteworthy feature of the machine described above at the A. O. Smith Corporation is the way in which rivets are brought to the riveting machine from their basement storage space. There is a line running from the basement to the machine for each and every riveting point. In the machine, as it is set up at the present time, this means 137 such lines. The individual rivets are fed into hoppers in the basement. They come out of the hopper into a circular device which automatically positions them to be fed into the pneumatic air lines one at a time. Upon activation of the compressed air, one rivet will be blown through the line into the waiting rivet hole in the automobile frame on the jig above.

4. Handling Metal Chips

This has always been a messy problem where machine operations are involved. Turnings, swarf, chips, and the waste products of machines dripping with coolant oils pose a problem of handling, from the one-machine shop in the basement to the largest mass-production plants.

One method of collecting involves the use of containers of various types. These will often have a wire frame on the inside to permit drainage of oil from the chips. They may be collected at periodic intervals by a skid truck or fork truck and carried to a central disposal place where they may be dumped directly into a waiting rail car.

The handling of chips involves three problems: (1) collecting from individual machines and bringing to a central point; (2) processing, including separating oil from metals and whatever segregation and sorting of types of metals being done to obtain highest prices for scrap; (3) final disposition, which is usually by rail car but may be by truck for smaller quantities.

Larger pieces of scrap from presses engaged in sheet-metal work may be carried by a four-wheel trailer to a baling or compressing machine. There the irregular pieces will be compressed into small metal bales for ease in handling.

Chips may be carried from machines by overhead trolley conveyors.

---

[4] For further description, see *Modern Materials Handling,* May, 1948, p. 13.

The operator will hang a small bucketful on the conveyor hook as it passes. In other cases a conveyor may be installed under the floor. These will include winch-operated four-wheel containers on rails, slat conveyors, V-type pan conveyors, and various types of drag-scraper units. At the Kansas City plant of Pratt and Whitney, a pneumatic handling system was installed to take care of 3,333,000 pounds of aluminum chips per month. These chips were collected from an area of over 1,500,000 square feet.[5]

In processing, large pieces of scrap, rags, and other foreign matter may be removed at raking plates before crushing. Wet chips have the oil removed from them in centrifugal driers. Coolant extracted may be drawn away to settling tanks. Chips are stored in large bins at the conclusion of processing.

Elevated bins permit chips to be unloaded to rail cars by gravity chutes. Conveyors (pneumatic, scraper, bucket) are used to raise contents from lower bins. Larger pieces of scrap and compressed billets are commonly unloaded by magnet attachments from overhead cranes or from mobile yard cranes.

QUESTIONS

1. What problems are involved in the handling of heavy materials?
2. What are the main factors affecting the selection of handling equipment? Explain.
3. Discuss the movement of heavy materials along a single horizontal plane.
4. Discuss the use of various types of cranes for the movement of heavy materials.
5. Discuss the use of positioning devices.
6. In what ways are overhead handling systems used in moving materials between machine operations?
7. What conditions favor the use of gravity roller conveyors for movement of materials between machine operations?
8. In what ways are portable conveyors used in connection with machine operations? What are their main advantages?
9. Describe the use of industrial trucks to move materials from one machine operation to the next.
10. Discuss the different ways in which the handling function is built into the body of a machine.
11. What problems are involved in the handling of metal chips?
12. What types of equipment are used to handle metal chips?

---

[5] Sidney Reibel, Three Systems for Handling and Storing Metal Chips, *Transactions of American Society of Mechanical Engineers,* Paper 46-A-26, 1946.

Sidney Reibel, World's Largest Aluminum Chip Handling System, *Mill & Factory,* December, 1945.

PROJECTS FOR FURTHER STUDY

1. Make a study of manufacturers' catalogues for examples of the handling of metal chips.

2. Prepare a report on the use of industrial trucks for handling between machine operations.

3. Prepare the same report for use of overhead conveyor equipment.

4. Prepare the same type of report for use of portable handling equipment.

CHAPTER 29

WAREHOUSING ACTIVITIES

1. Importance of Planning

The phenomenal savings in handling constantly being shown on new installations reveals the importance of handling in all phases of warehouse operations. Rising labor rates and higher construction costs for new warehouse construction have not been matched by corresponding increase in charges. The difference in most instances has been made up from economies of new materials-handling systems.

The savings in money and time due to mechanized handling is illustrated in the following examples:

1. Ferro Machine and Foundry, Inc. Before the use of fork trucks and pallets, it took 10 men 2 hours to load a truck full of castings at a cost of $20. But with unit-loaded castings, a fork truck can do the job in 1 hour at a cost of $1.88 (60 cents for operation, maintenance, and depreciation, and $1.28 for driver). Calculations show that the fork truck can pay for itself in one year by loading 0.6 of a truck per working day, which is not an unreasonable expectation.

2. A & P Warehouse. Formerly, it cost $44 to unload a boxcar of coffee sacks. Present cost with fork truck, $7.

3. Sherwin-Williams Co. The number of orders that can be handled has been increased from 800 per day to 1,200 per day and saves $288,000 per year through coordinated use of conveyors, monorails, fork trucks, and pallets.

4. International Harvester Co. This company built pallets for shipping engines and saved $38,000 for every 27,000 engines built. Their investment of $9,000 was returned in 32 working days.

5. Kraft Foods. Before the use of fork trucks, the company could store 700 boxes of cheese in the cold storage room and 1,800 boxes in the dry storage room. With the use of fork trucks, they can now store 1,300 boxes and 4,500 boxes, respectively, in these same rooms. They also noted much easier inventory control due to unit loads, and less damage and pilfering.[1]

6. Kellogg Company, Battle Creek, Mich. This company redesigned shipping, receiving, and storage and increased efficiency at their warehouse by 60

[1] Adapted from Materials Handling; the New Word in Industry, *Fortune,* Vol. 37, p. 96, June, 1948.

per cent. Unit costs were lowered, and distribution to consumers and dealers was increased by 12 per cent.[2]

Still another picture of what planning can do to warehousing costs is the results obtained at the Greeley General Warehouse Company. A complete planning of handling facilities for storage operations resulted in the following:

1. Increased the number of cartons stored in the appropriate bay by some 40 per cent.

2. Cut the work hours required to handle newsprint by over 50 per cent.

3. Changed the handling of carbon black from a dirty job to one that is close to lily white.

4. Cut over-all loading and unloading time by 50 per cent.[3]

The new pallet system of the Greeley General Warehouse Company permitted 16,000 cases to be stored where 9,000 to 10,000 cases were previously stored. Small electrically operated hand lift trucks combined with these double-base 40- by 36-inch pallets to move and store to the ceiling in unit loads.

Efficient material handling results in a direct tangible reduction of cost, but there are many intangible savings that are also brought about. Some of these less obvious savings are as follows: [4]

1. Better utilization of space; therefore the need to plan on future building is reduced.

2. Results in better housekeeping, cleanliness, and orderliness.

3. Can take inventory easier and more often. Hidden material is easily uncovered.

4. Can ship quicker which means satisfied customers. Can store quicker; therefore, purchasing department can take advantage of good buys.

5. Material is not so susceptible to damage if stored properly; can be moved quickly in case of fire or flood.

6. Better working conditions; reduces fatigue.

7. Smaller labor turnover.

8. Reduces the number of accidents because fatigue is lessened.

9. By faster loading, can save on demurrage.

2. Receiving Operations

There are various methods of receiving goods at a warehouse. Material from outside will be received by rail car or truck, although a very few firms will have direct barge or ship loading facilities. Materials from

[2] John O. Archer, Efficient Storage Saves Us $50,000 a Year, *Factory Management and Maintenance,* September, 1949, p. 111.

[3] R. C. Greeley, There's No Monopoly in Brains, *Distribution Age,* December, 1949, p. 30.

[4] Matthew Potts, Materials Handling Bonuses, *Distribution Age,* June, 1948, p. 35.

within the plant will come by way of conveyor or fork truck. In a few instances the service may also be by overhead monorail conveyor or a bridge-crane system.

When material is received by rail car or truck, the sidings should be enclosed to permit unloading in all kinds of weather (Fig. 239). This is particularly important in the Northern states. A large number of unloading sites should be provided to permit unloading a number of cars

FIG. 239. View of receiving dock of the Purchasing, Receiving, and Stores Building of the Schenectady works of the General Electric Company. Inside unloading from both rail car and trucks is provided. Traveling bridge crane covers entire unloading area. Note portable sections of gravity wheel conveyor. (*General Electric Company.*)

or trucks at the same time. This may save demurrage charges. Height of the loading dock should correspond to the height of the car or truck door. Variations in truck loading height can be compensated for by means of adjustable hydraulic platforms which can be lowered or raised to the height of the truck bed.

Materials will be removed from the car by means of conveyors (set up in portable units), fork trucks, industrial-truck cranes, or by hand.

Heavier units may be unloaded with overhead monorail or traveling bridge crane hoist.

Some requirements for the location of receiving areas are given by the U.S. Department of Commerce: [5]

[5] John R. Bromell, "Dry Goods Wholesalers Operations," U.S. Department of Commerce, p. 49.

1. Contain a desk and other office equipment necessary for essential clerical work.

2. Be large enough to accommodate a large van load of goods stored on four-wheel trucks, skids, or semilive skids (those with two wheels at one end) without causing undue congestion.

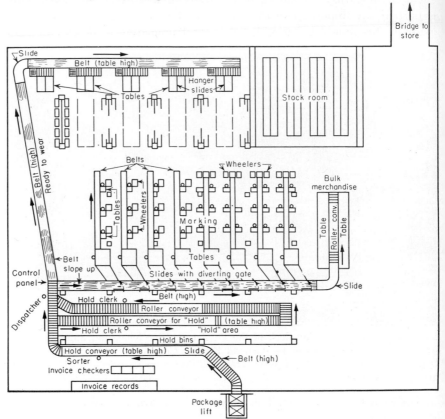

FIG. 240. Gravity roller and power belt conveyors speed up receiving and marking activities for Thalheimer's department store in Richmond, Va. (*Business Week,* *Dec.* 18, 1948, *p.* 78.)

3. Be distinctly separated by distance from the shipping area to avoid confusion and congestion.

4. In a one-story building be located as conveniently as possible to the point of storage so as to reduce hauling to minimum.

5. In a multi-story building be located adjacent to the elevators on which goods are to be conveyed to the upper floors.

General merchandising stores are faced with the problem of handling in large volume packages of a wide variety of sizes, shapes, and weights.

Thalheimer Bros., Inc., of Richmond, Va. (with a $25 million volume in 1948) mechanized receiving and marking facilities with the following results (Fig. 240): [6]

Merchandise now averages only 697 feet from the dock to the sales floor instead of 1,297 feet.

Packages are handled 17 times instead of 23.

Work area in the marking room has been increased 30 per cent; dock space 810 per cent.

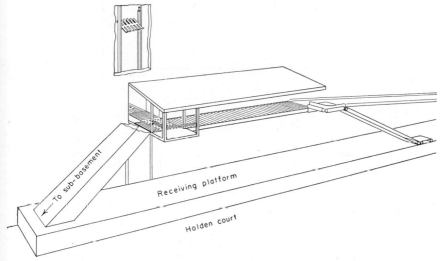

Fig. 241. Elevating belt conveyor raises incoming packaging to level of main conveyor leading to ball transfer section at left side of diagram. Packages are then guided either to chute leading to basement or to suspended tray-type elevating conveyor. (*Marshall Field & Company.*)

The receiving and shipping area of Marshall Field and Company is located midway in the building, running north and south from Washington Street to Randolph Street. With the 125 truckloads of material received daily in peak periods, unloading time per truck becomes a very important factor.

The receiving dock is a platform on the west side of the areaway 8 feet wide and 120 feet long. Three movable ascending conveyors carry packages from the receiving clerk's position at the delivery truck tail gate upward at an angle of 20 degrees to a point above the level of the main conveyor belt (Fig. 241).

This main conveyor belt is 4 feet wide and is suspended against the wall 8 feet above the dock. Near the south end of the dock, packages as-

[6] "Disassembly Line" for Store, *Business Week*, Dec. 18, 1948, p. 78.

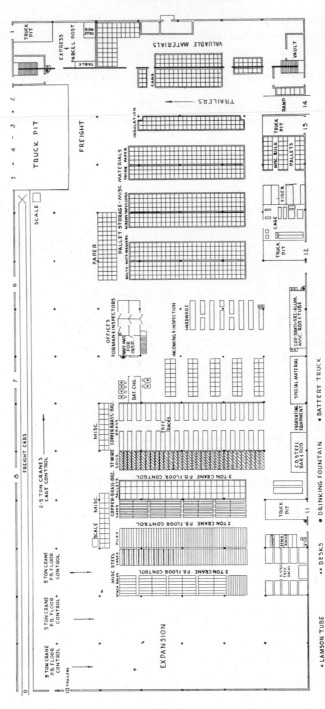

Fig. 242. Floor-plan layout of purchasing, receiving, and stores building of the Schenectady works of the General Electric Company. (*General Electric Company.*)

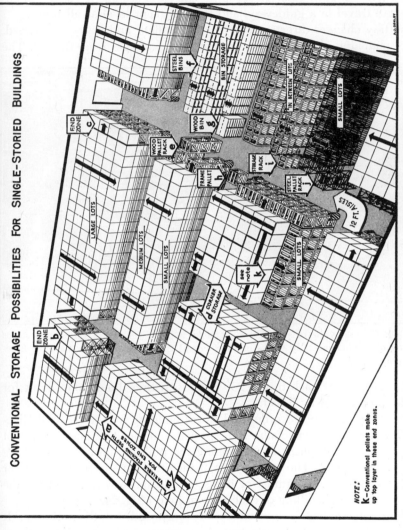

CONVENTIONAL STORAGE POSSIBILITIES FOR SINGLE-STORIED BUILDINGS

FIG. 243. Conventional storage possibilities for single-storied buildings. End zones are used for small-quantity items. Types of racks, bins, and pallet racks are also illustrated. (*Official U.S. Navy drawing.*)

signed to the subbasement opening rooms are guided to a gravity chute. The other packages are carried to the receiving and marking rooms on the eleventh floor. This continuous-moving lift, of an automatic pickup and discharge type, consists of trays at 10-foot intervals. A tray passes the pickup point at each 10 or 12 seconds. The trays are on swiveled suspensions and travel in a guideway, and thus are kept level at all times.

The tray changes direction on the twelfth floor and starts downward, where matching platform fingers remove the packages from the lift. The

Fig. 244. General view of pallet storage racks in right section of order and stores building of the Schenectady works of the General Electric Company. (*General Electric Company.*)

maximum load for each tray is 250 pounds, with a dimensional limit for packages of 3 by 4 by 5 feet.

A recently constructed order and stores building for the General Electric Company in Schenectady, N.Y., provides an outstanding example of what can be accomplished by planning the building around a handling and storage system. The latest types of facilities have been provided for the handling of a wide range of items. Ample space is provided for the most expeditious handling of each type of item (Fig. 242).

The receiving bay is located on the north side of the building. It is served by two 5-ton cage-controlled cranes and three 5-ton floor-controlled cranes. Sunken tracks within the building accommodate eight or nine freight cars. Special truck pits are provided to accommodate eight trucks at a time. This truck bay is completely enclosed and heated during the winter months. Unloading is carried on with the aid of tractor-trailer cranes, fork trucks, and other materials-handling equipment. Much of the material is received on a standard-sized wooden pallet 26 by 48 inches long. Long bar stock and other larger pieces are easily handled by the 5-ton crane service. Special steel racks provide for the high stacking of irregular materials. The variety of storage and handling facilities included in this installation is illustrated in Fig. 244.[7]

3. Storage

The storage of materials involves provision for buildings and physical facilities and equipment for moving materials into and out of storage. The cost elements are primarily the rental or amortization of the building and the space it occupies plus the cost of auxiliary storage and handling facilities and the cost of labor.[8]

a. Physical Facilities. For many years multi-story buildings were most commonly used for storage purposes. High land costs of central locations, low stacking heights, lack of heavy handling equipment with lighter floor-load requirements favored the construction of these multi-story buildings. With the advent of the trucking industry about 1927, central locations became less important; in fact because of congestion in downtown areas they became objectionable and expensive. Pallets and stacking frames used in connection with fork trucks and portable elevators raised stacking heights and the weights now imposed upon the floor-load. Costs of handling, especially with elevators, were much more than with new horizontal handling systems.

In determining the type of structure to erect, the positive advantages of the one-story warehouse should be seriously considered. Some of these are:
1. Lower operating cost. Few question the fact that goods can be handled with less cost on one floor than on several. The following reasons show why:
   a. Greater use can be made of available space since none will be taken up by stairwells, chutes, elevators, and so on.
   b. Usually there is at least one extra handling involved in chuting orders to the shipping platform from upper floors.
   c. Incoming goods can be stored in less time on the first floor than they can on upper floors.
   d. No power cost for elevators and no elevator men needed.
2. Less time lost in assembling the order. The entire order can be filled on one floor, thus obviating the necessity for assembling the parts of the order coming from different floors.
3. Quicker service. An order, or group of orders, can be filled more quickly from one floor than from several.

[7] Matthew W. Potts, Designed for Industry, *Distribution Age*, June, 1944, p. 12.
[8] See section on Live Storage in Chap. 12.

4. Higher type of help. Several suburban firms in another trade report that such employees (drawn from the immediate neighborhood) are markedly more satisfactory than those employed from downtown or congested areas.

It is believed that, in the vast majority of cases, when the advantages and disadvantages are properly evaluated, the facts will weigh heavily in favor of the one-story structure and that nearly all wholesalers who are in a position to build will finally decide on a one-floor goods-handling operation. Most exceptions will probably be among those who are located in large metropolitan centers where land values are extremely high.[9]

Fig. 245. Arm racks for heavy loads of steel bars (approximately 90,000 pounds), served by overhead traveling crane, in the order and stores department of the Schenectady works of the General Electric Company. (*General Electric Company.*)

Where materials to be stored do not adapt themselves to high stacking by reason of their shape either with or without pallets, special racks and frames will have to be provided in order to utilize the cubic content of the warehouse (Fig. 244). Special arms or supports on pallets will permit the palletizing of automobile tires, chairs, or brooms. Special collars will be used for high stacking of cylinders, such as oxygen tanks. Special frames will provide multi-tier stacking for divans and overstuffed furniture, ceramic materials which will not support additional weight, and a wide variety of other items which do not lend themselves to high stacking.

Storage of long lengths such as pipe and bar stock poses a special problem of its own. A-frame racks may be provided for both (Fig. 245).

9 Bromell, *op. cit.,* p. 27.

A. O. Smith Corporation utilizes frames 10 feet square for storage of 24-inch pipe sections.

Aisles are the traffic arteries not only of the industrial plant but of storage areas also. They provide accessibility for the materials being stored. Where a large number of items in small quantities are involved, this last becomes very important.

In Fig. 246 the new layout aisle space occupancy in the remaining space increased from 50 to 80 per cent with a net gain of 25 per cent.

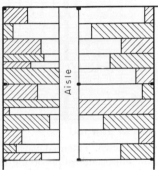
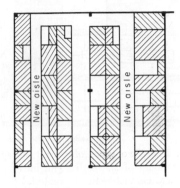

Old layout – A comparatively small number of inefficient storage spaces, 30 and 40 feet deep– only 50 per cent occupied on the average. One-half of complete storage area as shown in above diagram

New layout – With half again as many storage spaces, but only 8 to 16 feet deep—80 per cent is occupied on the average. Despite space used up in new aisles, there is a net increase of 25 per cent in occupied area, while handling in and out of storage is easier and much more efficient

Fig. 246. Old and new layouts in the same warehouse. The new layout shows the greater percentage of occupancy obtained by increasing the *b* number of aisles. (*Industry and Power, October*, 1949, *p.* 78.)

In this instance shallow areas were more efficient than deep narrow ones.

The following summary offers a detailed analysis of the original and new layouts: [10]

Original Layout	Square Feet	New Layout	Square Feet
Gross storage area	10,400	Gross storage area (original	
50 per cent average occupancy	5,200	layout)	10,400
		Deduct area lost in new aisles	2,200
		Gross storage area (new layout)	8,200
		80 per cent average occupancy	6,560

Gain in average occupancy ....1,360/5,200, or 25 per cent

b. Handling. High stacking is the keynote of modern storage methods. This may be accomplished in a number of ways. The shape and density of

[10] Sidney Reibel, Aisles Can Affect Efficiency of Handling and Storage, *Industry and Power*, October, 1949, p. 78.

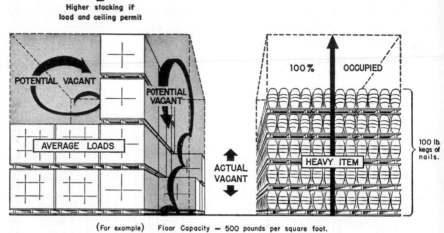

Fɪɢ. 247. Two types of vacant storage space are shown. Potential vacant space is the amount of space that can be reclaimed with proper utilization of the cube and physical characteristics of materials and the building. (*Official U.S. Navy drawing.*)

Fɪɢ. 248. General view of pallet storage in left section of order and stores building of the Schenectady works of the General Electric Company. (*General Electric Company.*)

the packages may adapt them to stacking without assisting facilities. The General Electric Company, for example, stores crated refrigerators four high. Waldorf Paper Products Company of St. Paul, Minn., stores rolls of paper five and six high without the use of pallets. Bagged goods may also be stacked to 20-foot heights.

Pallets are most commonly used in connection with high stacking of materials. Barrels, boxes, bagged goods, flat stock, bricks, and crates will

Fig. 249. Heavy rolls of rugs are raised to mezzanine storage area by electric hoist on overhead monorail system. This installation, in the warehouse of the F & R Lazarus Company at Columbus, Ohio, utilizes a special grab for rug and carpet handling. Note the fork truck in the lower right corner which is also used to elevate items to the mezzanine floor. (*Cleveland Tramrail.*)

be handled in unit loads and stacked on top of each other. After all, when the average storing height is increased from 4 to 8 feet, the cubic content of storage space has been doubled. At a new construction cost of $6 to $9 a square foot the utilization of these "air rights" may mean the difference between profit and loss to the company.

Fork trucks are used generally for the stacking of pallet loads or large crates or boxes prepared with skid bottoms. Portable elevating conveyors are used for high stacking of bagged goods and cartons where pallets are not used. Overhead traveling bridge cranes and monorail systems are also employed for high stacking (Fig. 250). An added advantage of these systems is the fact that aisle space for handling and movement of materials does not have to be provided. Overhead handling of materials also makes it possible to move objects such as heavy rolls or crates without

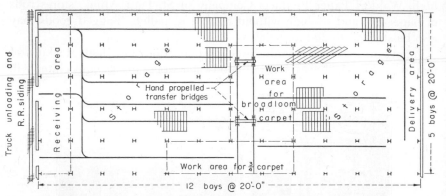

Fig. 250. Diagram of layout showing monorail system serving the storage area in the warehouse of the F & R Lazarus Company at Columbus, Ohio. (*Cleveland Tram-rail.*)

Fig. 251. High stacking of bales of pulp paper is achieved with safety at the Hammermill Paper Company in Erie, Pa. A special screw grab with three motor-driven screws or augers secures the bales when in movement. With this system 200 tons are easily handled into and out of the warehouse in an 8-hour day. (*Cleveland Tram-rail.*)

workers having to work around the stacks of material. Operations can be controlled from a cab, and all danger of accidents to workers is eliminated (Fig. 251).

Portable elevators are used in smaller establishments where the quantity handled does not justify more expensive handling equipment.

4. Outgoing Operations

The movement of materials out of storage involves the selection or sorting from stock, its preparation for shipment, and the physical movement from an outgoing loading dock. The economical movement of a wide variety of materials through these processes requires a considerable amount of advanced planning in order to establish the most efficient progression of operations with a minimum of handling and travel (Fig. 252).

a. Order Filling and Sorting. Basically, the same problem is faced by Marshall Field and Company in Chicago, the parts depot of International Harvester Company in Chicago, and the order room of McGraw-Hill Book Company, Inc., in New York (Fig. 253). An engineer recently charged with the assignment of laying out an order-filling department in an automobile plant received many of his most useful ideas from a large mail-order house.

The types of order pick lines to be used will depend upon (1) the structural features of the building in which the shelf stock is kept, (2) the number of items carried in stock, (3) the number of items appearing on individual orders, and (4) the amount of order-filling activity.

Some of the common types of order pick lines which have been developed are:

1. *Outside lines.* In this type the order picking line runs along the outer walls. This line is longer than other types and is difficult to justify.

2. *Inset lines.* The lines form a horseshoe which divides the length of the building at about 25 per cent of the distance from each outer wall. It provides the shortest walk-in aisle for each foot of order pick line and therefore usually gives the shortest order pick walk. If building measurements warrant, it is believed to be the most advantageous.

3. *Center lines.* A center line runs down the center of the room toward the shortest possible order pick line and is particularly adapted to narrow buildings less than 75 feet wide. Its effectiveness decreases in direct proportion to the width of the building.

4. *Double lines.* This type is in reality a combination of the outside line and the center line. Its purpose is to increase the number of orders which may be picked from a given shelf-stock area in a given time.

5. *Multiple-loop lines.* This is the type used in buildings that have large square or oblong floors. The large floor is divided into smaller units by employing a length of line for each 50 to 75 feet of building width and by

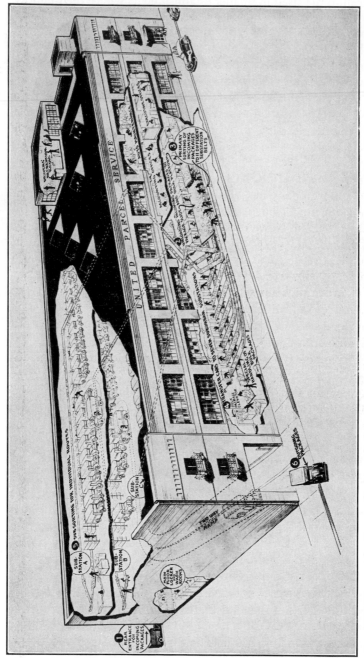

Fig. 252. Line production methods applied to package handling at the United Parcel Service, New York City. Numbers in diagram indicate sequence of operations by which thousands of packages per hour are sorted and distributed.

1. All packages picked up from the stores are brought into the building through the court entrance in the rear.
2. Incoming packages are unloaded onto a slide if they are of ordinary size or are placed on the bulk platform if they are unusually large.
3. Sorters take the packages from the slide and place them on one of the 11 conveyor belts which distribute the packages to various parts of the building.
4. Seven of the conveyor belts lead directly to large transfer cars, into which the packages are loaded for delivery to suburban stations.
5. Four of the conveyor belts lead to city stations within the building. Here packages are marked and sorted for individual delivery routes.
6. Delivery cars loaded with outgoing packages leave both the upper floors by a wide, two-way ramp to the street. (*Abbott, Merkt & Company.*)

connecting these lengths at appropriate alternate ends. The use of a multiple-loop line should be avoided if possible.

6. *Twin lines.* This type is used when the floor area is very large and the number of orders handled is great. It may be advisable to set up two full shelf stocks and pick complete orders from each. If this is done, each stock should be arranged from an inset order pick line, horseshoe in shape.

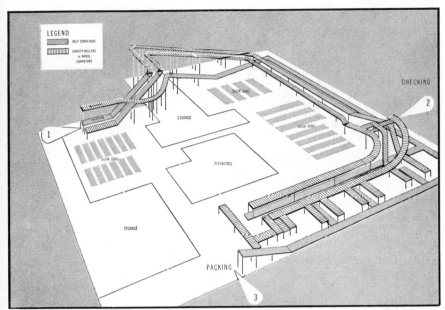

FIG. 253. Order filling and shipping for the McGraw-Hill Book Company, Inc., has been made easier for workers and output has been increased by the use of a 1,525-foot system of belt, roller, and wheel conveyors. Order-collecting carton starts empty at point 1. At point 2, the complete assembly is checked against the order and dispatched to one of several wrapping stations. At point 3, it is weighed for postage before passing to the outgoing elevators.

7. *Worm line.* This is a line described by the push truck when the truck accompanies the picker through the walk-in aisle. In this operation the push truck often does not penetrate the walk-in aisles but remains in a main aisle which constitutes the order pick line, while the picker brings the goods to the truck by hand. This method is used commonly by dry-goods wholesalers. To be more effective, the shelving should be arranged in long rows with occasional break-through aisles. These aisles need be only wide enough to permit easy passage of the push truck.[11]

[11] Bromell, *op. cit.,* p. 59.

b. Packing and Packaging. From the small retail store and plant to the largest mail-order stores, preparation of the product for shipping requires packaging. The small plant or retail store may have a single bench on which materials are prepared for shipment. The large mail-order store or parts depot will have a packing line to provide for the efficient movement of packages. These individual packing units are often arranged at

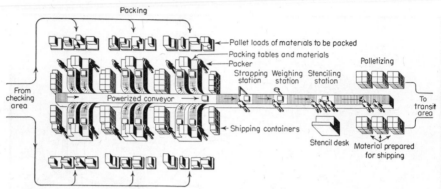

Fig. 254. Flow of materials through a typical mechanized assembly packing line. An analysis of the packing assembly operation will reveal that continued efficiency demands standard methods for performing assembly packing-line operations. The typical assembly packing line shows the general arrangement of equipment necessary for an efficient flow of work. Note that equipment is arranged in a production-line sequence, so that the work is performed at specific working stations. This permits assignment of personnel to definite detail operations and an even flow of work, making efficient supervision possible. Larger equipment and/or containers, which are centrally handled for preservation or packing operations, may also be efficiently handled by applying the same production-line principle as outlined above, adapting a conveyor movement system to facilitate working stations together with mechanical movement throughout the system. (*Official U.S. Navy photograph.*)

right angles to a conveyor, powered or gravity, upon which the finished package is put. These conveyors will carry it directly to the mailing or shipping room or area (Fig. 254).

c. Shipping Dock. This is the reverse of the receiving dock and will often be located on the opposite side of the building from it. In any case there will be a complete separation of the two functions to avoid confusion and recrossing of the two functions. As in receiving, it is important to have sufficient dock space and to have this enclosed if weather is an interrupting factor.

One problem often encountered on the shipping dock is that of moving materials in a steady stream to a large number of loading points on the dock. One solution to this problem is a patent device called the Spiramatic classifier.

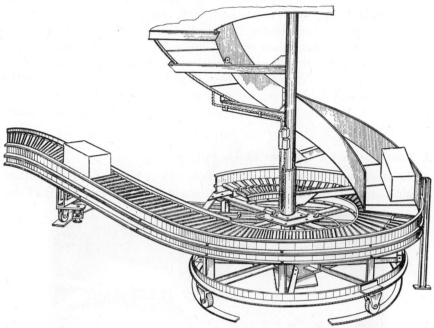

FIG. 255. Spiramatic classifier is used at the bottom of a spiral chute as a means of directing packaging to a number of different lines. (*Modern Materials Handling, May,* 1951, *p.* 58.)

FIG. 256. System now in use has three different docks and 17 conveyor lines. Packages are held on conveyor lines if a truck or trailer is not ready to receive it. (*Modern Materials Handling, May,* 1951, *p.* 58.)

The Spiramatic classifier is a ring of spiral gravity roller conveyor with a pitched tangential runoff section. It receives goods from a spiral chute and directs them to the specific line of conveyor desired.

In the Boston, Mass., plant of the Gillette Safety Razor Company, the Spiramatic classifier directs shipments from a spiral chute to one of 17 lines of gravity roller conveyors. These shipments may be loaded directly to a truck or may be held on a section of conveyor until a truck is ready to be loaded. As many as 4,000 of these parcels pass through the classifier in a single working day.[12]

5. Zone System for Efficient Order Filling

The efficient distribution of foodstuffs to a large number of retail outlets requires considerable ingenuity and a consideration of every part of the

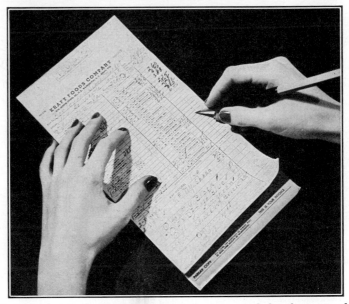

Fig. 257. First step in the Zonor system of the integrated distribution is this salesman's order form. The simplified form with its carbons replaces all the usual paper work of bookkeeping, shipping, etc. The same form goes to the warehouse for order filling. (*Modern Materials Handling, May,* 1951, *p.* 31.)

operation. The Zonor plan developed by Kraft Foods Company was reported by that company to save 25 per cent over every other system used to date.[13]

[12] It's a Conveyor That Acts Like a Hose, *Modern Materials Handling,* May, 1951, p. 38.

[13] E. J. Schwartz, Zonor System Speeds Distribution, *Modern Materials Handling,* May, 1951, p. 31.

The success of this system is due to the following four features:

1. *Zone selling and delivery routes.* These delivery zones are carefully planned to provide each delivery truck with a maximum pay load. Sales routes are adapted to these zones. Salesmen call on each store the same day of the week at regular intervals.

2. *Simplified bookkeeping system.* The salesman's order slip serves as a warehouse order, customer's invoice, and a permanent record of the

Fig. 258. Heart of the Zonor system is its novel truck-loading mechanism. Continuous roller chains powered by the truck's battery move pallet loads back into position in the truck after they have been placed with a fork truck. (*Modern Materials Handling, May,* 1951, *p.* 31.)

transaction. A copy is delivered with the order for the customer's record and another is signed by him as a receipt for the goods. The signed slip is returned to the bookkeeping department where the prices are extended and the bill totaled.

3. *Efficient order-assembly area.* Goods with the highest turnover and the biggest tonnage are located nearest to the center assembly point. A single order assembler works in a U-shaped area. Reserve stocks are moved to this area by fork truck.

The orders are assembled on specially developed flat pallets 32 by 48 inches. This pallet rests on a double wood track for fork pickup. The loaded pallet is then stored in a rack to await loading to the delivery truck. The pallets are carefully arranged so that they will be loaded into the truck in the order in which they will be unloaded on the delivery routes.

4. *Chain unloading device.* Two pallets are placed in the truck side by side on raised sections of the truck bed. The center rib under each section has a chain by means of which the loaded pallets are moved back into the truck. This chain is operated from the truck battery. With this device eight pallet loads or the equivalent of 12,000 pounds of goods can be loaded in approximately 8 minutes. As the orders are loaded to come off in the proper sequence, the driver never has to climb into the truck.

QUESTIONS

1. Discuss the main results of planned handling for storage operations.
2. What are some of the intangible benefits resulting from planned handling?
3. What are some of the monetary savings effected by the use of planned storage procedures and handling methods?
4. Discuss the physical means of receiving materials at a warehouse.
5. Discuss the use of specific types of equipment in receiving operations.
6. Name the requirements for the location of receiving areas.
7. Describe the receiving facilities of Marshall Field and Company.
8. What are the advantages of the single-story warehouse?
9. Discuss the physical plant and equipment used for storage operations.
10. The outgoing movement of materials involves what specific operations?
11. Describe some of the common types of order-picking lines.

PROJECTS FOR FURTHER STUDY

1. From current magazines prepare a list of firms which have developed new or improved warehousing methods. What types of equipment were involved? What savings were listed for each installation?
2. Prepare a report on order filling. This may be based on local wholesale warehouses, mail-order companies, or spare-parts depots.
3. From manufacturers' sales catalogues make a list of the different ways in which various types of equipment are used in warehousing operations.

CHAPTER 30

ASSEMBLY

Materials handling applied to assembly operations may be classified into two categories: (1) the problem of moving materials and parts to the line and (2) the problem of moving the assembled pieces on the line itself. The use of any particular method or system of equipment for either of these problems is dependent upon the following factors:

1. The size, weight, and shape of the assembled product and its constituent parts

2. The quantity of production desired

3. The restrictive influences of factors of the building and all other existing facilities

4. The economics of the above systems and methods to determine the most economical one for that particular purpose

5. The amount of money available for capital expenditures, particularly in view of long-term activities of the company

1. Feeding Material to Lines

In the early days of the automobile industry, it was customary for assembly crews to search for their own material. The individual parts would be stacked in neat piles immediately adjacent to the assembly area. As an assembler needed a particular part, he would go to a stack of these items and search until he found the one he needed. With this method, workers spent considerable time searching for materials.

At a later date, a stock collector was assigned to each assembly group. This individual was responsible for keeping stock up to a certain level. The efficiency of these stockmen was adjudged on the basis of their ability to maintain stock levels even in the face of plant-wide shortages. Therefore, considerable competitive spirit developed. Shortage of four-wheel carts commonly used for transporting heavier objects was also the object of spirited competition. In one firm these stockmen would dump a load of finished crankshafts on to a concrete floor in order to obtain the cart for their own use. This competition for carts and parts was very wasteful in manpower as well as damaging to parts.

The system gave way to the more formal systems under closer control

which we have today. In the early 1920's, a number of the leading automobile manufacturers were seeing the need for control in the movement
of materials and were setting up handling systems to provide this control.

a. Conveyors. The use of conveyors provided the degree of control
needed in assembly operations. Even today the control over assembly
production is one of the big benefits of the system.

Materials have been moved to assembly areas in two ways. The first
involved the movement of materials to the assembly area itself, pref-

Fig. 259. Trolley-conveyor system feeds complete list of parts to assembly areas.
(*Ferguson Tractor Company, Coventry, England.*)

erably to a place immediately adjacent to the assembly line. Trolley conveyors have commonly been used for this purpose. The fact that assembly
operations on subassembly lines involve moving the material to the assembly area should not be overlooked, however.

A second method, developed quite early in the history of modern production methods, involved the use of a kit complete with all parts necessary to fabricate a certain assembly. In 1919 and 1920, a number of
automobile companies used a modification of this system. Studebaker,
Packard, Hudson, and Ford motor companies were some of the many
which were using these methods at that time.

At the Studebaker Motor Company a large A frame was mounted on
the assembly-line conveyor. This frame contained fenders and all parts
necessary to complete the assembly at that point. When the car was
finished at the end of the line, the A frame was lifted on an overhead

conveyor and taken to the second floor. This floor was used as a stock area, and there the frame proceeded back along another assembly line at the end of which the frame would be completely loaded with all the parts needed for another car. This kit would then be lowered to the beginning of the finished chassis line. It should be noted that the Packard Motor Car Company used the same system about this time. It was later taken out and was not reinstalled until the summer of 1947 when it was an-

Fig. 260. Complete kits of all parts accompany each engine block down the assembly line. (*Standard Motor Company.*)

nounced as being a new system of supplying parts to the assembly lines.

Todd Protectograph and a number of other companies used the same system at about the same time, using belt conveyors and a wide variety of other conveying devices. One of the most outstanding installations of this system in operation today is that of the Ferguson Tractor Works in Coventry, England. Complete kits of parts are gathered in an area adjacent to the assembly area. Therefore, there is no movement of materials or parts in the assembly area itself. This eliminates a great deal of congestion in the assembly areas and allows the assembly workers to proceed with their work without interruption. Furthermore, there is the assurance of a steady stream of materials waiting for them at working height. That is also conducive to easier and faster work.

The economics of this system is a source of much argument among engineers in the automobile industry. For a particular application it requires a very careful study of the costs of handling under both methods. It is, however, a system worthy of very careful consideration where mass-production assembly is involved.

In the Toledo, Ohio, plant of the Willys Overland Company an overhead trolley system provides a constant source of supply of parts for the assembly line. Permanent boxes and bins have been attached to fixtures on the conveyor; thus nuts, bolts, and screws are readily available for the assembly workers.

At the Packard Motor Car Company in Detroit, Mich., component assemblies (front ends, seats, bumpers, etc.) are assembled on a series of balconies running parallel to final assembly lines. These components are then dropped by conveyor to point of assembly on the line.[1]

b. Unit Handling. The handling of a number of units at one time has introduced revolutionary changes in the entire handling production picture. Companies which have been conveyorized from A to Z for 20 or 30 years or more have replaced a number of these conveyors with fork-truck systems. After all, materials moved by conveyors have to be put on by one man and taken off by another. Each separate loading and unloading point requires another person.

In one automobile assembly plant, a study showed that it was more economical to move materials from a rail car direct to an area adjacent to the assembly line than it was to utilize the existing conveyor system wherein one man would put the materials on the conveyor at one end and another man would take them off and store them as needed at the other end.

Materials should be moved as little as possible. The accepted thinking in automobile circles today is, whenever possible, to move the materials direct to an area immediately adjacent to the assembly workers. This movement should be made by pallets, skids, or some other unit-handling method.

c. Bins and Portable Boxes. Unit handling of small parts is accomplished by means of bins and portable boxes. This may be done in small metal or cardboard tote pans or boxes or trays of various types. It also includes the use of racks on which a number of circular or irregular objects may be carried. The main advantage of the rack is that it permits the worker to reach for a part without too much time lost in searching or sorting. For increased portability and movability, these racks are often mounted on pallets to be moved by fork trucks with sidearm extensions to

---

[1] Floyd J. Bird, Synchronizing Sub-assemblies to Main Line Needs, *Factory Management and Maintenance,* April, 1948, p. 56.

be picked up by overhead cranes. They also may be mounted on castered rollers or may have rollers attached to the base of the frame itself.

d. *Cranes and Overhead Handling Devices.* Where large unwieldy and irregular-shaped component parts are involved, the handling of most of these items to the assembly areas may be done by an overhead handling system. The most complete coverage of this type is provided by an overhead traveling crane. In the main fabricating shed of the A. O. Smith Corporation of Milwaukee, Wis., a large overhead traveling crane services

Fig. 261. Small parts and subassemblies are brought to the assembler on wheeled racks holding an assortment of bins and containers. (*Rack Engineering Company.*)

the entire area. Operating under this are a number of small semigantry cranes which serve local areas.

Jib cranes of a wide variety of types are also used to provide for movement of heavy parts to the assembly line or to the actual operation itself. In the manufacture of farm tractors, one company moves the completed engine to the final assembly line by means of an overhead monorail track. An electric hoist running on the track enables them to transport the heavy engine block from the end of the engine line to the place on the final assembly line where it is lowered into the chassis.

2. Assembly Operations

Products may be assembled in one of two ways, stationary or progressive assembly. Stationary assembly, the earlier from an historical standpoint, involves considerably more movement of component parts and practically no movement of the item being assembled. This is done in an assembly area with one individual or a crew performing the entire assembly operation. On the other hand, progressive assembly generally implies the movement of the product past workers as they perform various assembly operations. In this latter method, the movement of the assembled item from one station to the next becomes a very important handling problem. It is, therefore, necessary to accomplish this with a minimum of

Fig. 262. Moving chains carry automobile bodies along assembly line while finish operations are performed. (*Mechanical Handling Systems, Inc.*)

cost and a maximum of control according to the manufacturing requirements.

a. Trolley Conveyors. These overhead systems of conveying are used more for the movement of component parts than for the products being assembled. They were used during the Second World War in the assembly of wing sections for aircraft.

b. Chain Conveyors. This is the system most commonly employed for the assembly of heavy items. It is also one of the earliest conveyor systems to be used. In this system a cable connects a number of carts by means of power. The cable and the entire line of carts are drawn forward to the next work position.

In the assembly of airplanes, a single or a multiple chain drag connects the airplanes being assembled. At stated intervals, the line is cleared and all units are moved forward to the next position. In other instances, there is a slow steady movement of the same units. In the early stages of the same assembly, the various parts may be carried on elaborate wheeled jigs and fixtures which move along with the chain. Sometimes a channel track is set in the floor to provide more control over the path of travel.

Quite commonly in the assembly of engines the main assembly is carried on a wheeled platform. The platform or bogie rides on tracks or

Fig. 263. At the new St. Louis assembly plant of the Ford Motor Company, Lincoln and Mercury cars are assembled on the same conveyor lines. Front ends, including such parts as radiator grilles, front fenders, and stone deflectors, are assembled on a carrousel-type conveyor, located adjacent to the final assembly line. (*Mechanical Handling Systems, Inc.*)

rails and is connected by the chain conveyor. Some companies have turnover devices to permit the turnover of the engine block. In mass-production foundry operations, molding and pouring are generally set up on such a system.

Automobiles are often assembled on a similar raised section consisting of tracks with a chain conveyor pulling along the various chassis. Upright dogs or hangers engage the chassis and pull it along at a steady pace.

During the Second World War, to hasten the final assembly of mosquito bombers, the company divided the process into 10 parts and mechanized each one as best suited it. Among the innovations was a system consisting of four parallel tracks on which the fuselages moved on dollies. When the end of these tracks was reached, bogies were rolled up to transport the fuselages to the final assembly tracks. The entire operation was serviced by overhead cranes and the finished product was hauled away by industrial trucks.

Another aircraft manufacturer took a different approach and moved the final assembly line by resting the fuselage in a cradle and moving the cradle by a continuously driven chain from below. Smaller subassemblies were transported to the final assembly line by overhead power-driven chains and monorails equipped with electric hoists. Stock rooms were

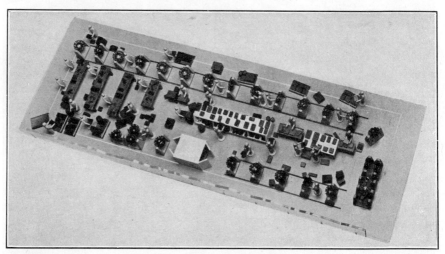

Fig. 264. This scale-model presentation of a new layout shows turnover jigs moved on double tracks set in the floor. (*Rack Engineering Company.*)

completely eliminated, being replaced with the above live storage of the subassemblies and bins for the smaller parts placed parallel to the assembly line and only a few feet from it.

In place of the wheeled bogies, a complete platform may be provided. This results in what is commonly known as the slat conveyor, which provides a flat surface for assembly operations. Although these are often mounted flush with the floor level, they may be raised to working height. In wider units, they consist of crosswise flat wood or metal segments. In narrower units, especially those used in the handling of bottles and small packages, the connecting ends are rounded to provide a smooth surface, even when the chain is moving around a curve.

c. Belt Conveyors. A smooth movement of the belt conveyor adapts itself to the assembly of parts while the conveyor is still in motion and without removing the object from the conveyor belt itself. However, it is used primarily for the movement of parts and very seldom are some of the operations performed on the belt itself.

d. Hand-pushed Units. Where more flexibility in the sequence of operations is desired, hand-pushed units are employed. Lack of quantity production and frequent change-over from one style or product to another may make this flexibility necessary. These units are mounted on wheels and may consist of wheeled platforms, jigs, frames on wheels, or elaborate turnover wheeled structures. They may run free on the assembly floor, which permits them to be moved about at will. They may be installed with a channel track, and they may be used in connection with a rail set

Fig. 265. Belt conveyor feeding parts from one operation to next. Assembly worktable with conveyor in center serves two lines of operators. Note troughed slides for progressing assemblies and parts across belt. Longitudinal partition rails on belts keep parts separate. (*Alvey Conveyor Manufacturing Company.*)

in the floor or raised to working heights. One assembler of radio sets has a small wooden platform and frame approximately 12 by 14 inches mounted on roller-skate wheels. These run in a channel track at working height in front of the worker. As each worker finishes his operation, he simply gives it a slight push, which shoves it down to the next operator.

Perhaps not all manufacturers can use tracks to the same advantage as the Lionel Corporation, maker of toy trains. When the electric locomotive is completely assembled, it proceeds under its own power past inspection to the area where it is packaged.

At the Belmont Radio Corporation, Mason City, Iowa, assembly of radios is facilitated by means of a small wooden fixture. This fixture enables the operator to move the assembly easily to the next station by means of a wheel conveyor.

e. Cranes. Whenever the movement of large unwieldy or heavy subassemblies is required, overhead-crane handling systems often provide the flexibility needed. This is particularly adapted to the assembly of large parts in which the operations are long and movement is made from one assembly station to another at rather infrequent intervals.

Assembly of amphibian planes at the Montreal, Canada, plant of Canadair, Ltd., provides an interesting example of the handling and maneuvering of unwieldy assembly parts. This is accomplished by a system of overhead cranes (Fig. 266).

Fig. 266. Two electric hoists on traveling bridge crane move the hull section to next work station. (*Cleveland Tramrail.*)

This overhead handling system transports completed hulls through testing for water pressure and painting and then on to the head position in one of the primary assembly lines. The entire wing section is 104 feet long. Engines, fuel tanks, and accessories are mounted into the hull as a complete unit. The crane performing this operation is equipped with two electric hoist carriers which handle the load by means of an equalizer beam.

QUESTIONS

1. Discuss the factors which will determine the use of specific types of handling equipment for assembly operations.

2. The problem of materials handling for assembly operations falls into how many separate classifications? Explain.

3. Describe the earlier methods of assembling products.

4. Describe the uses of conveyors in supplying parts to the assembly lines.

5. In what ways does unit handling speed up supply of parts and supplies to the assembly line?

6. How can bins and portable boxes aid the supply of parts to the assembly line?

7. Where are overhead cranes used for the supply of subassemblies and parts?

8. Discuss the ways in which complicated products may be assembled.

9. How are chain conveyors used to move assemblies through successive operations?

10. Explain the use of various types of hand-pushed units through progressive assembly operations.

11. How are overhead cranes used in assembly of products?

PROJECTS FOR FURTHER STUDY

1. Prepare a list of handling equipment used in connection with assembly operations. Provide an example of the use of each.

2. Contrast the problem of handling in the assembly of heavy products such as automobiles with the assembly of light products such as radio sets.

3. Prepare a report on the cost factors to be considered in determining whether to move parts to the assembly lines by trolley conveyor or by fork truck.

CHAPTER 31

AIR CARGO HANDLING

1. Characteristics of Problem

Shipment of cargo by air is one of the most recent innovations in the field of materials handling and transportation. The first air express shipment was made by the Railway Express Agency, Inc., in 1919, but a scheduled air express service was not established until 1927. During the Second World War, the movement of cargo by air became a major mode of transportation and this impetus carried over into the postwar years. In 1932 seven carriers joined with Postal Telegraph Company and formed a group known as General Air Express. All these carriers were combined with the Railway Express Agency, Inc., by contract in 1936. In 1944, airfreight as such (in distinction to air express) came into being. The American Air Lines was the first carrier to offer an exclusive airfreight service.

In 1945, 1,500,000 freight-ton miles were flown by the air lines. By 1948, this had increased to 75,000,000 freight-ton miles, and the prediction for 1950 was 150,000,000 freight-ton miles. This terrific growth of the industry has placed a premium upon new materials-handling methods.

Shortage of flying units made it imperative to reduce terminal time, *i.e.*, the loading and unloading of prime units. Time lost by costly and time-consuming handling methods often meant the difference between profits or loss for the operation. Speedier methods of handling both in terminal operations and in the loading of the planes became necessary.

The nature of the materials being handled had to be considered. In an effort to replace hearsay with factual data, a number of studies have been made recently on this phase of air cargo. The Railway Express Agency, Inc., recently conducted a study of the handling of express shipments at the Chicago terminal office of the United Air Lines. It showed that there was much less variation in size and weight of packages than commonly supposed. The average weight of packages for air express in the near future was projected at between 20 and 25 pounds.

Although a greater dimensional variation was anticipated, there would be a greater increase in packages of small size. The density of the cargo (pounds per square foot) must also be considered. The same study showed that extreme density cargoes now constituted a less serious part of the problem than formerly.[1]

For example, garments are flown to distant cities suspended on a rack protected by a cloth or paper covering. In other instances, orchids will be flown to market in light paperboard trays. After arrival they will be met by personnel trained in the proper handling of the blooms and transported in special refrigerated trucks.

During the Second World War the air forces had at one time more than 200 employees working night and day repackaging contents of overweight containers. The economy of the operation can be appreciated when it is revealed that within one month the equivalent of 125 flight loads of cargo destined for Europe, Africa, and Asia was saved by this repackaging. It was estimated that every dollar spent on labor, materials, and overhead for containers and repackaging saved more than $20 for the taxpayer. Savings in gross weight ranged from 15 to 80 per cent by improved methods of packing.[2]

2. Terminal Handling and Operations

The movement of material from a point in one city to a point in another city by air involves much more than the use of a plane. The items involved must be picked up from the shipper's place of business and brought to the air terminal. There it must be sorted and combined with other packages to the same destination. These will be carried out to the field and loaded into a plane. At the end of the plane ride they will be unloaded from the plane and transported to the terminal where they will be sorted for city delivery. Transference to regional air carriers or to surface carriers may further increase the handling.

This pickup and delivery service is a responsibility of Air Cargo, Inc., whose 21 stockholders are air-cargo carriers. This is accomplished entirely under a Standard Service Contract between Air Cargo, Inc. (for and on behalf of its air carriers at each point) and a carefully selected cartage agent. Shipments are then picked up or delivered by order and in the name of the air carrier who thereby assumes liability, responsibility, and service for the complete haulage. Such standardization (plus the professional supervision of Air Cargo, Inc.) has been reflected in considerable improvement of ground service in the last four years.

The problem of sorting is similar to that encountered by both rail and truck operators. It involves individual package handling, and at the same

[1] W. W. Davis, "Cargo Aircraft," Pitman Publishing Corp., New York, 1946.
[2] Charles L. Saperstein, Air Cargo Packing Problems, *Distribution Age,* October, 1946, p. 40.

time maintaining control on the path of each item. It may be expected then that as volume increases to the point presently handled by other transport agencies, the air lines will employ similar methods of sorting.

Handling of packages through these operations is now done in a wide variety of ways. In some instances, particularly in the smaller airports, the two-wheeled hand truck or, more commonly, a four-wheel unit, is used. Where sorting is done direct to the truck, these packages can be pulled by a tractor to the plane for loading without further handling. The following equipment is being used: [3]

Type	Advantages	Disadvantages
Wheeled vehicles: 1. Fork lift 2. Lift platform 3. Lift motor truck 4. Belt conveyor on truck 5. Crane boom on truck	Flexibility for all door heights. Useful for transfers on field. Needed at medium-sized airports where traffic does not justify large installations.	Tend to clutter field if cargo volume is large. Except for lift platform, do not always have enough capacity for entire cargo of plane in one loading.
Conveyors: 1. Belt (power) 2. Gravity rollers 3. Chutes 4. Portable belt ramps	Direct and continuous flow reduces handling. Small initial installation may be expanded as volume grows. Removes vehicle from field. Can be run underground.	Calls for somewhat larger initial investment and must be set up with a freight building designed for the purpose. Provide handling capacity beyond postwar needs. Cannot handle heavy or large units.
Overhead equipment: 1. Monorail hoists 2. Overhead cranes 3. Elevators	Monorail and crane planned for installation on aircraft. Elevators might be useful to load from conveyor tunnels.	Uses believed rather limited and depend on special design of aircraft.

A survey of air-line utilization of materials-handling equipment was recently conducted by *Distribution Age*. It was found that the major air lines (seven lines were included) used 109 fork trucks, 56 portable conveyors, 91 sections of gravity conveyors, 100 industrial tractors, 84 nose loading stands, 123 pallets, and 29 industrial trailers. In addition, the following conclusions were drawn.[4]

1. Leading transport companies relied largely upon certain types of equipment. For instance, it was noted that Slick Airways use gravity conveyors primarily while other lines utilize portable belt conveyors.

[3] George Herrick, Postwar Cargo Handling, *Air Transport,* October, 1943, p. 22.
[4] Materials Handling Equipment, *Distribution Age,* October, 1949, p. 20.

2. There is considerable variation between airlines on utilization of supplementary equipment. It was noted further that there is spotty use of chutes, pallets, and nose loading stands.

3. There is evidence that the air lines have made good use of available types of equipment and that considerable investigation has been made of handling methods.

3. Loading of Planes

Although the old hand-to-hand bucket-brigade method is still seen in smaller airports where the amount of loading may not justify the installation of equipment, materials-handling equipment of all types has found a wide use and adaptation in the loading of planes. As indicated in the above survey on equipment, the major air lines have already invested heavily and are constantly investigating the advisability of further expenditures in order to lower handling costs and cut loading time of the expensive prime mover—the cargo plane.

The materials-handling equipment and the loading techniques most commonly used in the loading of planes are:

1. *Bucket-brigade method.* This involves the passing of cargo items from man to man. In loading planes, handlers sometimes utilize ladder stands. Because of the design of the fuselage this method must often still be used, even where other equipment is used for the lifting to the plane.

2. *Chutes.* These are unloading devices utilizing gravity to move cargo from the plane to the ground. It is generally mounted on wheels for complete mobility. In some instances it has cut unloading time to 20 per cent of that required by the bucket-brigade method.

3. *High-platform truck.* This truck has a platform mounted on the roof at cargo-door level. Cargo is then loaded or unloaded at compartment level. The main disadvantages are that the height of the platform is fixed and cargo must often be raised by hand in the terminal.

4. *The lift bed truck.* This unit was developed to meet some of the objections of a stationary platform truck. It consists of a truck bed adjustable to any height desired. It is hydraulically operated and can be lowered to standard truck-bed height for loading or unloading at the terminal.

5. *The belt conveyor.* Although personnel is required at both ends of the conveyor, it is a speedier method of loading and unloading when large quantities of items are involved. These units are usually gas-engine-powered and mounted on wheels for mobility. They are frequently mounted on tractors, and even on jeeps, as well as trucks, for greater speed in positioning the device for unloading.

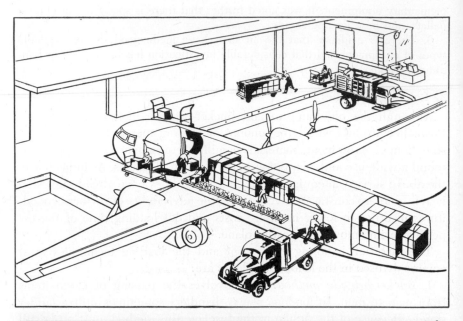

FIG. 267. The new Curtiss-Wright CW-32 is designed for faster loading. Dock-level cargo floor permits loading from dock or truckbed. (*Flow, November,* 1949, *p.* 38.)

FIG. 268. Portable belt conveyor speeds up loading of DC-4. Highway truck, four-wheeled trailer, and fork lift trucks are also used at the same time. (*Eastern Air Lines, Inc.*)

FIG. 269. Four-wheel carts and industrial tractor used to handle mail. (*Delta Air Lines.*)

6. *Industrial tractors.* When used in connection with four-wheel carts, the industrial tractor provides a flexible means of handling to and from the plane and of moving materials elsewhere in the terminal. Preloading of carts speeds plane loading. It must be used in connection with other equipment to raise and lower items to and from the plane (Fig. 269).

7. *Fork lift truck.* Although it may pull a small number of carts to the loading plane, this unit will be used to elevate the carts, pallets, or con-

Fig. 270. Freight agent supervises loading of airfreight. Fork lift truck is used to load heavy pieces of machinery. (*Delta Air Lines.*)

tainers to the compartment level. This speeds the loading operation (Fig. 270).

8. *Portable hoists.* The handling of heavy freight items is done with the aid of mobile cranes, portable hoists of various types, including small portable leg derricks.

A comparison of time required for loading of a plane by different methods was provided in a recent test. This involved the loading of 5,000 pounds of cargo in 300 pieces (without the use of preloading containers). The plane to be loaded was 400 feet from the terminal. The cargo loading doors of the plane were 48 inches wide by 72 inches high and were 10 feet off the ground. Two men were used with the tractor-lift and high-lift trucks and three men with the bucket-brigade and the conveyor methods.

The results of the test are given in the table for loading and unloading time.

LOADING AND UNLOADING TIME *

Method	Movement to plane and positioning	Loading time	Unloading time	Return to express room	Total
Tractor-lift train.........	2.0	11.5	6.5	1.0	21.0
High-lift truck...........	1.5	10.5	6.0	1.0	19.0
Belt conveyor............	2.0	16.0	13.0	1.0	32.0
Bucket brigade...........	2.0	25.0	18.0	1.0	46.0

* W. W. Davies, "Cargo Aircraft," Pitman Publishing Corp., New York, 1946.

4. Handling within the Aircraft

As the size of cargo planes increases, the need for handling equipment within the plane increases. The handling of unit loads requires mechanical aids. The distance from loading doors also increases the need for equipment. Larger planes also mean greater investment; hence, there is a greater urgency to cut down loading times and keep the unit in the air as much as possible.

Because of the necessity of keeping weight down, there is an objection to having handling equipment built into the plane itself. On the other hand, concentration of floor-loads is limited, which restricts the use of industrial trucks.

Some of the handling methods now being used within the plane are:

1. *Hand handling.* This includes the bucket-brigade system as well as the hand stowage of items into compartments. Both are wasteful of man power. The inefficiency of this method also increases with the size of the plane. Nevertheless, except in the largest cargo carriers with extensive built-in handling facilities, this will continue to be a common method of stowage.

2. *Roller conveyors.* These may be built into the floor of the plane or may be removable, consisting of light sections, which may be quickly put together to form a complete handling system. These sections are generally 4 or 5 feet in length. This speed of assembly is part of the total handling time and must be considered in computing the savings in handling time. Gravity wheel conveyors of magnesium are easily positioned by one man. Small packages may be handled on them with considerable dispatch.

3. *Cargo bins.* The bins are designed to fit the contour of the aircraft and are preloaded and speed up handling. They are generally used with auxiliary equipment.[5]

4. *Monorail hoists.* Most of the new cargo planes of the larger types have some type of overhead monorail system built into them. On the new

FIG. 271. Built-in hoist operating on inset tracks provides overhead lifting service for the Martin Mars. Note tracks extending through fuselage and under wings on both sides. (*Flow, October,* 1949, *p.* 22.)

Boeing Stratofreighter an electrically operated hoist will handle baskets up to 5,000 pounds traversing a 74½-foot main deck (Fig. 272).

5. *Elevating platforms.* Movable sections of the bottom deck are lowered by four overhead electrically operated winches. Packages and other items of freight (even jeeps) are loaded onto the platform and raised into the body of the plane (Fig. 273).

[5] See John R. Immer, "Layout Planning Techniques," p. 319, McGraw-Hill Book Company, Inc., New York, 1950. See also *Distribution Age,* October, 1947, p. 28.

FIG. 272. Built-in power hoist travels on full length monorail and permits positioning the load to any desired stowage location. (*Boeing Airplane Company.*)

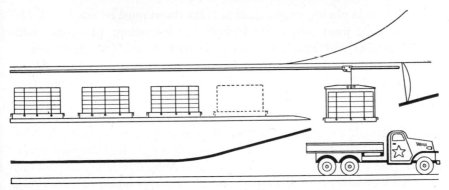

FIG. 273. Sketch shows pallet load being hoisted from truck for loading in plane. (*Flow, October,* 1949, p. 22.)

5. Tie-down Methods

With aircraft cargo there is always the problem of tying down or stowage. On the passenger planes, bins are used for the storage of such things as mail, baggage, and other small pieces. Very little tying down is required because the cargo cannot shift more than within the confined area of the bin.

Fig. 274. Cargo nets are used to fasten down cargo to prevent shifting. Special tie-down fixtures speed up time of this operation. (*Eastern Air Lines.*)

On the cargo planes, some means of tying down must be employed. The methods used most frequently include the following: (1) ropes with special fittings and attachments, (2) leather straps, (3) steel rods or beams adjusted and held in place by jacks and locks, and (4) cargo net (Fig. 274). All of these are secured through rings in the walls and floor of the plane.

When using the rope method, no knots are required. The rope is simply looped through a metal hook designed to grip the rope loop firmly. This hook engages the cabin floor tie-down ring. The length of the rope necessary to pass completely over the cargo is determined roughly, and another rope hook is attached and slipped into the corresponding tie-down ring. A rope tightener, a metal-rod device over which rope is twisted or wound, is then utilized to remove the slack and tighten the rope snugly over the cargo.

With the rod-and-beam device to hold cargo in place, the rods are of varying lengths to accommodate shipments of different sizes. These rods have hooked ends which are inserted in the tie-down rings in the cabin floor. One rod is placed on each side of the cargo to be lashed down, and a wooden beam is slipped over each rod and held in place with simple friction-type locks. A small hand jack is then slipped over each rod in order to bring the lock tight against the beam and to bend the beam slightly to hold the load secure.

Partitions of various types are used to cut down the time of tying down and provide greater stability for cargo while the plane is in flight. American Airlines, a few years ago, had their engineers develop a new interior for the carrying of cargo. The result was 1,200 pounds additional payload over the normal passenger interior. This arrangement of cargo compartments provided for quickly cutting off each section. It eliminates tie-down facilities except for extremely heavy cargo.

In general, however, fixed compartments within the main cabin have not been found generally practical, as they do not provide the elasticity necessary to handle the various odd shapes and sizes which must be carried. Modifications providing movable partitions have been found to be much more practical. These frames can also carry a heavy treated canvas fire wall to isolate various sections of the cabin and thus afford greater effectiveness to the cockpit-controlled carbon dioxide extinguishers.

The Evans Products Company of Detroit, Mich., designed and manufactured the first tie-down equipment specifically intended for aircraft use. The equipment is supplied in kits that contain varying quantities of units so that a special kit can be obtained for any type of cargo craft, depending upon the capacity of the plane and the service it is to perform.

6. Loading Requirements

A problem peculiar to the loading of aircraft is the loading restrictions imposed by flight balance requirements. In the course of flight, the center of gravity of any aircraft will shift because of the loss of weight from the consumption of fuel and oil or the shifting of cargo or passengers within the airplane. The design of the aircraft takes this into consideration and a range of safe center of gravity locations is established. This is broken down into a safe range of center of gravity locations for any cargo that is placed in the aircraft and must essentially be a more limited range, for a safe center of gravity at the beginning of the flight could lead to an unsafe location due to the burning of the fuel unless precautionary limitations of the cargo center of gravity travel is maintained. These requirements give rise to three loading-pattern restrictions.

1. The location of every heavy article must be prearranged in order to maintain proper balance in the cargo.

2. The maximum floor-load capacity must be kept in mind. This applies especially to excessive concentrations of weight which must be distributed by skids or dunnage.

3. The maximum allowable load that can be placed in compartments must be considered.

Armed with these three loading-pattern restrictions and the description of the articles as to weight, volume density, and size dimensions, the freight loader establishes a loading pattern that will hold the center of gravity within the specified limits and still allow for easy cargo handling for those doing the actual loading. To facilitate his work, he makes use of a freight-loading slide rule that can be calibrated in either foot-pounds or inch-pounds and sets up a summation of moments about some determined set of datum planes. His work is of extreme importance and should be carefully checked. In addition, the experienced pilot when boarding the aircraft will examine the arrangement of the cargo for any apparent mistakes in stowing.

7. Recent and Proposed Developments

a. Air Terminals. The development of an acceptable standard prototype for air terminals has been hindered by the uncertainty of the shape, size, height, or mode of propulsion of the cargo aircraft to come. Satisfactory air-terminal facilities involve considerable expenditure, which must be amortized over at least a 10-year period. At the present time there is no reasonable certainty as to what the cargo aircraft of 5 years hence will look like. The air-cargo industry is watching developments along this line very closely, and several patterns for the development of future air-cargo terminals have received a wide acceptance at least in principle.

One of the most promising of these is the Basic Air Freight Terminal Layout devised by the engineers of Lockheed Aircraft Corporation. In the selection of this layout two prerequisites were considered. First, that the arrangement be as simple as possible commensurate with efficient and adequate facilities. Building dimensions were selected that would permit the use of standard components.

The second prerequisite was to spot the cargo planes as close to the dock as possible, commensurate with adequate areas for aircraft-loading docks and truck-loading ramps. The latter can be accomplished by a hexagonal, octagonal, or circular grouping of buildings. A V-shaped arrangement was finally selected as offering the most efficient combination of all the desirable features of the terminal layout. The dock height finally selected was 100 inches above the ground level. By selecting a floor level most closely approximating that of the majority of the commercial cargo planes in operation, all raising of cargo is eliminated.[6]

b. Douglas C-124 A. In new designs a number of handling devices have been designed into the plane itself. In the Douglas C-124 A, capable

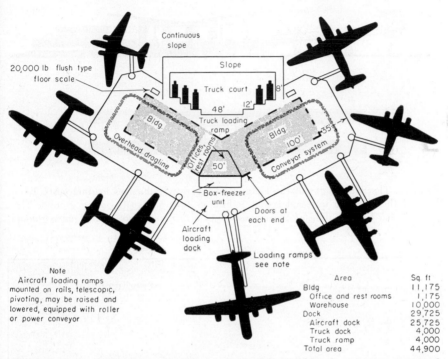

Area	Sq. ft
Bldg	11,175
Office and rest rooms	1,175
Warehouse	10,000
Dock	29,725
Aircraft dock	25,725
Truck dock	4,000
Truck ramp	4,000
Total area	44,900

FIG. 275. Basic air freight terminal layout devised by Lockheed engineers, composed of two rectangular structures to form an open V arrangement, provides for two freight operators or for a consolidated freight terminal. (*Air Transportation, May,* 1950, *p.* 18.)

of carrying a payload of 50,000 pounds, the main loading doors will be of a clamshell type opening directly below the pilot's compartment. A full-sized truck or trailer may be backed through this opening. Fork trucks may also be used to bring pallet loads into the plane through the same opening. In addition there will be an electrically operated elevator and well opening midship with an electrically operated hoist on a monorail track.[7]

[6] L. R. Hackney, Planning the Air Freight Terminal, *Air Transportation,* 1950, March, p. 10; April, p. 10; May, p. 11.

[7] Flight Equipment, *Distribution Age,* October, 1949, p. 24.

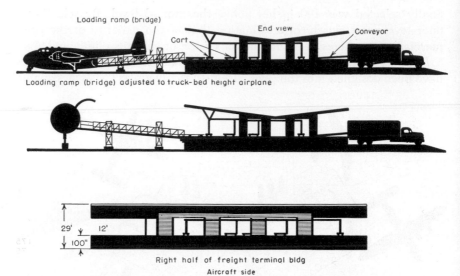

FIG. 276. The floor height of the loading dock greatly influences loading costs. Floor level of the basic air-terminal layout is located 100 inches above the ground. This permits near-level loading of the newest types of air freighters. (*Air Transportation, May,* 1950, *p.* 19.)

FIG. 277. Location of the four loading doors on the Boeing Stratofreighter permits simultaneous loading. This is made possible by their wide separation. (*Boeing Airplane Company.*)

c. The Boeing Stratofreighter. This plane incorporates a monorail extending the full length of the upper cargo fuselage upon which an electrically operated cargo hook operates. The following advantages are cited for this equipment:

1. Lifts are hoisted aboard by the motor-driven hook and swung forward to the desired point (Fig. 278).

Fig. 278. Pallet load goes aboard by cargo hook. (*Flow, October,* 1949, *p.* 22.)

2. Lifts can be made from the ground or from a truck. Hook can also be used to tow nonpowered vehicles up the ramp.

3. Loading ramps, highway truck bodies, and high-lift fork trucks are accommodated through these doors (Fig. 280).

4. Preloaded pallets of 5,000 pounds can be handled.

5. With this equipment, 20,000 pounds of cargo can be loaded and stowed in less than 30 minutes.

d. Douglas Globemaster. The newly developed C-74 utilizes three electric cranes. Two of these are of the underslung, bridge type traversing

FIG. 279. Cargo elevator shown lifting vehicle aboard Globemaster. (*Flow, October,* 1949, *p.* 22.)

FIG. 280. Heavy-duty ramps are provided in the Boeing Stratofreighter for loading wheeled vehicles onto the main cargo deck. Ramps are retractable into the airplane by means of the powered hoist or may be readily detached and left on the ground at the direction of the airplane operator. (*Boeing Airplane Company.*)

double rails running the length of the cargo area (Fig. 281). Each crane has a load limit of 8,000 pounds, and cranes can be combined to hoist 16,000 pounds. The third crane operates on a boom which can be swung in and out from the side cargo door of the fuselage; its capacity is 4,500 pounds. The major advantage is a detachable floor area at the rear which serves in conjunction with the twin cranes as an electrically operated cargo elevator. Palletized loads, large bulky objects, and small vehicles

Fig. 281. Light-alloy twin-bridge crane and detachable floor make up cargo elevator in Globemaster. (*Flow, October, 1949, p. 22.*)

can be easily handled by either lifting from this platform in lowered position or by lifting the platform and load as a unit.

e. Unitized Cargo Container for the Flying Wing. The Northrop Flying Wing of tailless design features total enclosure of crew, engines, and cargo space within the wing structure. Individual cargo bays extend spanwise within the wing. This arrangement enables air-cargo handlers to adopt the airborne equivalent of the railroad practice of "cutting out cars" at terminal and intermediate points. The artist's sketch shows that the car is a unitized cargo container (Fig. 282). Since the cargo compartments are individual bays accessible from under the giant wing, preloaded cargo baskets are used for shipment of "through" loads. The material handling is accomplished by means of an industrial lift truck, as portrayed in the artist's sketch. Northrop officials predict that long-range Flying Wing cargo planes will be in use by 1960.

Fig. 282. Artist's sketch shows handling of preloaded cargo unit from Flying Wing cargoliner of the future. This tailless design features total enclosure of aircrew, engines, and cargo within the wing structure. (*Flow, November,* 1949, *p.* 38.)

Fig. 283. Package fuselage (arrow) will be hauled by tractor and flown by motive part of Pack-plane, according to plans. (*Flow, November,* 1949, *p.* 38.)

f. The Pack-plane. The Fairchild C-120 will be the first transport to apply fully the principle of the truck trailer to the airplane. (See artist's sketch, Fig. 283.) Production is expected to begin within a year. The cargo fuselage will be loaded at the factory, as an example, and coupled to a truck or tractor and then towed to the airport. The fuselage will then be attached to the C-120 wing to complete the flight unit. After arrival at the airport nearest the cargo destination, the fuselage will be delivered

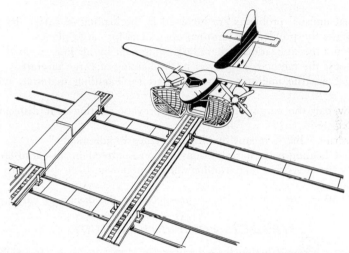

FIG. 284. Mobile platforms with preloaded metal containers speed up loading and unloading time of Bristol freighters in New Zealand. (*Flight, September* 7, 1951, p. 337.)

to the user's plant or warehouse. On the return trip, another loaded fuselage will be flown to some point along the line of flight. It is expected that the Fairchild C-120 will be in use by 1955.

The same idea has already been developed by the Straits Air Freight Express, Ltd., of New Zealand. The problem was to lift 14,000 tons of deadweight mixed cargo between two terminals only 72 miles apart. Loading and unloading time per flight was 60 minutes while the flying time was 30 minutes.

As shown in Fig. 284, the new method consists of preloaded containers which fill the hold of the freighter. These are loaded from two traversing trolleys which roll on two sets of parallel railway lines. Loading and unloading time with the new equipment is estimated at a total of 10 minutes.[8]

Much thought has already been given to the design and use of con-

[8] *Flight*, Sept. 7, 1951, p. 337.

tainers for preloading. These have been mainly the wire-basket type, the box or hamper type, or bags, either canvas or mesh. The post office and air express in particular use this last type. It is light and weatherproof and is easily stowed in any cargo compartment. Pallets have also been used but these offer no means of tie-down, nor do they give the additional protection of the enclosed container.

QUESTIONS

1. What unusual problems are involved in the loading of cargo aircraft?
2. Discuss the problem of terminal operations for cargo planes.
3. Discuss the utilization of handling equipment by air lines to load planes.
4. Discuss the methods employed in the loading of cargo aircraft.
5. What are the methods currently used for handling materials within a plane?
6. How can the cargo be secured to prevent shifting and dislocation in flight?
7. Describe what is meant by "flight balance requirements."
8. What loading-pattern restrictions are encountered in air-cargo stowage?
9. In what ways has material-handling equipment been built into recent cargo planes?
10. What are some of the future prospects for the design of cargo planes?

PROJECTS FOR FURTHER STUDY

1. Prepare a report listing the advantages and disadvantages for each major type of handling equipment as regards its use in loading cargo planes.
2. Make a study of the methods used in handling air cargo at the local airport. Include recommendations for improvement in method or for equipment.
3. Make a survey of subjects covered in articles on air-cargo handling within the previous 12 months. Use the Periodical Index to Current Literature as a guide.

CHAPTER 32

RAILROAD AND TRUCK HANDLING

1. Rail Terminal Operation

The importance of mechanizing handling for railroad operations is emphasized in a guest editorial by William T. Faricy, president of the Association of American Railroads.[1]

The freight station and LCL transfer problems are of peculiar difficulty in the adoption and use of mechanical handling devices. Railroads are called upon to handle virtually every type of merchandise manufactured. Packages come to the railroads of every size and weight and of every shape and type. Mechanical handling equipment, therefore, to be of the greatest usefulness on a railroad must be adaptable to dealing with this great variety of goods and this demand for versatility applies not only to the goods themselves but to the places in which the equipment must be used. In giving consideration to the use of mechanical handling equipment, the physical layout of particular stations must be studied. In many cases older stations will not permit the efficient employment of mechanical freight handling equipment. It becomes necessary, therefore, to provide adequate operating areas for the handling equipment.

In the building of new and modern freight terminals as well as in remodeling existing facilities, most railroads are making necessary provision for the efficient use of mechanized freight handling equipment.

Studies are continually under way on the railroads to determine the nature of the tonnage received at particular stations and to see whether or not they can be adapted for the use of mechanical handling equipment. Such studies involve the detailed analysis of all facts concerning the size, shape, and uniformity of the packages to be handled; concerning the type of equipment needed; concerning the methods of employing these new devices and techniques. In making these studies, the railroads have enjoyed the cooperation of the manufacturers of the widely diversified types of handling equipment.

Less-than-carload (lcl) freight shipments account for about 2 per cent of the railroads' originating tonnage but around 30 to 40 per cent of the loss and damage claims. Because of the large amount of handling involved, lcl freight contributes heavily to the operating costs of the

[1] William T. Faricy, *Modern Materials Handling*, November, 1949, p. 11.

railroads; in fact, about 80 to 90 per cent of all terminal costs can be attributed to the handling of lcl freight.[2]

In the past, most freight handling has been done manually, but the recent trend has been toward the installation of mechanical-handling methods. The Pennsylvania Railroad estimated that mechanization of freight handling in their Polk Street Station in Chicago made possible savings of 85 cents a ton on inbound freight and 58 cents a ton on outbound freight. In addition, loss and damage has been cut 50 per cent, and production in pounds handled per man-hour increased by 23 per cent.

Freight shipped in carload lots entails no great problem for the railroads; the car is loaded by the shipper and unloaded by the consignee; thus the carrier's sole function is that of "spotting" the car for loading and unloading and moving it from origin to destination without the problem of cargo handling and terminal storage. Less-than-carload freight, on the other hand, is handled a great deal more by the carrier. When the shipment is brought to the railroad's freight house, it is weighed, checked, and loaded aboard the proper car. At the destination, it is unloaded and placed in the carrier's freight house to await removal by or delivery to the consignee. In addition, lcl freight can frequently be transferred and reloaded into other cars at junction points en route. It is quite obvious that this amount of handling will increase cost and also increase chances for loss and damage.

A comparison of the old and new methods of handling is provided by the following description of operations in the Polk Street Station of the Pennsylvania Railroad in Chicago.

This station serves as an inbound, outbound, and transfer station for lcl freight destined to and from points within the Chicago switching district as well as Gary, Ind., and overhead freight routed to and from connections at Chicago. It covers 7½ acres of land, measures 745 by 420 feet, and consists of a track level below the street surface, a street level, and two upper floors containing office and warehouse space. The Pennsylvania Railroad in its lcl operations uses 12 house tracks with a total capacity of 240 cars which are served by 130,216 square feet of platform area.[3]

One handling difficulty is the incoming tracks on the below-street level. This level is served by two 5-ton and two 10-ton elevators to the street-level platform. Before mechanization, the procedure was to have a gang unload the freight on four-wheel trucks, according to zone number. The trucks were then moved to the platform elevators, lifted to street level,

[2] Railroad Materials Handling Problem, *Railway Age*, Feb. 14, 1948, p. 346.

[3] Freight Station Mechanization Helps Offset Trend of Rising Costs, *Railway Age*, May 8, 1948, p. 42.

and towed by tractors to loading areas. They were unloaded by hand upon the platform until the freight was loaded into motor trucks. In this operation the packages would be handled by hand from the platform onto hand trucks and then into the motor truck.

After mechanization, the freight is loaded onto pallets in the railway cars. The pallets are lifted by fork trucks onto four-wheel trailers, which are raised to street level and hauled to the platform where the pallets are unloaded by fork truck. When loading the motor trucks, the pallets are lifted by fork truck into the truck intact and unloaded by hand. This results in the saving of two hand handlings of the freight: (1) the unloading from the four-wheel truck to the platform and (2) loading from platform onto hand trucks. Palletizing also made better use of the platform space by allowing higher piling of materials.

Outbound traffic is handled by Buda choreboys which are loaded directly from delivery trucks, backed up to the platform, into street-level railway cars spotted on six tracks. Heavier material is unloaded onto pallets and transported by fork trucks. The railway cars are spotted six abreast and connected by temporary platforms extending from car to car.

At the Gratiot Street Station of the Missouri Pacific Railroad in St. Louis, a steel lift bridge connects a series of island platforms and provides a smooth floor surface for operation of tractors and trailers. Pallets are used extensively for handling of merchandise from truck to car. At the Kansas City terminal, gravity wheel conveyors are used to handle a heavy movement of merchandise in standard packages.[4]

2. Truck-terminal Operation

The efficient handling of packaged merchandise in modern truck terminals provides an interesting example of the way handling systems evolve. According to Stanley W. Wasie, president of Merchants Motor Freight, Inc., St. Paul, Minn., their terminal in St. Paul was designed after visits to similar terminals to observe the success of the systems in operation there. As a result, a number of refinements were incorporated in their plans.

In turn, as part of the research in preparation of the new truck terminal in Newark, officials of The Port of New York Authority studied the St. Paul installation in considerable detail. Its influence can be observed in the description of the terminal operations for the Newark terminal as it was finally completed in July, 1950. Still later, Stanley W. Wasie and his group returned the visit in search of new ideas for their Chicago terminal on which construction was started June 1, 1950.

[4] Railroads Looking to Mechanization, *Modern Materials Handling,* July, 1949, p. 32.

In freight-terminal operations, goods are received and held for temporary storage until outgoing loads can be "collected"; then they are loaded to outgoing trucks. At Merchants Motor Freight, Inc., in St. Paul, goods are unloaded from incoming trucks on the receiving side of the terminal to four-wheel trucks. These are hooked to a conveyor system consisting of 56 small four-wheeled trucks measuring about 3 by 5 feet, connected

Fig. 285. Portable conveyor used to load truck. (*Food Machinery Corporation.*)

by chains to an overhead trolley system running the full circuit of the dock. The conveyor tows the trucks around the dock floor on a regular circuit.

Control of merchandise is effected with an intercommunication system and a pneumatic-tube system. The original bill of lading is used for checking. After it has been signed by the checker, it is shot through the pneumatic-tube system to the billing office, where it is rated and billed. These bills carry a complete record of the handling of the shipment from the pickup at the shipper's dock to and including its loading on the outgoing trailer. In the loading of outgoing trucks, as each conveyor truck is emptied the bills go to the business office via pneumatic tube. Thus, billing is done as freight is loaded and the truck is ready to leave in a matter of minutes after the loading is completed.

Other advantages of the system are:

1. Most shipments are kept together intact on a single truck, thereby eliminating loss caused by splitting the order.

Fig. 286. Two-ton packs of steel sheets being unloaded from truck with a chain hoist and hand-operated sheet lifter. They are moved inside by overhead monorail. (*Cleveland Tramrail.*)

2. Reduces physical handling of freight. It is now handled only from the pickup truck to the conveyor truck, and from the conveyor truck to the trailer. Cross traffic of hand trucks is eliminated.

3. Reduces errors. Each piece is checked by loaders as it is placed on the conveyor trucks. With the two-wheel trucks pieces were often moved in stacks without this individual checking.

4. Dockmen have more time in which to check shipments and load freight more carefully because the freight is moved mechanically.

5. Damage claims have been practically eliminated.

6. Conveyor trucks have enough reserve capacity to absorb peak periods of incoming freight until outbound loaders can be loaded with speed and consistency.

7. Loading time of trailers is reduced. Terminal time of these units is nonreproductive time. Departure time of trucks has been shortened by 1 to 2½ hours.

The Taylor Street terminal of the Standard Freight Lines in Chicago uses a fleet of gas fork trucks with a stock of 800 pallets 36 by 42 inches. In addition, skids and skid jacks as well as the usual two-wheel hand trucks are used. An overhead crane is used for items weighing over 3

Fig. 287. Local shipments are loaded to the "mosquito fleet" for early morning delivery to local zones. Over-the-road carriers load and unload from the terminal and no longer have to make their own deliveries in the metropolitan area. (*The Port of New York Authority.*)

tons. An intercommunication system speeds up dispatching and provides closer control.

The terminal is 44 feet wide with apron and 360 feet long. It also has a reefer box 20 by 20 feet for temporary storage of perishables. The success of the system is attested to by B. D. Prince, director of operations:

Our mechanical handling methods have permitted us to cut our labor costs by 60 per cent. Use of the fork truck and the pallet method of shuttling freight across the platforms has also yielded great savings in time, and has helped to eliminate damage to freight.[5]

The Newark Union Motor Truck Terminal, completed in July, 1950, is a consolidating terminal at which lcl common carrier truck traffic (mixed

[5] N. C. Hudson, Trucking Terminals Embrace Mechanical Freight Handling, *Traffic World,* Mar. 13, 1948, p. 781.

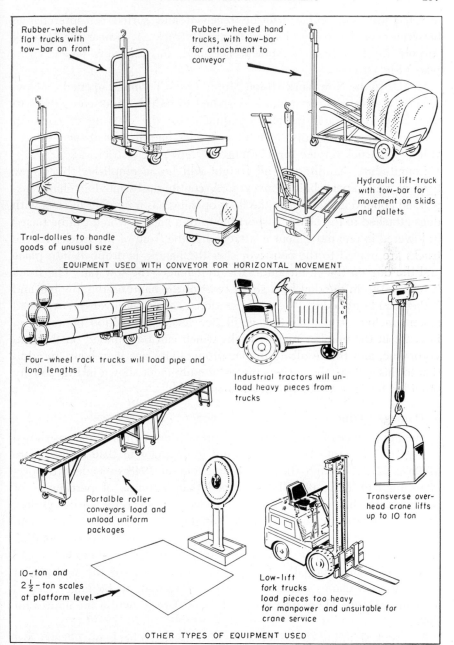

Rubber-wheeled flat trucks with tow-bar on front

Rubber-wheeled hand trucks, with tow-bar for attachment to conveyor

Hydraulic lift-truck with tow-bar for movement on skids and pallets

Trial-dollies to handle goods of unusual size

EQUIPMENT USED WITH CONVEYOR FOR HORIZONTAL MOVEMENT

Four-wheel rack trucks will load pipe and long lengths

Industrial tractors will unload heavy pieces from trucks

Portable roller conveyors load and unload uniform packages

Transverse overhead crane lifts up to 10 ton

10-ton and $2\frac{1}{2}$-ton scales at platform level.

Low-lift fork trucks load pieces too heavy for manpower and unsuitable for crane service

OTHER TYPES OF EQUIPMENT USED

FIG. 288. Although the greater part of the horizontal movement of materials at the Newark Terminal is by the underfloor chain conveyor, a large number of auxiliary and supplementary pieces of equipment are used. (*The Port of New York Authority.*)

merchandise shipments) will be received and sorted for interchange between over-the-road units and local city trucks. It is near the Newark Airport, the Port Newark Marine Terminal, and the New Jersey Turnpike (Fig. 287).

Similar to the New York Union Motor Truck Terminal opened on Nov. 1, 1949, the Newark Terminal is designed to reduce street congestion, to provide modern facilities and equipment for the clearing of common carrier mixed merchandise freight, to reduce handling costs, and to provide better truck service for The Port of New York district.

Longitudinal handling of all freight will be accomplished by a new type of underfloor chain conveyor. A continuously moving chain suspended about 5 inches under the floor opening has a number of slots with dogs attached to the chain. A short bar with a handle which can be raised or lowered in one movement is attached to the front of the trucks. As the trucks are moved to the conveyor slot, the handle is dropped into place and the dog on the chain automatically engages the tow bar. The truck is released from the dog by a slight twist of the hand on the tow bar and it then can be rolled to its desired section. Advantages over the overhead system include safe operation at higher speeds, reduction of noise, an increase in the number of flat trucks which can be handled on the conveyor line, and the resulting higher productivity per man-hour. In addition to this system, the various pieces of equipment shown in Fig. 288 are provided for increased efficiency in handling.[6]

3. Damage Claims

The importance of loss and damage prevention to the railroads is shown in Fig. 289. The total amount paid out in damages in 1949 amounted to $109,202,227. Although the claims paid out in 1948 exceeded the previous high of 1920, it will be noticed that in terms of percentage of revenue there had been a marked improvement since the earlier period.

The 1948 ratio of claims paid to freight revenue was 1.64 per cent. This was more than a full percentage point less than the corresponding figure in 1920 of 2.78 per cent. In addition, the total amount of claims paid in 1948 was an aftermath of conditions arising out of the war period resulting from claims charged to suspense account to be later charged to claim account. These improved conditions are shown in the figures for 1949.

A recent shipping-container study involved a check of 733,308 test

[6] For more detailed account, see Controlled Handling Speeds Freight Delivery, *Modern Materials Handling,* June, 1950, p. 25.

cartons shipped by rail.[7] It was found that 0.9 per cent of boxes in these shipments were damaged in transit; 0.2 per cent of boxes in these shipments were damaged enough to cause the consignee to file damage claims with the railroads. See description of study on pages 224 to 226.

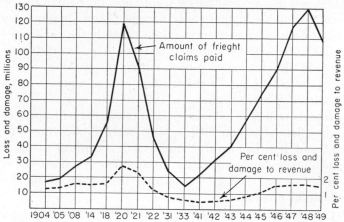

Fig. 289. Chart showing the total amount of freight claims paid and the per cent of claims to revenue. (*Freight Claims Division, Association of American Railroads.*)

It will be noticed that responsibility for the cause of damage found under the report was allocated as follows:

	Per Cent
Railroads	34
Shippers	54.5
Boxmakers	11.5
Total	100.0

Inadequate bracing and improper bulkheading were found to be the larger causes of damage. Some form of permanent flush-floor blocking as well as adjustable bulkheads was indicated as needed.

The rearrangement of causes of damage in Table 5 (page 224) gives a clearer picture of the responsibility for the damage noted. It also indicates the importance of the cause for each agency.

4. Damage Prevention

Although much attention of late has been given to railway damage and the claims resulting therefrom, the railroads have been actively concerned with it for some time. One of the first organized efforts at loss and damage prevention was the calling of a Meeting Extraordinary in 1907 of a

[7] W. B. Lincoln, Jr., Shipping Container Study, *Modern Packaging*, April, 1948, p. 168.

group of claims men in the Southeast. Other steps were soon taken and the whole movement quickly gathered momentum.

In 1914, the Interstate Commerce Commission called for an examination by the carriers into their situations and the making of special reports. In the same year the Committee on Cause and Prevention was set up by the Freight Claim Association (now Freight Claim Division, Association of American Railroads) with instructions to study the causes of loss and damage and to recommend remedial changes. The Association of American Railroads also set up a subcommittee on packing, marking, and handling of freight to handle the matter from an operating standpoint.

At a National Claim Congress in 1920 a plan was evolved for filing monthly reports of loss and damage claim payments with the secretary of the Freight Claim Division. The reports were broken down according to carload and less-than-carload traffic and according to the principal causes and outstanding commodity groups. These reports showed what each item of loss and damage was costing and served as the basis of the later prevention program.

Shortly thereafter regional Shippers' Advisory Boards were established to function in thirteen different sections of the country. Memberships of these boards are wholly industrial and cooperate with the railroads through contact committees regarding car supply and other matters, including loss and damage prevention. The railroads have also cooperated with the National Industrial Traffic League through joint meetings with its Freight Claims Committee.

Other trade associations with whom the railroads work on this problem include the Porcelain Enamel Institute, the National Canners Association, the National Association of Furniture Manufacturers, the American Newspaper Publishers Association, and others of like nature. Further contact is maintained with many individual shippers and receivers of freight and groups thereof.[8]

The activities of the Freight Claim Division of the Association of American Railroads may be summarized as: [9]

1. An educational campaign through personal contact with representatives of the various branches of the service, followed up by correspondence and supplemented by a bulletin service

2. Promotion of loss and damage activities on inactive lines, increase in effectiveness of active lines and coordination of effort of individual lines into a general prevention movement

[8] Lewis Pilcher, executive vice-chairman, Freight Claim Division, AAR, "Loss and Damage Prevention," speech given at Second Midwestern Institute in Rail Transportation, Minneapolis, Minn., Sept. 26–Oct. 8, 1949.

[9] *Ibid.*

3. Coordination of prevention activities of the sectional Freight Claim Conferences, which organizations, in turn, coordinate the activities of the carriers in their several territories

4. Assembling and analyzing statistics and other information necessary for the conduct of effective prevention activities

5. Contact with the public through industrial and commercial organizations, shippers' advisory boards, the public press, trade journals, railroad publications, and other means or avenues for securing the interest and cooperation of the public in claim prevention.

In addition to the work of the associations, individual railroads have conducted active campaigns of their own to reduce damage claims. The Union Pacific Railroad Company found that the number of freight loss and damage claims received by the company in 1947 totaled 168,191. At the close of 1948, this had been reduced by 14 per cent to 144,971. A further reduction of 19 per cent reduced this figure to 117,523 for 1949. Thus, an over-all cut in damage claims of 30 per cent was effected in two years.[10]

The program responsible for this showing was carried out in three concurrent phases:

1. Appeals to railroad management
2. Education of railroad employees
3. Cooperation with shippers and receivers of freight

Of the various media used to get its message across (see below) the most successful was a 16-millimeter sound-color motion picture entitled "Who Done It?" Luncheon forums attended by freight claim department representatives and freight handling and operating employees were also successful.

MEDIA EMPLOYED IN DAMAGE REDUCTION PROGRAM

Railroad Management	Union Pacific Employees	Shippers and Receivers of Freight
1. Correspondence	1. Correspondence	1. Correspondence
2. Literature	2. Literature	2. Literature
3. Conferences	3. Conferences	3. Container engineers
4. Railroad publications	4. Motion pictures	4. Business publications
	5. Freight service inspectors	5. Freight service inspectors
	6. Container engineers	6. Motion pictures
	7. Posters	

5. Carloading Patterns

Perhaps the most important single factor contributing to the prevention of damage [in loading of canned goods] is that of tight loading. Its importance

[10] O. J. Wullstein, general freight claim agent, Union Pacific Railroad Company.

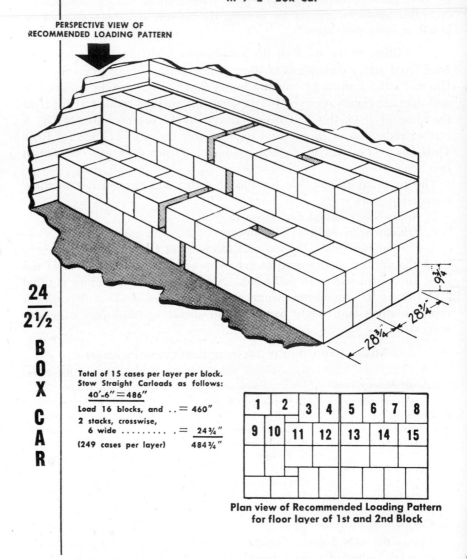

CASES OF 24/#2½

Approximate Outside Dimensions 16⅜″x12⅜″x9¾″

In 9′-2″ Box Car

PERSPECTIVE VIEW OF
RECOMMENDED LOADING PATTERN

24

2½

B
O
X

C
A
R

Total of 15 cases per layer per block.
Stow Straight Carloads as follows:

40′-6″ = 486″

Load 16 blocks, and .. = 460″
2 stacks, crosswise,
6 wide .... = 24¾″

(249 cases per layer)   484¾″

1	2	3	4	5	6	7	8
9	10	11	12	13	14	15	

Plan view of Recommended Loading Pattern
for floor layer of 1st and 2nd Block

FIG. 290. Diagram of loading pattern. (*"Recommended Carloading Patterns for Canned Goods, Commodity Pamphlet 1," Union Pacific Railroad.*)

cannot be overemphasized. Frequently the adoption of a loading pattern in which certain boxes are turned will result in a snug load.[11]

This introduction to a booklet on carloading patterns is only one example of the importance of carloading patterns for preventing damage in transit. Both Army and Navy services have devoted considerable attention to the development of patterns for specific commodities which they transport in quantity. Individual companies have also prepared elaborate diagrams and instruction sheets to ensure tight loading and prevent damage to products in shipment (Fig. 290).

6. Use of Racks and Bulkheading Devices

It was found in the study of causes of damage (Chap. 15) that approximately 15 per cent of total damage reported was due to inadequate bracing and another 15 per cent due to excessive slack in load. Railroads as well as shippers have been keenly conscious of this cause of damage and have devised a number of methods to remedy it.

The Pennsylvania Railroad has a new load-securing device which has caused widespread interest. It permits more efficient loading of less-than-carload freight and increases protection against damage. The new devices increase the average loading of merchandise freight as much as 133 per cent.

Steel gates with upper and lower sections are fastened to the sides of the car approximately 6 feet apart. When closed, the gates lock together to form bulkheads across the car from the floor to near the ceiling. Sectional steel and wood shelves are hinged to the top of each of the lower gates. When the gates are locked in position after the section is loaded, the shelves are swung up and rest on top of the adjacent gates, forming a second floor or deck between the floor and ceiling.

Used in a loaded car, the gates and shelves have the effect of dividing the car into small compartments. Freight piled in the upper compartments rests on the shelves, so that it cannot damage freight resting on the floor. The gates keep the freight firmly in position and prevent shifting while the car is in motion.

The Missouri Pacific Lines are converting boxcars into specially designed cars for efficient movement of automobile parts from factories to assembly plants. These cars are equipped with ingeniously designed racks, fasteners, and adjustable partitions.

One type of converted car is designed for engines and axle assemblies, and another for sheet-metal stampings such as doors and body and fender parts. Steel racks are built to support 72 eight-cylinder engines

[11] "Recommended Carloading Patterns for Canned Goods," Commodity Pamphlet 1, Union Pacific Railroad Company.

in double-deck arrangement, while the racks at both ends of the car will carry 72 gasoline tanks. The steel motor racks, or cradles, are removable so that the engines may be bolted in place in the factory and taken to the car on dollies. A section of monorail that connects with the factory's conveyor system can be bolted onto an angle iron at the top of the car door, and the cradles with their engines mounted can be swung in place with

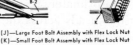

(A)—Locking Handle Assembly	(D)—Slide Housing Assembly	(J)—Large Foot Bolt Assembly with Flex Lock Nut
(B-1)—Large Tube	(E)—Slide Rack	(K)—Small Foot Bolt Assembly with Flex Lock Nut
(B-2)—Small Tube	(G)—Large Rubber Foot and Block	(L)—Special Cap Screw with Flex Lock Nut
(C)—Spring Loaded Lock	(H)—Small Rubber Foot and Block	(M)—Special Stud with Lock Washer

FIG. 291. Use of patented bulkheading equipment to secure load of truck. Close-up of parts. (*Jordan Equipment Company.*)

a crane. As each cradle enters the car, it is set on the permanently anchored angle-bar tracks and pushed toward the car ends. A long pin secures each cradle in place on the track support. This is a faster method of fastening each motor rack in place than by time-consuming bolting.

7. Loading of Cars and Trucks

Within the last few years there has been a trend toward shipment of materials in palletized units. Handling in unit loads is considerably faster than handling the packages individually. Damages to materials in transit have been reduced. One disadvantage of the use of pallets has been the weight of the pallets themselves. These carry the same freight rate as the packaged materials being shipped. There has also been the cost of returning the pallets to the shipper.

One approach to this latter problem has been taken successfully by Don Kelsey of Detroit. Interested in the development and use of wire pallets and containers, he early recognized the importance of commodity freight rates in influencing the use of pallets in inter-plant shipments. The recent adoption of a pallet return rate of one-half of fourth class for intra-state shipments has greatly encouraged the use of pallets in this area.

Fig. 292. Loading lumber with a 12,000-pound-capacity fork truck. Straddle truck spots load beside rail car to speed loading process. (*The Ross Carrier Company.*)

The use of expendable or one-way pallets provides another approach to the problem. Although these pallets may be made of thin wood sections, the most successful types to date have been the cardboard pallets. Although fairly heavy loads may be accommodated, their capacity is limited by the concentration of the weight of the load. Thus they are ideally suited to handling of flat materials, packaged items, and other materials with a broad base. They have been used successfully for handling bagged goods, steering columns, spring coils, etc.

Fork trucks are commonly used to load rail cars whether in rail terminals or at company docks. Palletized goods are picked up in the car and brought out to the loading dock. In smaller scale operations, the fork truck carries the load to the storage area and stacks it. If the distance traveled is 250 feet or more and operations are extensive, the fork truck will deposit the load on trailers spotted on the loading dock convenient to

Fig. 293. Scale models of railroad flatcars used in studies of loading arrangements. Flatcars and farm machinery reproduced at scale of one inch to one foot. Templet shown in top photograph is used for correct positioning of securing blocks before equipment is loaded on flatcars. (*International Harvester Company.*)

FIG. 294. Palletized loads of Dow chemicals being unloaded by fork truck at Port Newark. (*The Port of New York Authority.*)

FIG. 295. Railroad loading dock in warehouse of the Metal Goods Corporation, Dallas, Tex. Overhead bridge crane covers entire loading area. (*Cleveland Tramrail.*)

the rail car. An industrial tractor will then pull a loaded trailer train to the storage area where another fork truck will unload and stack. In the meantime, the tractor has returned to the dock with a string of empty trailers.

Conveyors, both portable and fixed, are commonly used for loading. With portable conveyor units, nonpalletized items can be delivered to

Fig. 296. Grab for handling bundles of sheet steel from car to storage. Order and Stores Department of Schenectady Works. (*General Electric Company.*)

the point of stacking. Extra units can be added or taken off as the distance between the cargo and car door increases or decreases. The same units will be used in the same manner for the loading of trucks. When these portable units are at the dock end of a larger conveyor system, items being loaded may be brought direct from the end of production lines or from storage areas direct without extra handling.

The lifting and loading of irregular materials may be accomplished by fork trucks with crane attachments or by a number of industrial-truck cranes. Loading of packages of 3 to 5 tons or more on flatcars is often done with mobile traveling cranes or with fixed-leg derricks. Extended monorail tracks or traveling bridge cranes often extend out over rail car or truck bays and provide rapid and efficient loading service for heavier materials.

In addition to the above devices used for loading of rail cars, trucks utilize in-built hoists and tail-gate lifting mechanisms. Both of these units are generally hydraulically operated. The hoists swing out of the way when not in use. The other lifting device moves up into the customary end gate position.

8. Unit Containers

For a number of years companies have been experimenting with methods which would permit them to load materials into a container at the

Fig. 297. Containers developed by Southern Pacific Company for handling of package freight. There are approximately one thousand of these now in use on this line. Their use has resulted in reduced cost per ton handling expense, faster handling at transfer points, and reduced loss and damage. (*Southern Pacific Company.*)

shipper's plant and then have them moved as a unit to the buyer's plant. Capital investment and the problem of container return have been the main stumbling blocks. Two-way utilization is often needed for economical operation of such a system. Nevertheless, there has been a considerable amount of success with the special applications of unit containers.

The Dravo metal container shipping unit, more fully described in Chap. 31, has been used for rail and truck shipments. Long before this, English railroads used a similar container which was loaded at the plant and then taken to the rail car by truck and there slid off by means of rollers.

Various railroads have also developed special containers which have been handled in similar fashion, transported on flatcars, and unloaded to flat-bed trailers at the other end. Special refrigerated units have also been devised. The complete trailer-sized container developed by the Gulf Canal Lines will carry a maximum of 20 tons from supplier's plant to

Fig. 298. A fleet of straddle trucks is used in one of the world's largest canneries to unload truck loads of pineapple in one operation. (*The Ross Carrier Company.*)

destination without any individual handling or listing of the contents. This also eliminates individual item checking at each transfer point.

9. Bulk Handling

Bulk materials are loaded on rail cars by means of conveyors, cranes, trucks with scoop attachments, and by gravity. Discharge from overhead bins either directly or by means of chutes is common for many commodities.

Belt conveyors provide rapid and continuous loading. Coal and similar products are commonly loaded by crawler cranes with buckets. The same crane may be used with a magnet lift for the handling of scrap metal or flat sheets.

Unloading will be speeded by the use of bottom-opening gondolas,

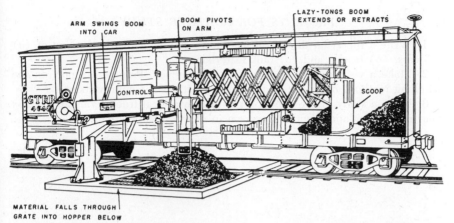

ARM SWINGS BOOM INTO CAR

BOOM PIVOTS ON ARM

LAZY-TONGS BOOM EXTENDS OR RETRACTS

CONTROLS

SCOOP

GTRR 4642

MATERIAL FALLS THROUGH GRATE INTO HOPPER BELOW

FIG. 299. Mechanical arm reaches into car to scoop out grain, sand, and similar materials. Lazy-tongs arm is hydraulically operated. Materials are pulled through door and fall into open grate with hopper underneath. (*Popular Science, March,* 1950, *p.* 138.)

special car dumpers, or other tippling devices. Special unloading mechanisms have also been devised (Fig. 299).

QUESTIONS

1. Discuss the importance of mechanized handling for railroads.

2. How does lcl freight affect the problem of freight handling?

3. Discuss the use of mechanized equipment in rail-terminal operations.

4. Compare the freight-handling methods of the three truck terminals described in the text.

5. Discuss in detail the handling and control system used at Merchants Motor Freight, Inc.

6. Discuss the importance of damage claims to handling costs.

7. What steps have been taken to reduce the amount of claims arising from damage to goods in shipment?

8. Outline the activities of the Freight Claim Division of the Association of American Railroads.

9. What have the railroads done individually to reduce damage claims?

10. How do carloading patterns affect damage to goods in transit?

11. Discuss the use of racks and bulkhead devices.

12. Discuss the problems arising from and the advantages of the use of pallets for shipping goods by truck or by rail.

13. Discuss the means by which rail cars are loaded and unloaded.

14. Discuss the means by which trucks are loaded and unloaded.

15. In what ways are large-sized unit containers used to speed up loading?

PROJECTS FOR FURTHER STUDY

1. Write a report on the use of handling equipment for the loading of (*a*) rail cars, (*b*) trucks, and (*c*) bulk materials.

2. Make a visit to a local railway express agency. Prepare a report on the handling methods observed, and make suggestions for improvement.

3. Make a study of the handling problem in a local truck terminal. Discuss your recommendations with the person in charge of operations.

CHAPTER 33

SHIP AND BARGE HANDLING

1. Importance of Cargo Handling

The importance of efficient cargo handling can readily be seen when one realizes that the cost of loading a ship at New York and discharging her in Melbourne, Australia, is often far more than the cost of operating the ship during the voyage. Approximately one-half the total cost of operating the Federal Barge Line in recent years is taken up by loading and unloading of barges.

Increased labor rates increase costs unless handling operations can be speeded up. In some instances an adequate labor force may not be available to unload cargo by former, more wasteful methods. To the ship owner, the time the ship is tied up at the dock is nonproductive time. One often quoted figure is that it costs a large cargo ship over $2,000 a day for every day it is in port.

In 1947, the President's Advisory Committee in the Merchant Marine made public a report which included recommendations for the study of cargo handling.[1]

Ocean shipping has lagged in the application of the new techniques and methods of handling materials developed during the last 10 to 15 years. The great percentage of dry cargo is still handled into and out of holds of vessels with cargo booms and winches, in a method which has experienced little improvement except in the winches themselves in the last hundred years. This procedure involves many handlings of individual items of freight. It is slow and expensive.

Although cargo-handling cost is an important factor in all shipping, its impact on certain domestic trade, because of relatively short hauls and because of competition with land transportation systems, is particularly severe. According to the study made by the Graduate School of Business Administration, Harvard University (The Use and Disposition of Ships and Shipyards at the End of World War II, dated June, 1945), cargo-handling costs in domestic shipping in prewar years averaged 41 per cent of the cost of transporting general cargo by water. Representatives of the industry indicate that this portion of the total cost has increased to approximately 50 per cent.

[1] *Report of President's Advisory Committee on the Merchant Marine,* 1947.

Reduction of handling costs can come through the application of suitable mechanized systems for moving cargo into and out of ships, through the modernization and improvement of port and terminal facilities and through the development of ships of specialized type where their utility for the service in view is indicated.

In view of the wide application and importance of improved cargo-handling procedures and facilities in the national economy and in the development of

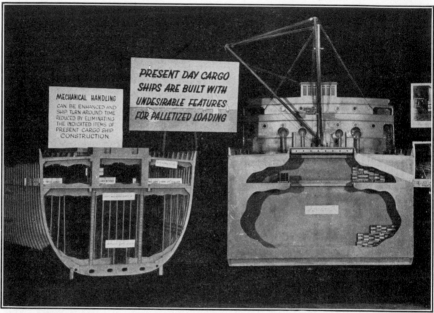

Fig. 300. This comparison between present-day ship holds and one ideal for the stowage of cargo illustrates some of the difficulties in present-day cargo handling. (*Official U.S. Navy photograph.*)

American flag shipping, the Committee recommends that the Government sponsor a concerted cooperative effort by shipping companies, shippers, ship designers, maritime labor, port authorities, and interested governmental departments toward the reduction of cargo-handling costs.

This need for the coordination of the efforts of a wide variety of activities and interests concerned with maritime shipping in one country is multiplied further by the number of other countries which are faced with the same problems and the same difficulties in solving them. To meet this need, the International Cargo Handling Co-ordination Association was formed in 1952 with its central office in London.

In May of 1952 this association held its first international technical conference in Rotterdam. This meeting was attended by representatives from 11 nations. The association issues weekly bulletins on causes of delay in the turn-around of ships and makes special studies of cargo handling problems. It also serves as a clearing house for information and, with its world-wide membership, is able to bring together the divergent groups in different countries whose assistance is often needed in solving a shipping problem.

2. Classification of Cargo Movement

There are two distinct movements involved, "transference" of cargo from ship to wharf and "handling" of cargo on the wharf. Transference is of two kinds: from side ports, as is the case in lake and coastwise or river boats, and from the hatch, as in the case of ocean vessels. The first is a lateral movement and the second a vertical movement, or the first is a low trajectory and the second a high trajectory.

Handling the merchandise on the wharf consists of three general operations: sorting, tiering, and delivery to various land and inland water carriers. The speed at which a ship can be discharged or loaded depends chiefly upon the efficiency of port equipment and organization, ship's winches and derricks, division of cargo holds, and other aids to assist dispatch.

3. Transference of Cargo

a. The Quay or Wharf Crane. This crane is the most widely used device in the movement of cargo between ship and shore except for United States ports. Its advantages are numerous. It can hoist and lower through a considerable vertical distance and can cover a length of quay front equal to twice its radius. Other advantages are (1) the crane traverses a load horizontally instead of raising it as in the case of a jib crane; (2) free movement of the jib while the load is being hoisted or lowered and the crane is traveling or slewed; (3) low power requirement to move the jib; (4) speed of moving crane unit.

This level-luffing crane is a revolving unit mounted on a gantry running on rail tracks along the quay front. The gantry permits easy movement of the whole unit for discharging cargo. With the 360-degree traverse of the crane arm, it is ideally adapted to reaching awkward areas within the hold and transferring direct to rail car, truck, or terminal transport units (Fig. 301).

b. The Semiportal Crane. This crane operates on two rails, one of which is attached high on one wall and the other is adjacent to the base. One advantage of this type is its suitability for single-story structures, and another is that the entire weight of the crane is supported by the floor instead of the walls. It may also extend through doors a few feet; and while it does require floor space along the base of the wall, its carriage is narrow and very little room is actually needed. It may be used to advantage on smaller scale operations and is less expensive than the heavier gantry crane (Fig. 301).

c. *Industrial Trucks.* Where ships are loaded from the side—as on the Great Lakes waterways—fork lift trucks, small industrial trucks with

Fig. 301. Two semigantry 15-ton revolving cranes service the new 1,100-foot pier dock at the Port of Norfolk. These cover the 35-foot apron and two rail tracks for loading directly to and from ships. (*American Hoist and Derrick Company.*)

crane attachments, mobile cranes, and two-wheel hand trucks are used in loading cargo. In the loading of deck barges, the trailer-train system is often used. An industrial tractor pulls a line of loaded trailers into the barge or ship where a waiting fork truck lifts off the palletized loads and stacks them for shipping. Often, however, the loaded pallet will be put down adjacent to the stacking area and the goods will be stowed away by hand (Fig. 302).

d. *Mobile Cranes.* These are commonly used in the loading of barges and may have either a crawler or four-wheel truck-type mounting. For bulk commodities, clamshell or orange-peel type buckets are used. A magnet attachment may be employed for the loading of scrap metal or for other ferrous metal products where little care is required in handling. Special grab units expedite the handling of bundles of sheet steel. These

usually come in 5-ton units, although, because of limited handling facilities, many smaller firms use the 3-ton package.

Several barge terminals constructed recently have a covered craneway
extending out over the water and resting on extended piers. This permits
the use of a traveling bridge craneway and expedites the handling of
heavier loads even on the far side of the barge.

Fixed crane equipment is also used in many places where a specialized
problem of handling is involved. This is particularly common at company-

Fig. 302. Fork truck backs out of river barge with double pallet load of bagged
material during unloading operations. (*Clark Equipment Company.*)

owned wharves or loading docks. A single derrick leg guyed to outlying
riggers may be operated with an electric or gasoline motor. Fixed-mount
level-luffing cranes also provide coverage for a limited area which
may be sufficient for the particular installation. They are less expensive
than the traveling gantry and provide greater lifting capacity for the same
size of unit.

e. The Burtoning System. Finally, mention should be made of the
system of blocks, tackles, and winches which is often used in conjunction
with similar equipment on board the ship and the ship's booms. Especially
in ports without the above equipment these facilities are used for cargo
loading or unloading.

In United States ports the most common method used for loading and
discharging general cargo is by means of the ship's own gear or tackle.
This is in marked contrast to the general practice in many European, Far
Eastern, and South American ports which are generally equipped with

overhead or gantry cranes. These are used almost exclusively for handling cargo between pier and ship, the ship's gear being employed only occasionally in a supplementary manner.

The scope of a ship's own gear in handling her cargo tends to be overlooked but becomes quite important in the case of outlying ports lacking

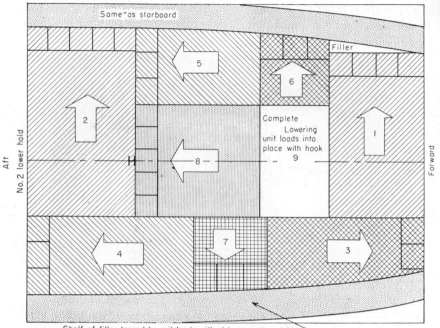

FIG. 303. For maximum use of unit loads in cargo stowage in Liberty ship, this diagram shows the recommended order of stowage. The numbers indicate the sequence in which each palletized lot should be stowed. Unit loads will be put in place with fork trucks, except in the last area where the unit loads will be dropped into place by overhead hook. (*Official U.S. Navy photograph.*)

necessary loading devices. By combining the winches and derricks of a ship berthed at quayside with portable winches on shore, the ships may be loaded without the use of shore cranes. This is known as the burtoning system and is in wide use today (see page 487).

In this system, besides the ordinary derrick rigging, a second wire for each derrick is also rigged on shore, passing from a portable winch over a sheave hooked to a metal rail which runs along above the sea face of the transit shed and down to a hook ring on to which the ship and shore wires are secured in common. By alternating ship and shore winches of hauling and slacking off, loads can be raised from the ship's holds and

FIG. 304. Uniformity of unit load can be obtained despite irregularity of cargo. Cylinders, cans, plywood drums, cartons, and cases are palletized and put in place by fork truck in the lower hold. (*Official U.S. Navy photograph.*)

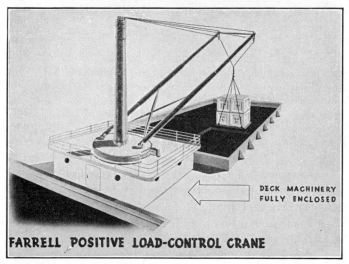

FIG. 305. The positive load feature of this revolving crane overcomes pendulumlike swinging of loads, which prevented fast rotation. Deck machinery is enclosed in a watertight house to prevent its exposure to salt water. (*T. V. Farrell.*)

transferred to the shore, and vice versa. Without the electric winch the ship's derricks may simply drag suitable cargo up a skid to the dock or load to barges.

There has been a rapid development in the hoisting equipment of steamships as to the winches, masts, and gear. The hatch masts are usually constructed to carry a cluster of booms of 5-ton lift. Certain large hatch

Fig. 306. Gas-powered fork truck stows heavy boxes in the lower hold. Truck will be lifted out by overhead hook, and center section will be filled by lowering directly into the hold. (*Clark Equipment Company.*)

(27-foot) vessels have one or two 10-ton and even a 20-ton boom to each hatch. There has been a tendency in new vessels to build two masts connected by a bridge. This is the prevailing Maritime Board type, and although cumbersome in appearance it is considered efficient.

Loading of refrigerated cargo has been speeded up on the new S.S. *Cleveland.* Two parallel retractable beams are arranged overhead in the handling space above No. 4 hold. These extend out through the open side port, port or starboard side as required, and are locked in place. Each beam carries a hoisting trolley. The two units can handle a load of 3,000 pounds and a maximum of 72 long tons per hour. The hoisting winch has a lifting speed of 150 feet per minute.

This unit eliminates top deck booms and winches necessary for operation of the hatches. It eliminates all rehandling of cargo on A deck and makes this space available for other use. Furthermore, no equipment on shore is needed. It is expected that this one unit will load almost two-thirds of the ship's stores.

Reefer barges constructed on the West Coast during the Second World War were provided with a complete electrified trolley system for handling refrigerated cargo. Hinged jib cranes connect the barge handling system to similar monorail systems in terminals and fold up out of the way when not in use.

Fig. 307. Topping off the lower hold No. 2 with bagged cargo. Notice filler cases topping off 'tween deck unit loads. (*Official U.S. Navy photograph.*)

The Federal Maritime Board of the Department of Commerce has done considerable experimenting with new types of unloading equipment putting emphasis on ship-mounted crane units. The *Sea Hawk*, for example, was a C-3 vessel built during the war on which was installed a crane runway over the three forward hatches. Other plans using the same idea involve traveling gantries covering a number of hatches, crane runways running crosswise on the ship, and retractable boom cranes supported by special frames built into the ship.

A vessel recently designed for carrying pulp has a whirley which travels the length of ship on a set of rails. It was found that 10 stevedores and 1 winch operator could accomplish practically the same work that was done previously by 6 winch operators and 40 to 60 stevedores. The whirley can handle up to 280,000 pounds of freight an hour, swinging it a radius of 55 feet. It can handle 250,000 tons per year at a cost (in 1940) of 9 cents per ton in contrast to 86 cents per ton by more conventional means.[2]

[2] Self-propelled Diesel and Diesel Electric Deck Whirleys, *Diesel Power*, March, 1947, p. 50.

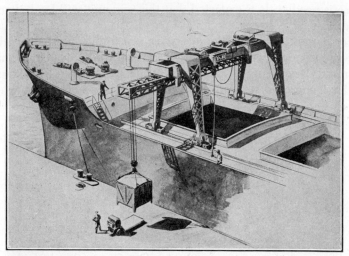

FIG. 308. The retractable boom crane adapted to shipboard installation has simple push-button control for all hoisting, boom, and trolley motions. The gantry operates on rails and is driven through gears and racks fastened to the ship's decks. The gantry legs can be made collapsible to permit the crane to be lowered in stowed position. This materially reduces the ship's center of gravity. (*Harnischfeger Corporation.*)

FIG. 309. Overhead runways running crosswise of a ship speed up handling, particularly where heavy loads are involved. The first installation of this type on a ship employed a 5-ton crane on No. 1 hatch, a 10-ton crane on No. 2 hatch, and a 30-ton crane with two 15-ton hooks on No. 3 hatch. Jibs, used to extend the runway beyond the ship's side, folded against the side when not in use. (*Harnischfeger Corporation.*)

Still another system recently devised to speed up cargo loading consists of a set of coordinated rolling wing decks. These are wheel-mounted platforms that can be loaded directly under the hatch and then rolled to the wing storage area. This eliminates rehandling to the wing areas. After removal to wing position, the hatch area is then loaded. A system of cables provides stability for the platforms when the ship is under way. This system was first demonstrated on the Victory ship, *Private Francis X. McGraw.*

4. Loading of Bulk and Other Nonregulated Materials

a. Fluids. In the loading of bulk tankers, fluid is piped to and from the tanker with the aid of pumps which are generally stationed aboard the vessel itself. The pumps on the *F. S. Bryant* of the Standard Oil Company of California record on a tape the amount of fluid pumped into each tank on the vessel. Another tape record is made when the products are discharged at the other end. The vessel has a capacity of 3,500,000 gallons.

The pumps aboard the tanker *Stanvac Calcutta* have a combined capacity of 5,600 gallons per minute. The tanker has two motor-driven cargo pumps and two steam reciprocating cargo stripping pumps. This provides a flexible arrangement so that several products can be handled at one time. This is one of a fleet of 29 tankers owned by the Petroleum Shipping Co., Ltd.

b. Grain. This is now usually loaded and unloaded by means of pneumatic handling equipment. This may be a permanent fixed installation or mounted on rails for more flexibility of movement. R. & H. Hall, Ltd., has a plant of the latter type at a northern English port. An electric winch lowers the conveyor tube into the hold. Grain is sucked up through these pipes to an automatic weigher from which it falls by gravity to rail cars or to conveyors which carry it to the granary. It has a capacity of 150 to 180 tons per hour.

Pneumatic handling plants are also mounted on small ships. This type of equipment is used primarily when shore and dock loading facilities are busy and the grain must be loaded to lighters or barges. During the Second World War the British outfitted six small Dutch cargo vessels into similar transferring units. Thus dock facilities were not needed for the loading of grain ships.

The International Elevating Company of New York City uses this same method for loading grain. Barges with elevating equipment permit them to load grain from the off-dock side of the vessel at the same time other cargo is loaded from the dock. Two of their elevating barge units use pneumatic handling, while six other units use bucket conveyors

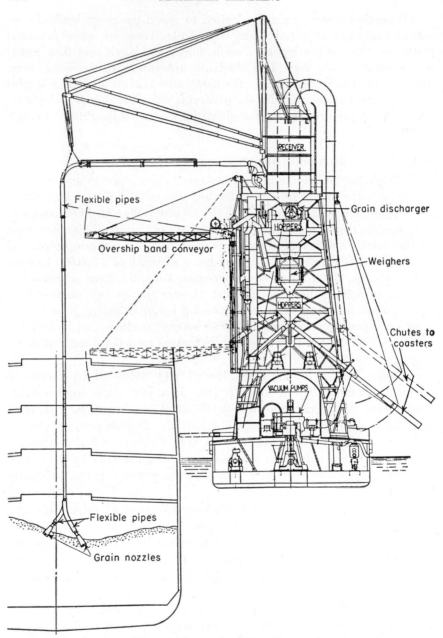

Fig. 310. This floating pneumatic elevator handles 250 tons of grain per hour, which can either be discharged to barges by means of chutes or unloaded to shore by means of an overship belt conveyor. [*Spencer (Melksham) Inc. Ltd.*]

for elevating the grain. In each case the product is weighed in the tower before being dropped into the receiving unit.

These vertical bucket elevators which may be raised and lowered are commonly referred to as "marine leg elevators." The leg must also be moved horizontally from one side to the other. Some of them are equipped with telescoping sections so as to be able to take care of deep-hold vessels and extremely wide tide variations. When mounted on shore, changes in water level caused by the tide have to be compensated for by the vertical position of the leg. In addition to grain, bucket elevators may be used for loading and unloading of cottonseed, nuts, copra, coal, and other similar materials.

c. Other Materials. Loading of barges and open-deck vessels is commonly done with movable cranes, mounted on wheels, crawler treads, or rail cars. Traveling gantries and ore bridges are used. These latter are equipped with belt conveyors for collection or distribution of materials over a wider storage area.

5. Terminal and Wharf Handling

The modern terminal must provide for fast and efficient transfer of a wide variety of materials from steamship to truck, rail car, or storage. As much as possible, materials should be unloaded from the ship directly to rail car or truck without any intermediary handling.

a. Ship Terminals. Proper facilities and equipment must be provided for the loading of ships, the rapid transfer of material, and the internal movement of materials within the terminal area. It is not surprising then to find a wide variety of equipment being used. For example, the Jules S. Sottnek Company in Brooklyn, N.Y., stevedores and terminal operators, has a fleet of more than 100 fork lift trucks, tractors, mobile cranes, and other mechanized cargo-handling equipment.

In a study recently made by the author, a number of operators of terminals and stevedoring firms declared that handling has to be done with unit loads in order to keep pace with increased loading demands and higher labor rates.

b. Barge Terminals. Although barge terminals also prefer to load directly between barge and rail car or truck, they too must often rehandle or in some instances provide temporary storage. In many instances an extra stevedoring charge is assessed for this rehandling. Another terminal allows a charge of one-half the usual rate if the products are palletized.

The Houston Barge Terminal of Houston, Tex., illustrates many of the desirable features of barge-terminal layout. With 800 feet of workable dock space, three barges can be unloaded at the same time. Over 24,000 square feet of covered storage area is provided. It has a capacity of 12

FIG. 311. Pier No. 4, Hoboken, N.J., provides the latest answer to rapid wharf and cargo handling. A U-shaped truck boulevard provides unimpeded access to all parts of the pier without interfering with cargo operations. Space is provided for unloading of 120 trucks at one time. The three-track rail spur in center is depressed to place car doors at deck level. Combined with the two services on the north apron, 70 rail cars can be spotted at one time. (*The Port of New York Authority.*)

FIG. 312. The Houston Barge Terminal, Houston, Tex., moves materials directly from rail car or over-the-road trucks to barges by means of mobile cranes and a traveling bridge crane which extends out over the barge. Other horizontal movement is accomplished by means of industrial crane trucks and fork trucks. (*Houston Barge Terminal, Inc.*)

rail cars at the dock. As many as 12 trucks have been handled at each barge (Fig. 312).

A 10-ton traveling bridge crane serves an outdoor covered area and provides direct loading from barge to rail car or truck. Along the dock, crawler cranes are used for loading. One is of diesel type and the other two are gasoline powered. The floor surface for the entire area is concrete. Several fork trucks and tractors are all of the gasoline type. Everything is palletized.

6. Unit-load Handling

Unit-load handling with pallets is accomplished with the aid of fork trucks, tractor-trailer systems, and the conventional boom slings. Goods are palletized either at the point of origin or on arrival at the wharf, the work in the latter case being done by the stevedore. At the wharf, the loaded pallets are lifted from the vehicle by a fork truck and stacked in the transit shed.

When ready to be loaded on the ship, a fork truck unstacks the palletized load and deposits it on a trailer. An industrial tractor pulls a string of trailers to the dock area where they can be picked up by special slings from an overhead boom. After the cargo is swung into the hold of the ship, another fork truck removes it from the sling and stacks it to the desired height in the hold.

Where side ports are available, these trailer trains may often be driven directly into the hold. Elevators within the ship may be used to lower trailers to the lower decks. In the loading of barges, the complete trailer train may be driven onto the main deck. The pallets are then loaded by fork truck.

Another system involves a large metal container approximately 7 feet square. The container is made of welded steel construction, and it can be padlocked or sealed and transported to the destination as a single unit. Several firms report that savings in pilferage losses alone justify the use of the containers (Fig. 314).

Lenthéric, Inc., reported the following savings and advantages of the use of containers on shipments to San Juan, Puerto Rico, on the AGWI Lines: [3]

1. Savings in export packaging materials, including wooden cases, excelsior, waterproof paper, iron strapping, etc., estimated $120 for every container used.

2. Savings in man-hours necessary for packing, marking, weighing and handling export shipments—approximately 36 hours per container.

[3] Steel Shipping Containers Reduce Costs for Shipper and Ship Operator, *Marine Age.*

3. Reduction in breakage—75 per cent.
4. Reduction of pilferage losses—100 per cent.
5. Savings in marine insurance rates—50 per cent.

FIG. 313. Unit loads speed both transference of cargo and its movement at the wharf. *Top*—Fork truck loads palletized bags of sugar to trailers by which they will be conveyed to storage. Note the open-end cargo-type pallet. (*Clark Equipment Company.*) *Bottom*—Straddle truck handles Yugoslavian oak in unit loads. (*The Port of New York Authority.*)

An even larger container is currently being used on the Gulf Coast. This is a unit 7 feet, 6 inches by 7 feet, 6 inches by 26 feet. Although it is designed to carry 20 tons, load restrictions in various states limit its average capacity to approximately 12 tons. Its main characteristic is that it is handled with regular trailer facilities, *i.e.*, a conventional over-the-road tractor unit. The container and the flat-bed trailer on which it is transported together weigh about 5 tons.

Fig. 314. Shipping container loaded with cigarettes is swung aboard an AGWI freighter at New York. At Puerto Rico, it is reloaded with rum, mail, express goods, and other articles for the return journey. (*Dravo Corporation.*)

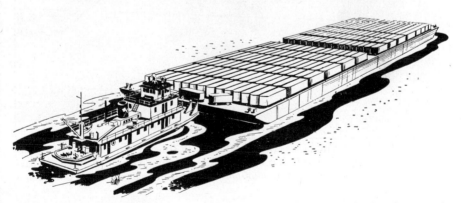

Fig. 315. Over-the-road trailers are carried on top of oil barges and other flat-topped equipment. Multi-story barges, now used for down-river transport of automobiles, are also used to transport loaded trailers. (*Commercial Barge Lines, Inc.*)

These trailer units may be loaded on a flat deck barge or on top of an oil barge when properly reinforced. The only loading facility required for this loading operation is an inclined ramp by which the trailers are drawn up on the barge.

This service is now available along the Gulf Coast from Brownsville, Tex., to Mobile, Ala. The service is soon to be extended throughout the Mississippi and Ohio river systems. Arrangements with truck lines permit them to be transported inland from the water terminating point.

At least one line operating in the Caribbean is considering arrangements for transporting the units complete without reloading. The U.S. Maritime Commission has authorized the construction of two ships for the transport of similar units. These vessels will operate between Los Angeles, Long Beach, and San Francisco. Each ship will have space for 176 trucks and 385 passengers.

7. Special Handling Facilities

The new coal and ore handling facility at Toledo, Ohio, recently constructed at a cost of $20,000,000 is designed to handle 20,000,000 tons of

Fig. 316. Air view of ore and coal and ore docks at Toledo, Ohio, showing the coal-car dumpers on the left, the Hulett ore unloader at the right slip, and the 5,500-car-capacity receiving yards beyond. (*Lakefront Dock and Railroad Terminal Company.*)

coal and 4,500,000 tons of ore a year. This is accomplished with supporting rail yards of a total capacity of 5,400 rail cars, three electric coal-car dumpers, and two electric ore-loading machines (Fig. 316).

The car dumpers are of the elevating, turnover type and each will unload a car a minute. Each dumper has its own independent six-track loaded-car yard, holding approximately 250 cars. The cars are pushed forward by a 30-ton electric pusher to a point where the single car is engaged by an electric "mule." The "Barney mule" pushes the loaded car up the incline into position on the cradle. The preceding car (now empty) is given a push sufficient to send it down the opposite incline. Momentum from the kick-back trestle returns the empty car, slowed down by retarders, to the empty yard.

8. Special Ship-loading Facilities

The modern self-unloading vessel, commonly termed a "self-unloader," is a bulk cargo vessel furnished with conveying equipment which withdraws cargo

Fig. 317. Rail car is raised 25 feet, the contents are dumped into a retarding pan, and the coal is sprinkled with a chemical to reduce dust. A telescopic trimmer at the lower end of the pan deposits the coal in the bottom of the ship carefully in order to reduce degradation. (*Lakefront Dock and Railroad Terminal Company.*)

from the bottom of the hold, elevates it above deck to a boom conveyor which swings outboard and deposits the cargo on a dock, all without the aid of any shore facilities such as unloading towers, bridges, or cranes, and does this at a high hourly unloading rate with a small expenditure of power. [See Fig. 326.]

The commodities usually handled have been crushed limestone, coal, gypsum, and also coke, sand, gravel, and other free-flowing materials.[4]

[4] R. W. Eickenberger, The Self-unloading Vessel, *Marine Engineering and Shipping Review,* August, 1948, p. 36.

The first commercially successful self-unloading bulk cargo ship, the *S.S. Wyandotte,* was built in 1908 and is still in service. She carries more than one-half million tons of cargo per year. Although new hulls have been designed for this conveyor system, the majority of the self-unloading fleet consists of converted hulls.

In the earlier units, drag scrapers delivered the material to an inclined belt conveyor, feeding in turn to the swinging boom conveyor topside.

Fig. 318. Ore in unloaded by two Hulett ore machines, each of which can handle more than 15 tons per minute. These units unload the ore directly from the ship to empty rail cars which are moved out of the way by electric pushers. (*Lakefront Dock and Railroad Terminal Company.*)

Since 1932, belt conveyors running the length of the hold deliver material to an inclined chain-and-bucket elevator feeding the boom belt conveyor. Fifteen vessels have since connected to this latter system.

When handling crushed limestone weighing 90 pounds per cubic foot, the rate of discharge is given as around 2,000 net tons per hour and this figure is frequently exceeded.

A typical example of an improved type of vessel is the *S. B. Way* (renamed *Crispin Oglebay* after conversion). It has six cargo holds (with W cross section) with the hoppers opening to two 48-inch-wide longitudinal belt conveyors. Each conveyor delivers 1,100 long tons of stone per hour to the forward chutes. These direct the flow to the elevator conveyor made up of 96- by 30-inch pans connected by chain links.

The material is guided to the unloading boom by another chute which rotates with the boom. This boom is 240 feet in length and may be elevated to a maximum angle of 18 degrees. The conveyor belt is 60 inches wide and runs at 425 feet per minute.[5]

A proposed package freighter for the Great Lakes designed by the Leathen D. Smith Shipbuilding Company, of Sturgeon Bay, Wis., will have a traveling crane with a runway of rails on each side of the top deck extending the length of the ship. This will enable it to pick up containers from the dock and lower them into the hold. The hold of the vessel will

FIG. 319. Barrels are handled four at a time with special attachment for fork truck. Pallet loads may be doubled for higher stacking. (*Official U.S. Navy photograph.*)

have a number of slotted steel crossbeams instead of deck floors. Preloaded containers of 7 by 9 by 7 feet each and holding 8 tons of goods will then be slipped into the slots.

It is estimated that the new package can be loaded and unloaded in 24 hours. This is in contrast to the 2 or 3 days usually required for 300 stevedores to wheel package freight in by small units.[6]

QUESTIONS

1. What kinds of cranes are commonly used in the transference of cargo from ship to shore?

[5] Kent C. Thornton, Conversion of Lake Bulk Carrier S. B. *Way* to Self-unloader, *Marine Engineering and Shipping Review,* August, 1948, p. 40.

[6] New Type of Package Freighter Designed for the Great Lakes, *Distribution Age,* September, 1944, p. 49.

2. What kinds of cranes and other handling equipment have been installed on ships other than winches and swinging booms?

3. Discuss the problem of handling for ship-terminal operations.

4. Outline the special facilities provided at Toledo for the loading of coal.

5. What were the cargo handling recommendations of the President's Advisory Committee on the Merchant Marine in 1947?

6. Describe the use of industrial trucks in handling of ship's cargo.

7. Describe some methods of transferring fluids to a ship's hold.

8. Discuss handling and loading of materials at barge terminals.

9. What are some of the recent developments in cargo handling?

10. What kinds of movements are involved in cargo handling?

11. What is the burtoning system?

12. What are some methods used for the handling of grain from the ship's hold?

13. Discuss the problem of unit loading handling for loading of water-borne cargo.

PROJECTS FOR FURTHER STUDY

1. Prepare a report on the problem of stowage in a modern freighter.

2. Discuss the sources of information on cargo handling.

3. Make a study of the use of cranes for the loading of ships and barges.

CHAPTER 34

HANDLING BULK MATERIALS

The movement of bulk materials involves essentially conveyorized methods of handling. With few exceptions these materials have a high ratio of weight and bulk to value of the product; hence, handling constitutes a larger part of the processing cost. It is not surprising, then, to find that bulk handling has long enjoyed the application of many of the principles now just being considered for use in other manufacturing industries. Therefore, it may be seen that in general the handling of bulk materials has advanced to a finer point than other phases of materials handling.

1. Selection of Handling System

Many other types of materials-handling equipment require very little if any engineering for their successful application. Indeed, in some areas successful application requires a knowledge of business, of methods, and a general understanding of the handling picture rather than the application of any engineering techniques. This is not true, however, for most of the systems involved in the handling of bulk materials. In most instances these systems are designed tailor-made to fit a particular application. Therefore, a high degree of engineering knowledge and background is required in solving this type of problem.

In the selection of the particular system or type of equipment to be used for handling these materials there are a number of factors to be considered.

a. Size of Particle. This will largely determine the specific type of equipment to be used. Fine-powdered or fluffy materials have different handling requirements than gravel, coal, iron ore, and other irregular materials.

b. Nature of the Material Being Handled. There are a number of characteristics of the material which affect the choice of handling systems to be used. Whether the material is fragile or hard, dusty or sticky, abrasive or nonabrasive, free flowing or sluggish, are only some of the items that have to be considered. Sometimes the materials are highly corrosive or toxic. At other times a dust caused from the particles may provide an explosion hazard.

When the element of dust is combined with certain atmospheric conditions, danger of explosion becomes imminent. Other materials such as sulphur develop static electricity through friction and when discharged onto a chute develop a voltage equalized by a spark discharge. This static discharge must be dissipated harmlessly by lining the chute with aluminum bronze.

Some materials must be handled in such a way as to prevent pulverizing or disintegration, which rules out screw conveyors and high-speed elevators. In the transporting of carbon pellets, gentle handling is essential, and conveyors having a grinding action cannot be used. A number of other materials also require very careful handling, which must be considered in the selection of a specific type of equipment.

c. Quantity of Material. This will determine the amount of capital which can be invested in handling equipment. If the quantity is limited, various types of portable equipment will have to be considered. Where more than one kind of material is to be transported over the same system or by the same type of equipment, self-cleaning characteristics may be required.

The quantity of material to be moved between fixed points will also have to be considered. Where both points are permanent, one type of equipment can be used; where one or both points change, another type will be required.

2. Fluids and Materials in Suspension

Fluids are generally transported through pipes. After the initial cost of the original installation has been incurred, the cost of transporting materials by this means is negligible. In some chemical processes it has been found expedient to convert materials to a semifluid state in order that this means of transport may be utilized. In the handling of blackstrap molasses, the material is piped into the barge in a semifluid state. There it is dehydrated in order to permit a larger quantity to be transported. At the delivery end, water is again added to the mixture so that regular pumps and pipes may be used to carry it out of the barge.

These materials are generally stored by means of tanks wherever possible. Tanks will vary considerably in size according to the storage requirements of the specific installation. They may be made of wood or steel and lined according to special requirements of the materials being handled. For some products, glass or rubber-lined tanks may be used.

For ease of transport in larger quantities, barrels and small containers will be utilized. Because of the weight generally encountered with the size of barrel ordinarily used, this handling has long constituted a serious problem. With the advent of fork lift trucks, cranes, and other devices for the handling of heavier units, this problem has been simplified.

Large numbers of barrels may be stored in high stacks by means of the above-mentioned overhead handling devices. In other instances, special racks have been devised to permit multi-tier storing of these items.

One source of economy in the handling of these materials is the utilization of gravity. By equipment, this includes chutes, troughs, and open fall devices. In a number of instances, ground or granular materials may be transported with a water medium, thereby using troughs or sluices. Even large logs and other heavy items are often transported by this means.

3. Fine-ground Materials

The movement of fine-ground materials or fine fines, as they are called in the industry, poses a number of handling problems very similar to that of the movement of fluids and materials in suspension. For all practical purposes this classification of material will be considered in the same way as the former. In general, the flowability of the material is rather high, and the material lends itself to a mixture with another medium such as air. With the use of mechanical conveying systems, however, a few additional difficulties are encountered.

a. Pneumatic Handling. Pneumatic conveyor systems are used for handling a wide variety of bulk cargoes at a rate from 1 to 100 tons per hour.

Some of the advantages of this type of handling are (1) flexibility, as the nozzle and flexible hose of the unit can be quickly moved to the material; (2) low labor costs, as fewer men are required to operate this equipment than most other systems of handling; (3) dust is kept to a minimum, the material is transported through a closed system, and dust does not have an opportunity to enter the atmosphere.

The successful handling of soda ash developed a number of years ago opened the way for the conveying of borax, lime, grains, sugar, and other bulk products. Other operations taken from different fields are:

In a chemical process plant a unit handles 5 tons per hour of hydrated lime from kiln to processing or to any one of 12 storage tanks from 100 to 300 feet distant. It also serves to pick up from any storage tank and return to processing. Maintenance costs of this unit in use for 6 years is negligible.

In a borax plant a unit unloads raw and calcined borax from railroad cars to processing or storage. The vertical dip is 70 feet and the horizontal distance is 210 feet. Capacity of the unit is 15 tons per hour which is now being increased to 25 tons per hour.

In a brewery a pneumatic machine unloads grain and rice from railroad cars to any one of six storage tanks. Rate of handling is 7 to 10 tons per hour. No operator is required when moving the grain from storage tanks to process, and during the unloading from the railroad car only one man is required. Another advantage of the equipment is that a clean, thorough unloading job is the rule, for the flexible portable metallic hose can be guided to get into small corners.

In an almond plant a unit moves 50 tons per hour of almonds in the shell from warehouse to processing, a distance of 250 feet. After the nuts are shelled, the air goes through the blower and on the delivery side of the blower the air picks up the shells and blows them about 100 feet.[1]

b. Enclosed Conveying Equipment. The most effective and economical means of movement is the enclosed chute or pipe. This provides absolute control of the route of travel and protects the transported materials from contamination from outside sources, and no power is required for movement, gravity doing all of the work.

The use of gravity in this connection may be so important that the entire process will be designed around this fact. For example, grain elevators and similar processing industries are usually built entirely upon a vertical plan, allowing for the fall of gravity of material from one process to another.

Movement of materials may be accomplished by belt conveyors, generally of an enclosed type, or by using a mechanical device. The continuous movement of this device within the enclosed area of the conveyor converts the material to a continuous core, and is ideally suited to the movement of flowable, granular, or pulverized materials.

Still another device for the movement of this material is the spiral conveyor. The helicoidal action of the mechanical unit forces the material forward in a steady stream. Use of this method is also limited in the length which may be applied to a particular situation. Another device which uses a continuous moving mechanical device within the conveyor wall is the Hudson helicoid. This consists of an endless steel helicoid with spaced coils on which the materials are moved forward. This has had limited application to date.

At the O'Sullivan Rubber Corporation, Winchester, Va., the method of handling powder black has been changed from bags to an enclosed dustproof system. Carbon black now arrives at the plant in tank-car lots and an enclosed screw conveyor lifts it from the pit under the railroad

[1] Robert S. Clark, Pneumatic Handling of Bulk Cargoes, *Distribution Age*, March, 1948, p. 22.

siding and feeds it through two sections of a horizontal screw conveyor to a steel-encased bucket lift. The conveyor line from pit to bucket elevator is 195 feet long. The elevator then lifts it 65 feet to the storage bin.[2]

Under certain conditions, fine, dry materials can be made to flow like water. When fluffed up by a low pressure of air, the specific gravity of the mass is lowered considerably, which changes the angle of repose of the material. When this is accomplished, the angle of repose may be only 2 to

Fig. 320. Fine-ground abrasive particles are handled and stored at the Minnesota Mining and Manufacturing Company in large metal containers which are designed to nest into each other. (*Minnesota Mining and Manufacturing Company.*)

3 degrees. The angle will depend upon the physical characteristics of the material.

Since the only power required is to drive a fan which supplies the low-pressure air, it is extremely low in operating cost. There are no other moving parts, and therefore maintenance is very low. This method has been used to convey gypsum, soda ash, barite, bentonite, lime, fly ash, iron ores, alumina, phosphate, silica flour, fillers, flour, and talc. One cement plant also uses it to transport up to 40,000 tons of portland cement a day.[3]

c. Special Cars and Tanklike Devices. Where materials are exceptionally fine or unusually volatile in nature, special handling containers are

[2] From Bags to Bulk, *Factory Management and Maintenance*, March, 1947, p. 78.
[3] Pour Them Like Water, *Modern Materials Handling*, May, 1951, p. 61.

required for over-the-road or distance movements. Rail cars will often consist of a single tank of complete car capacity. One special type, called the Trans-Flo Bulk Car, is designed specially for the bulk handling of dry, granular, or powdered materials such as flour, dried foods, etc. It uses a pneumatic unloading system to empty each of the separate hoppers.[4] Barges and ships used for the transport of these materials are gen-

FIG. 321. Flour can be transported and stored in these carton-lined wire-pallet containers. Handling costs are reduced, and entire pallet load can be elevated by fork truck and emptied to mixing machines. (*Clark Equipment Company.*)

erally divided up into a series of compartments and even these quite often have interior battle plates to prevent a shifting of the cargo.

    d. Unit Containers. The Minnesota Mining and Manufacturing Company recently discovered that fine particles of abrasive materials could be handled more economically in special-sized metal containers than by customary handling methods (Fig. 320).

    Still another application of unit handling to the movement of bulk materials has been the use of wire-frame collapsible pallet containers. By means of a reinforced paper liner resting upon the wire mesh a total load of 1,500 pounds of flour may be handled at one time by a fork truck. They have proved not only of value for the bulk handling of this material but

    [4] *Modern Materials Handling,* May, 1951, p. 51.

also for bakeries. There, the fork trucks equipped with a rotation device pick up the complete unit and empty its contents into the bin without any other handling (Fig. 321).

4. Granular Materials

These materials with a larger particle size than the previous group considered still have a high degree of flowability and are well adapted to bulk methods of handling. Because of the outstanding characteristics the discussion of handling specific commodities illustrates the problem of handling for the group as a whole.

a. Grain Handling. One of the oldest methods and still the most common way of handling grain is with a bucket elevator. This consists of a wide belt made of duck or canvas, coated with rubber for traction, with small metal buckets fastened to the belt at intervals of from 10 to 18 inches. The shaft is usually built vertically or nearly so. There is a large pulley or wheel at the top and the bottom upon which the belt runs. The elevator is generally powered by an electric motor of appropriate size for the capacity or load of the elevator.

Buckets on the moving belt pick up the grain from a pit at the bottom of the elevator and discharge it at the head or top. As the grain is carried around the top of the elevator, it is thrown by centrifugal force into a hopper. It then flows by gravity through pipes and chutes to the desired bin.

A newer method of moving grain either vertically or horizontally is by air blower. This consists of a heavy-bladed metal fan into which grain is fed from a hopper. The fan propels the grain along with the stream of air. Fans are used primarily on farms and in small elevators where a portable grain mover is needed. The disadvantages of the fan are the dust it raises, a tendency to clog, and the frequent cracking of grains such as wheat or rye by the blades.

A worm-screw type of conveyor may be used in tight places or for short distances. This consists of a spiral blade within a hollow round casing which carries the grain with it as the blade turns. Although satisfactory for horizontal movement of grain, it is inefficient and requires considerable power to carry grain upward at a steep angle.

An endless belt conveyor is a much more rapid method for horizontal handling of grain. The belt may be of any width from a few inches to 2 or 3 feet. The belt may be flat, but is usually trough-shaped to lessen spilling. It is usually made of a long-wearing rubber-covered fabric and is supported by rollers every few feet. Speed of the conveyor may be varied.

The pneumatic handling of grain has been used for a number of years in the unloading of ships and barges and more recently of rail cars and for other vertical handling needs. The use of flexible tubes makes their use extremely flexible. Considerable power is required to operate them and the speed of the particles being transported is limited. Nevertheless, they offer a large number of advantages over other types of vertical conveying machinery (see Fig. 310).

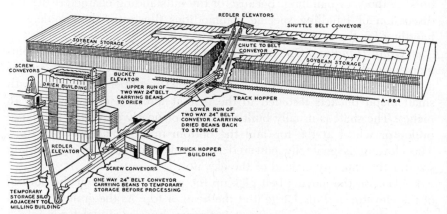

FIG. 322. A variety of conveying equipment is used by the Drackett Company in storing and processing soy beans. Not shown on the diagram is a vibrating screen which screens the beans before they go into storage. (*Stephens-Adamson Manufacturing Company.*)

The heart of the pneumatic conveyor system is the pump, which may be a reciprocating cylinder or a rotary type. This unit evacuates the air from the pipe which runs into the grain to be lifted. Air and grain are admitted together at the nozzle, which has an air vent to admit extra air along with the grain.

The exhausting unit or discharger is constructed so as not to break the vacuum in the suction pipe. This is accomplished by enlarging the receiving end, which slows down the air and causes it to lose its carrying power. Thereupon the grain drops out of the moving air stream into chutes which carry it to the desired bin.

b. Sand and Gravel. Materials handling is a large part of the processing cost of sand and gravel. Value in relation to weight is extremely low; hence handling and movement of materials must be accomplished at a very low cost per ton. A standardized method of processing results in an almost completely conveyorized type of operation.

Formerly conveyors were reserved for vertical travel and short horizontal movement. These distances have been extended until for some

Fig. 323. A tramrail system for the supply of molder's sand for the Standard Automotive Parts Company, Muskegon, Mich., utilizes a 24-cubic-foot capacity operating on a double track. The entire system is operated and controlled by one operator. (*Cleveland Tramrail.*)

Fig. 324. Molder's stations, with hopper above each station. Automatic dispatch system shown in Fig. 323 is overhead. (*Cleveland Tramrail.*)

time there has been a very definite trend toward long conveyorized handling systems. These often replace fleets of trucks formerly used.

In California aggregates were moved nearly 10 miles from the plant to the Shasta Dam site. Old theories of the economic limits of conveyor transportation are constantly being revised and extended.

In laying out a new plant in California, the owner was faced with the decision of building one of two types of establishments—a sprawling plant that would be hard to supervise and which would require many operators if he used a 100 per cent conveyor system of handling materials, or a compact and easily supervised plant wherein bucket elevators would be used to more than average extent. He decided on the latter and had engineers study and eliminate the weaknesses common to bucket elevators. Plenty of slope was allowed for each elevator so that the buckets discharged properly with little spillage. This is caught in a steel pan that partially houses the return side of the belt so that spillage returns to the elevator boot. Each elevator has a height of 76 feet with the tail pulley about 35 feet off vertical. Although these bucket elevators give the plant a very complicated flow sheet, the arrangement is such that the flow is really simple. The plant is completely electric controlled.

A new gravel plant at Phoenix, Ariz., is a good example of a conveyor system for a plant that one man can operate by push-button control. The sand and gravel is excavated from a nearby river bed and loaded into dump trucks for delivery to the plant. Trucks dump their load into a 40-ton screened hopper which limits size of the materials going into the primary crusher. The material is fed from the hopper by means of a 24-inch by 5-foot heavy-duty plate feeder which is driven by a variable speed motor. This enables the plant operator to change the feed to the plant to suit other operations. The feeder can be set from 30 to 90 tons per hour and delivers the sand and gravel to a slow-moving troughed belt conveyor 64 feet long which delivers the material to a 3- by 8-foot single-deck vibrating screen.

The materials are then screened, with the oversized materials going by conveyor to a jaw pressure machine. They then move into a 141-foot conveyor that elevates them to the top of the plant. Materials are washed and graded into various sizes by two double-deck vibrating machines. Any oversized rock is again conveyed to a crusher and back again. By changing the mesh on the screens, the operator can make several different grades of sand. The sand is fed by gravity to two storage bins which have belt conveyors on them for loading trucks. This plant uses all standard equipment and it has reached this high degree of mechanization and efficiency by proper planning and utilization of equipment.

In quarries distant from the main plant, haulage units must be used to some extent. The capacity of haulage units has been greatly increased in recent years. These units comprise large trucks with hydraulically operated end dump bodies, tractor and semitrailer combinations with a semitrailer chassis mounting one or two side-dump bodies, or some of the

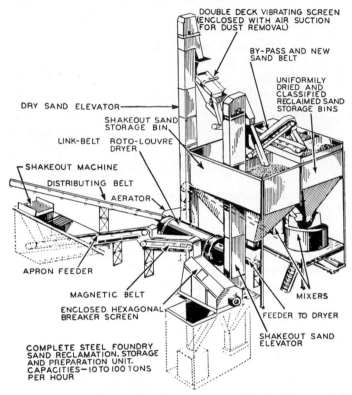

Fig. 325. A complete handling and reclaiming system for foundry sand. (*Link-Belt Company.*)

easily maneuverable haulage units that dump forward. All these types have applications for which they are particularly fitted. The side-dump semitrailer units are used extensively where the units move over a continuous roadway to the crusher hopper, side dump, and then move away without backing or turning. Some of these units are capable of handling in excess of 20 tons.

In sand and gravel pits, shovels very often have dispensed with any intermediate haulage units, as they load field hoppers over a movable conveyor belt which can be swung in an arc near the source of the raw material.

5. Lump Materials

The belt conveyor and the elevating bucket conveyor are the main types of equipment used for the movement of these materials. They form part of a comprehensive handling system which provides for the movement of the materials from receipt to discharge or use as the case may be.

For flexibility and wider adaptability, they are often combined with gantry cranes, portable stacking and elevating conveyors, marine legs, and swinging booms. For smaller inclines, the belt conveyor is also used for elevating materials.

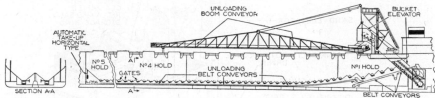

Fig. 326. Diagram of self-unloading ore vessel. (*Stephens-Adamson Manufacturing Company.*)

The most economical means of moving these materials is to provide for dumping of transporter units and gravity flow at the place of use. Thus rail cars will be tippled or dumped wherever possible. Loading of rail cars as well as ore and coal boats will be from chutes fed by overhead bins into which the above cars have dumped their contents.

a. Coal Handling. The handling of coal, from the standpoint of industry, generally starts with the unloading of rail cars. The user may not be able to dump cars as suggested above and other methods may have to be used.

The simplest method is with hand shovels. The shortage of labor and the difficulty in getting men to perform this type of work has made this method obsolete. With gondolas, portable conveyors which extend under the car move the materials out to a conveyor system to the stacking area. Portable conveyor loaders will complete the job. Cranes, overhead type in some instances but more often a mobile type, are also used. These are of truck type or caterpillar tread.

Barges and ships will be unloaded with conveyors on marine legs or with shore cranes. In some instances locomotive cranes will be used, but for the most part these have been replaced by portable types. For larger installations, gantry systems have been used to serve a larger storage area.

In large-scale handling of coal in coalyards, cranes of various types are employed. These range from large overhead gantrys to small crawler cranes, which provide a maximum of movement around the yard area. In addition, a wide variety of drag-chain devices will be used. In one installation an old Caterpillar tractor was used for the dead-man end and a movable winch was used at the other end. By means of this device the materials were skidded over to a hopper feed which dumped the material on to a conveyor. The conveyor in turn passed the material under the road to the processing plant on the other side.

FIG. 327. Standard types of earth-moving equipment are used to move coal in large storage areas. (*Caterpillar Tractor Company.*)

The Union Electric Power Company operates two plants in Illinois, each planned to handle coal into and out of storage. Their maximum rate is about 2,000 tons in 8 hours. At the Chakia plant, the main storage pile of 200,000 tons is located close to the unloading and reclaiming point with an average haul of about 300 feet each way.

Movement of coal is accomplished with three Caterpillar tractors. A bulldozer is used to maintain roadways and keep the pile trimmed and compacted. The other two units are equipped with 14-yard capacity scrapers. It was originally estimated that 750 tons per 8-hour shift could be handled by each unit. In actual practice, outputs of 900 tons per 8-hour day have been attained. Over a year's operation, the movement of ap-

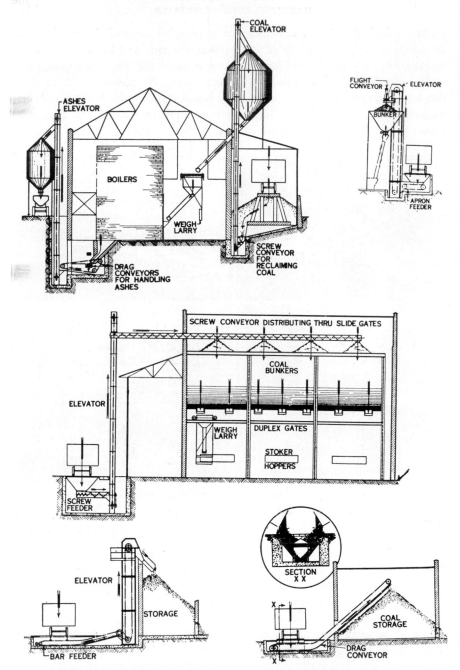

FIG. 328. To illustrate the variety of ways in which coal and ash may be handled, these nine typical arrangements of installations in boiler plants are presented by one equipment company. (*Link-Belt Company.*)

518

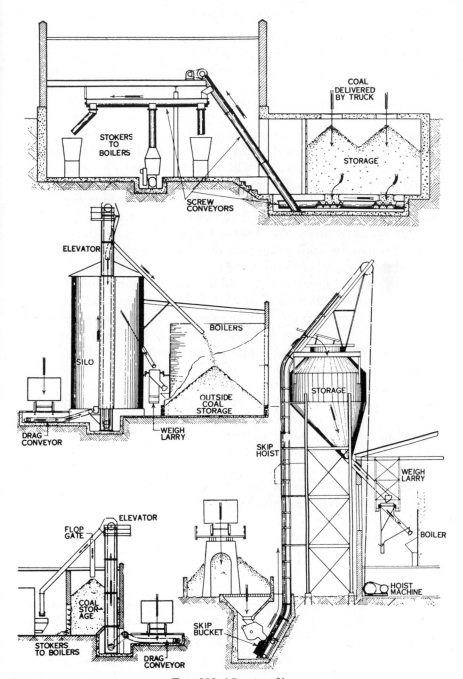

Fig. 328 (Continued).

519

proximately 350,000 tons of coal was accomplished at a cost of 8 cents a ton exclusive of loading costs and capital costs of tractor equipment.

At the Venice plant, the limitations of the plant site dictated that the coal storage would be located at a considerable distance from the unloading and reclaiming point. The average length of haul for storage coal at this plant is 2,500 feet one way. For this reason, considerable thought was given to the selection of equipment to be used. Crawler-tractor units were ruled out almost from the start in favor of rubber-tired tractors and scrapers. This storage operation will ultimately be set up for 2,000 tons of coal in 8 hours. It is expected that each of the three self-propelled rubber-tired tractor scrapers to be used will deliver into storage or reclaim 760 tons of coal per 8-hour day. Preliminary performance indicated that this can be realized. Two tractor bulldozer units will be used, one for general purpose compacting coal, maintaining roadways, shaping the pile, and so on; the other tractor will be used as a pusher when reclaiming coal from storage. Because of the additional operator required for the pusher, it is expected that the average cost of reclaiming coal from storage will be about 8 cents per ton, with an average cost into and out of storage of about 9 cents per ton per move based on early 1949 labor rates.[5]

An integrated system of handling coal has reduced the cost of handling and produced numerous other benefits for the Norton Company, Worcester, Mass. Coal is now brought in in hopper-bottom cars instead of gondolas. A large concrete-lined depressed pit permits the hoppers to be unloaded quickly and efficiently. A bulldozer is used to push the coal away from under the trestle and also to pile it in large piles in other parts of the pit. The material is then removed by means of a hopper opening and a belt conveyor to the coal bunker within the plant. Although it is estimated that the cost of the new system will be recovered in about 8½ years, other advantages are expected to cut this cost recovery period considerably.[6]

b. Ore Handling. Preparation for the loading of ore ships starts at the mine. Analysis is made of each carload. This is telephoned to the sorting yards prior to the train's arrival. Cars are weighed as they pass over scales at the rate of 2 miles per hour. The engines then assemble the cars in accordance with the chemical analysis. Thus, each boat's cargo will contain the correct amount of iron, phosphorus, silica, manganese, and other elements needed to comply with furnace requirements.

---

[5] E. H. Rudolph, Handling Coal by Tractor Equipment, *Power Generation,* March, 1949, p. 70.

[6] Allan Hardy, Jr., We Save Thirty-seven Cents a Ton on Thirty Thousand Tons of Coal a Year, *Factory Management and Maintenance,* February, 1950, p. 74.

Ore cars have hopper bottoms and are of standard length. These
lengths correspond to the width of the bins into which the ore is dumped
and the distance between ore hatches in the boats. The Duluth docks,

Fig. 329. Traveling-belt stacker conveyor is used for distributing coal in large storage
yard. (*Link-Belt Company.*)

claimed to be the largest in the world, are 2,004 feet long. Each dock
has 384 pockets with a capacity of 400 tons each. Total capacity of the
three Duluth docks is 460,000 tons.

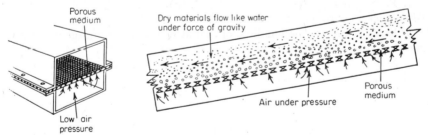

Fig. 330. Low air pressure fluffs up fine, dry materials so that they flow freely on a
slight gradient. (*Modern Materials Handling.*)

Before the boat arrives in the harbor, notice is sent to inform the dock
operators of the time of arrival, capacities, and requirements for that
particular load. With this information, ore cars of the proper grade ores
are selected and pushed onto the docks. This ore is transferred into the

ore pockets of the docks and is then ready for transfer into the hold of the ship. A 20,000-ton ship may be loaded in as little as 6 hours' time.

QUESTIONS

1. What considerations determine the selection of a system for the movement of sand and gravel?

2. Discuss the use of enclosed conveyor equipment in the movement of bulk materials.

3. Large reserves of coal built up for power-plant requirements present special problems in handling. Discuss some of the solutions used successfully to date.

4. Discuss the movement of fluids and materials held in suspension.

5. What are some of the ways by which grain is moved or handled?

6. What factors must be considered in the selection of a handling system for bulk materials?

7. What special problems are involved in the movement of fine-ground materials?

8. What types of equipment are most commonly used for the movement of lump materials?

9. How will the nature of the materials being handled affect the handling system to be used?

10. Can unit-load handling be applied to movement of bulk materials? Explain.

11. What types of materials can be moved by means of pneumatic conveyor systems?

12. Give a brief account of the operation of the ore-loading docks at Duluth.

PROJECTS FOR FURTHER STUDY

1. Prepare a report on the handling of (a) grain, (b) sulphur, (c) coal, (d) cinder and ash, or (e) carbon black.

2. Make a study of the handling of coal at power plants and generating stations.

3. Make a survey of the methods of handling used for loading and unloading bulk materials from ships and barges.

SELECTED SOURCES OF INFORMATION

TEXTBOOKS

APPLE, JAMES M.: "Plant Layout and Materials Handling," The Ronald Press Company, New York, 1950.

BARKER, FOOTLIK, YARHAM, and CARLE: "Industrial Materials Handling," Lincoln Extension Institute, Inc., Cleveland, Ohio, 1950.

Commonwealth of Australia (Ministry of Post-War Reconstruction): "Materials Handling," Angus and Robertson, Ltd., Sidney, Australia.

IMMER, JOHN R.: "Layout Planning Techniques," McGraw-Hill Book Company, Inc., New York, 1950.

MALLICK, RANDOLPH W., and ARMAND T. GAUDREAU: "Plant Layout," John Wiley & Sons, Inc., New York, 1951.

SUPPLEMENTARY BOOKS

ALFORD, L. P., and J. R. BANGS: "Production Handbook," pp. 993–1027, The Ronald Press Company, New York, 1945.

BARNES, R. M., and N. A. ENGLERT: "Bibliography of Industrial Engineering and Management Literature," Wm. C. Brown Company, Dubuque, Iowa.

CLEMENT, EDWARD J., and CARL C. HARRINGTON: "Plant Maintenance Manual," Chaps. 3 and 14–19 inclusive, Conover-Mast Publications, Inc., New York, 1949.

"Handbok i Industriell Driftsekonomi och Organization" ("Transporter vid ett Industrieföretag" by Erick Hj. Lindström), Natur och Kultur, Stockholm, 1949.

"Handbok i Industriell Anläggningsteknik" (Transportanordningar), Natur och Kultur, Stockholm, 1948.

MAYNARD, H. B., and G. J. STEGEMERTEN: "Operation Analysis," McGraw-Hill Book Company, Inc., 1939.

MUTHER, RICHARD: "Production Line Technique," McGraw-Hill Book Company, Inc., New York, 1944.

EQUIPMENT AND NOMENCLATURE

ATHERTON, W. H.: "Conveying Machinery," The Technical Press, Ltd., Kingston Hill, England.

ATHERTON, W. H.: "Conveyors and Cranes," Pitman Publishing Corp., New York.

BARSON, W. A.: "Electric Overhead Traveling Crane Design," The Technical Press, Ltd., Kingston Hill, England.

BROUGHTON, H. H.: "Electric Winders—A Manual on the Design, Construction, Application, and Operation of Winding Engines and Mine Hoists," E. & F. Spon, Ltd., London, 1948.

"*Flow* Directory of Materials Handling Equipment," *Flow* magazine, Cleveland, Ohio, annual.

GIVEN, I. A.: "Mechanical Loading of Coal Underground," McGraw-Hill Book Company, Inc., New York, 1943.

HETZEL, F. V., and RUSSELL K. ALBRIGHT: "Belt Conveyor and Belt Elevators," John Wiley & Sons, Inc., New York, 1941.

HUDSON, WILBUR G.: "Conveyors and Related Equipment," John Wiley & Sons, Inc., New York, 1944.

KOSHKIN, SIMON J.: "Modern Materials Handling," John Wiley & Sons, Inc., New York, 1932.

POTTS, M. W.: "Materials Handling Equipment," Pitman Publishing Corp., New York, 1946.

REIBEL, SIDNEY V.: "Trolley Conveyors," McGraw-Hill Book Company, Inc., New York, 1949.

STOCKER, H. E.: "Materials Handling," Prentice-Hall, Inc., New York, 1943.

TOURNIER, EDWARD J.: "Materials Handling Equipment," McGraw-Hill Book Company, Inc., New York, 1929.

ZIMMER, GEORGE F.: "Mechanical Handling and Storing of Materials," The Technical Press, Ltd., Kingston Hill, England.

PACKAGING

"Bonnell's Manual on Packaging and Shipping," Bonnell Publications, Inc., New York, 1950.

"Modern Packaging Encyclopedia," Packaging Catalogue Corporation, New York, annual.

CASE STUDIES

THE MATERIALS HANDLING INSTITUTE: "Modern Methods of Materials Handling," Prentice-Hall, Inc., New York, 1950.

URQUHART, LEWIS K., and CARROLL W. BOYCE: "Materials Handling Case Book," McGraw-Hill Book Company, Inc., New York, 1951.

SPECIAL REPORTS

"Materials Handling in Industry," Anglo-American Council on Productivity, 2 Park Avenue, New York, 1950.

"Safety Code for Conveyors, Cableways and Related Equipment," American Society of Mechanical Engineers, 1948.

"Safety Code for Industrial Power Trucks," American Standards Association, 70 East 45th Street, New York. (31 pages.)

"Safety Code for Elevators," rev. ed., American Society of Mechanical Engineers, 1945.

UNITED STATES GOVERNMENT PUBLICATIONS

(To be obtained from the Superintendent of Documents, Washington, D.C.)

Military

"Depot Operations, Space Reporting," ASF M-402-4, November, 1945.

"Depot Operations—Storage," Army Service Forces, ASF M-402, October, 1942.

"Depot Operations, Storage and Handling of Hazardous Commodities," ASF M-402-1, 1943.

"Depot Operations, Storage, Handling and Packaging of Engineer Supplies," ASF M-402-2, February, 1944.

"Depot Operations, Storage and Issue of Ordnance—General Supplies," ASF M-402-3, August, 1944.

"Materials Handling Manual," NAVSANDA Publication 13, Mar. 10, 1944.

"Navy Carloading, a Handbook on Loading and Bracing Methods," NAVSANDA Publication 65, November, 1945.

"Operator Selection and Training: Materials Handling Equipment," TM 21-302, February, 1945.

"Operator Selection and Training (Platform Trucks, Wheeled Warehouse Cranes and Straddle Trucks)," TM 21-302A, December, 1945.

"Quartermaster Materials Handling Equipment," TM 10-1619, March, 1945.

"Storage in the Zone of Interior," TM 38-402, March, 1946.

"Storage Methods of Aeronautical Parts, Assemblies, and Materials," NAVSANDA Publication 64, September, 1945.

"Storage of Quartermaster Supplies," TM 10-250, March, 1946.

"Warehousing and Materials Handling," ATSC Manual 67-9, Equipment Manual Series D, Headquarters ATSC, Wright Field, Ohio, Dec. 1, 1944.

Civilian

"A Study of Tobacco Wholesaler's Operations," U.S. Department of Commerce, 1946.

"Dry Goods Wholesalers' Operations," John R. Bromell, U.S. Department of Commerce, 1949.

"Effective Grocery Wholesaling," Economic Series 14, U.S. Department of Commerce, 1941.

"Effective Use of Drug Warehouses," U.S. Department of Commerce, 1947.

"Packaging and Shipping Containers," Business Information Service, U.S. Department of Commerce, 1949 (17 pages reference to other publications).

"Packaging, Marking, and Loading Methods for Steel Products for Commercial Overseas Shipments," Simplified Practise Recommendation R237-49.

"Pallets for Handling Groceries and Packaged Merchandise," Simplified Practise Recommendation R228-48, U.S. Department of Commerce.

"Principles of Box and Crate Construction," C. A. Plaskett, U.S. Department of Agriculture *Technical Bulletin* 171. (132 pages.)

"Streamlined Wholesale Grocery Warehouses," William H. Meserole, U.S. Department of Commerce, Industrial Series 18, 1945.

"Warehousing," Inquiry Reference Service, U.S. Department of Commerce. 1948. (Contains 8 pages reference to other publications.)

GOVERNMENT OF AUSTRALIA PUBLICATIONS

(Division of Industrial Development, 203 Collin Street, Melbourne, C.1, Victoria.)

"Materials Handling and Distribution," in preparation.

"Materials Handling in the Building Industry," No. 4, Part 1, September, 1947.

"Materials Handling in the Building Industry," Part 2, in preparation.

"Materials Handling; Packaging and Crating," in preparation.

"Pallets," No. 2, May, 1946.

"Unit Loading with the Fork Truck," No. 1, May, 1945.

"Warehouse Improvements," No. 3, 1947.

MAGAZINES

Materials Handling

Air Transportation, 10 Bridge St., New York 4, New York.

Distribution Age, Chestnut and 56th Street, Philadelphia 39, Pa.

Flow, 1240 Ontario St., Cleveland, Ohio.

Mechanical Handling, Dorset House, Stamford Street, London, S.E.1, England.

Modern Materials Handling, 795 Boylston St., Boston 16, Mass.

World Ports, 815 Washington Building, Washington 5, D.C.

Packaging

Modern Packaging, 122 East 42d St., New York.

Industrial Engineering

American Machinist, 330 West 42d St., New York 36, New York.

Factory Management and Maintenance, 330 West 42d St., New York 36, New York.

Industry and Power, St. Joseph, Mich.

Mass Production, Sawell Publications, Ltd., 4 Ludgate Circus, London, W.C.4.

Mill & Factory, 205 East 42d St., New York 17, New York.

Modern Industry, 400 Madison Ave., New York 17, New York.

Plant Administration, McClure Publishing Company, Toronto, Canada.

OTHER SOURCES OF INFORMATION

American Management Association, 330 W. 42d St., New York 36, New York. (Lists of booklets in Marketing, Production, and Packaging Series.)

American Society of Mechanical Engineers, 29 W. 39th St., New York.

American Society for Testing Materials, 260 Broad St., Philadelphia, Pa.

Association of American Railroads, Freight Loading and Container Section, Secretary, 59 E. Van Buren Street, Chicago 5, Ill. (List of 105 items covering containers, carloading, and packing instructions.)

Hinde and Dauch Paper Company, Little Packaging Library, Sandusky, Ohio. (Corrugated containers.)

International Cargo Handling Co-ordination Association, 7 Victoria Street, London, S.W.1.

National Safety Council, 20 N. Wacker Drive, Chicago 6, Ill. (Bulletins on accident prevention.)

Society of Industrial Packaging and Materials Handling Engineers, 20 W. Jackson Blvd., Chicago, Ill.

The American Materials Handling Society, 1200 Madison Ave., Indianapolis, Ind.

The Material Handling Institute, Inc., 1108 Clark Building, Pittsburgh, Pa.

"Trade and Professional Associations of the United States," 1942, U.S. Department of Commerce or Superintendent of Documents, Washington, D.C. (320 pages.) (There are over 400 materials-handling and packaging associations in the United States.)

CLASSIFICATION FOR MATERIALS-HANDLING INFORMATION

This classification was devised to provide a more comprehensive system for the organization of information in regard to materials handling. It is the result of the industry-wide cooperation afforded the author during the three years it took to develop it. This was an evolutionary process contributed to by many individuals, companies, and trade associations, many of whom undertook further research and study in order to develop particular sections.

The equipment classification was originally adapted from the code developed by Westinghouse Electric Corporation. Wherever possible, the appropriate classifications of the Standard Commodity Classification were followed. The Conveyor Equipment Manufacturers Association made available their detailed classification for conveyors. Reference was also made to the code developed by Chevrolet and others. A preliminary list was sent out by the Material Handling Institute, Inc., to 70 equipment manufacturers. Replies were received from the majority, and the list was further amended.

There has been a need for a long time of a system for classifying materials which would have some relation to difficulty of handling. The classification by weight and shape was suggested by Prof. Marvin Mundel of Purdue University. (See page 295 for further description of the use of this classification.)

10. MATERIALS-HANDLING EQUIPMENT

11. Cranes, derricks, hoists, and winches

11.1 *Cranes, railroad*
   11.11 Locomotive crane, steam-powered
   11.12 Locomotive crane, internal-combustion-engine powered
   11.13 Locomotive crane, electric-powered
   11.14 Locomotive cranes not otherwise classified
   11.15 Wrecking crane

11.2 *Overhead traveling cranes* (except gantry and monorail)
   11.21 Hand-racked or pushed
   11.22 Electric-powered
   11.23 Telpher type

11.3 *Cranes, portable types* (except revolving and industrial-truck)
   11.31 Portable gooseneck
   11.32 Portable telescopic
   11.33 Motor truck, rigid-boom type

11.4 *Gantry-type cranes and ore bridges*
   11.41 Full gantry
   11.42 Semigantry
   11.43 Cantilever-type
   11.44 Ore bridge

11.5 *Revolving cranes* (except locomotive type)
   11.51 Fixed-base
   11.52 Gantry
   11.53 Floating (mounted on barge)
   11.54 Crawler (caterpillar treads)
   11.55 Motor truck

11.6 *Bracket and pillar cranes*
   11.61 Cantilever jib
   11.62 Pillar (or column) jib
   11.63 Walking jib
   11.64 Wall-mounted traveling jib
   11.65 Stiff-leg derrick and derrick types
   11.66 Boom (ship)

11.7 *Crane accessories*
   11.71 Buckets
   11.72 Grab devices (including hooks, tongs, and grapples)
   11.73 Slings, cable and rope
   11.74 Lifting magnet

11.8 *Hoisting units* (skid and base-mounted)
   11.81 Air-powered
   11.82 Electric-powered
   11.83 Hand chain and rope
   11.84 Air cylinder
   11.85 Skip hoist
   11.86 Drag scraper
   11.87 Fixed-base
   11.88 Capstan

12. Conveyors

12.1 *Belt conveyors* (except portable)
   12.11 Troughed belt
   12.12 Flat belt
   12.13 Solid metal
   12.14 Mesh
   12.15 Chain
   12.16 Wire

12.2 *Elevator conveyors* (except freight or passenger-platform type)
   12.21 Belt-and-bucket type
   12.22 Chain-and-bucket type
   12.23 Arm-and-tray type, single-strand chain
   12.24 Arm-and-tray type, multi-strand chain
   12.25 Pivoted bucket conveyor
   12.26 V-bucket carriers
   12.27 Vertical screw conveyor

12.3 *Chain conveyors* (except portable)
   12.31 Apron type (steel and wood) including pan and slat conveyor (continuous bed)
   12.32 Flight, package or unit types (single- and multiple-strand)
   12.33 Scraper or flight (bulk materials)
   12.34 Single-chain drag
   12.35 Multiple-chain drag
   12.36 Car haul (chain under floor)
   12.37 Carrousel

12.4 *Roller conveyors* (except portable)
   12.41 Live roller
   12.42 Gravity roller
   12.43 Gravity wheel
   12.44 Gravity roller spiral
   12.45 Ball transfer heads
   12.46 Upender

12.5 *Overhead conveying units*
   12.51 Trolley conveyor
   12.52 Monorail (units propelled by hand or individual traction units)
   12.53 Telpher monorail
   12.54 Cableway (suspended from two elevated posts)
   12.55 Ropeway (long-distance cable or rope system)
   12.56 Screw type (for slow movement of hangers through processing)

12.6 *Enclosed conveyors*
   12.61 Screw conveyor
   12.62 Rope-and-button type
   12.63 Pneumatic type—package
   12.64 Pneumatic type—bulk
   12.65 Hydraulic tube
   12.66 Enmasse or induced-flow types
   12.67 Zipper

12.7 *Portable conveying units*
   12.71 Belt (package and car unloaders)
   12.72 Chain type (drag, slat, flight, or bar)
   12.73 Bucket type
   12.74 Extensible units
   12.75 Roller and wheel units
   12.76 Screw conveyor (twin screw for propelling bags)
   12.77 Segmented units (including narrow-belt type)

12.9 *Conveyors, others not classified*
   12.91 Vibrating or oscillating type (includes vertical spiral)
   12.92 Automatic pallet loader
   12.93 Magnetic separator
   12.94 Revolving fixed conveyors (including table, wheel, or arm type)

13. Industrial trucks, tractors, trailers, stackers and accessories, and wheeled devices used for handling (used for material handling on floors and paved surfaces in and around industrial plants, depots, docks, and terminals; excludes highway trucks and tractors and equipment used in mining, agriculture, logging, earth moving, and petroleum development)

13.1 *Hand trucks and dollies*
   13.11 Two-wheeled trucks (including third wheel for hand trucks)
   13.12 Platform-type trucks (three- and four-wheel trucks except casters and trailers)
   13.13 Dolly and attachable lift units (including casters)
   13.14 Lift truck, skid-type, manual-operated
   13.15 Lift truck, pallet-type, manual-operated
   13.16 Lift truck, skid-type, powered ("walkie")
   13.17 Lift truck, pallet-type, powered ("walkie")
   13.18 Other prime movers, powered and hand-operated
   13.19 Other not classified (including wheeled dump containers)

13.2 *Industrial tractors and trailers*
   13.21 Tractor, industrial, gasoline-powered
   13.22 Tractor, industrial, electric-powered
   13.23 Trailers, industrial
   13.24 Tractor, farm-type
   13.25 Tractor, accessories
   13.26 Tractor-trailer systems

13.3 *Industrial truck, gasoline-powered*
   13.31 Lift truck, fork-type, low-lift
   13.32 Lift truck, platform-type, low-lift
   13.33 Lift truck, fork-type, high-lift
   13.34 Lift truck, platform-type, high-lift
   13.35 Platform truck, nonlift
   13.36 Crane truck
   13.37 Straddle truck

13.4 *Industrial truck, electric-powered*
   13.41 Lift truck, fork-type, low-lift
   13.42 Lift truck, platform-type, low-lift

13.43 Lift truck, fork-type, high-lift

13.44 Lift truck, platform-type, high-lift

13.45 Platform truck, nonlift

13.46 Crane truck

13.5 *Tier machines* ("portable elevators")

13.51 Manual lift

13.52 Electrical lift

13.53 Gas-motor lift

13.54 Hydraulic lift

13.55 Portable elevators

13.56 Accessories (including crane attachments)

13.6 *Industrial-truck accessories* (except industrial-tractor and trailer accessories)

13.61 Scoops

13.62 Rams

13.63 Grab devices

13.64 Hydraulic pushers and push-pullers

13.65 Bridges (dockboards, loading plates)

13.66 Batteries and charging facilities

13.67 Gasoline and electric motors and accessories

13.68 Crane attachment

14. **Fixed-track equipment** (other than conveyors) (For car movers, see 11.88, also 14.46.)

14.1 *Standard-gauge track* (railroad)

14.11 Four-wheeled flatcars

14.12 Steel container on wheels or dump cars

14.2 *Track narrower than standard gauge*

14.21 Four-wheeled flatcars, including bogies

14.22 Steel container on wheels or dump cars

14.23 Channel-iron track

14.24 Intra-plant railway

14.3 *Track wider than standard gauge*

14.31 Wheeled tables or platforms

14.4 *Power units*

14.41 Switching locomotive, steam power

14.42 Switching locomotive, diesel power

14.43 Switching locomotive, diesel-power electric

14.44 Switching locomotive, electric power

14.45 Other electric-drive units

14.46 Wheeled car movers

15. **Elevating devices** (except elevating conveyors, stackers, and tiering machines and hoists)

15.1 *Chutes*

15.11 Spiral

15.12 Straight

15.13 Sluices and flumes

15.14 Passing boards

15.2 *Elevators*

15.21 Passengers

15.22 Freight

15.23 Short rise (sidewalk or floor)

15.24 Dumb-waiter

15.25 Man lift

15.3 *Endgate lifting devices*

15.4 *Adjustable platforms* (including loading aids and feeding tables)

15.41 Hydraulic loading platform

15.42 Other loading platforms

15.43 Feeding tables (adjustable lift or positioning tables)

15.44 Conveyor-lift section

15.45 Truckbed lift

15.5 *Electric stairways*

15.6 *Unloading machines*

15.61 Ore loaders (including Hulett)

15.62 Belt spreaders systems (for coal, ore, etc.)

15.63 Dock loading machines for packaged or unit goods

15.64 Car dumpers or tipples

15.65 Extensible arm unloader unit (for wheat)

16. **Industrial storage facilities**

16.1 *Skids and platforms*

16.11 Stationary skid, steel and wood

16.12 Semilive skid, steel and wood

16.13 Live skid, steel and wood

16.14 Platform, steel

16.15 Skid container, steel

16.16 Platform, wood
16.17 Skid, rack-type
16.18 Skid, dumping-type (container)
16.2 *Pallets*
16.21 Wood
16.22 Metal (except wire mesh)
16.23 Paperboard, cardboard, and fiberboard
16.24 Wire metal (includes collapsible container type)
16.25 Box type
16.26 Side support (for irregular materials)
16.27 Tray or tier type
16.28 Collapsible (other than wire metal)
16.3 *Dunnage and other palletizing materials* (except pallets)
16.31 Loose dunnage
16.32 Pallet omission (arranging material for unit-load handling)
16.33 Paperboard base
16.34 Paper and cloth binding
16.4 *Industrial containers*
16.41 Baskets and perforated containers
16.42 Tote pans (metal, wood, and fiber)
16.43 Trays (including trays for overhead conveyors)
16.44 Metal, large
16.45 Wood, large
16.46 Tanks
16.5 *Racks and frames*
16.51 Bar racks
16.52 Barrel racks
16.53 Tree or rotary type
16.54 Portable (all types)
16.55 Tier racks
16.56 Frames
16.57 Racks for tote pans
16.58 A frames
16.6 *Shelving, drawers, bins*
16.61 Shelves and drawers
16.62 Shelves and drawers on rollers
16.63 Bins, fixed
16.64 Bins, portable

16.65 Bins, assembly
16.66 Bins, rotary
16.67 Lockers
16.7 *Tables and benches* (except elevating tables)
17. Shipping containers
17.1 *Metal*
17.11 Barrels and drums
17.12 Metal casings, welded and lock side seam (except barrels and drums)
17.13 Stainless-steel shipping containers (except barrels)
17.14 Steel packages, kegs, and pails (except beer barrels and stainless containers)
17.15 Shipping containers, fluid milk and ice cream
17.16 Cylinders
17.2 *Wood*
17.21 Wire-bound
17.22 Nailed, solid
17.23 Barrels and casks
17.24 Crates
17.25 Skids
17.26 Plywood, cleated
17.3 *Corrugated cardboard and fiberboard*
17.31 Box, fiberboard
17.32 Drum, fiberboard
17.33 Box, corrugated
17.34 Box, corrugated, wood cleats
17.4 *Bags, cloth, and paper*
17.41 Bags, cloth
17.42 Bags, burlap
17.43 Bags, paper, single-wall
17.44 Bags, paper, multi-wall
17.45 Boxes, paperboard
17.5 *Other container material* (outer case used for protection)
17.6 *Corrosion-preventive materials*
17.61 Weatherproof papers
17.62 Cocoon covering
17.63 Metal treating
17.64 Resin and wax coatings
17.65 Cellophane and plastic materials
17.66 Grease type (including Cosmoline)
17.67 Desiccants
17.68 Vapor inhibitor papers

17.7 *Fastening devices*
    17.71 Steel wire and strap
    17.72 Wire stitching
    17.73 Thread stitching
    17.74 Nails and staples
    17.75 Adhesive tape
    17.76 Bolts and screws

18. Packaging materials and equipment
18.1 *Product container materials*
    18.11 Paperboard (not corrugated)
    18.12 Cloth
    18.13 Plastic
    18.14 Glass
    18.15 Metal
    18.16 Cellophane
    18.17 Paper
18.2 *Sealing devices*
    18.21 Glue and adhesive materials (except tape)
    18.22 Adhesive tape
    18.23 Twine stitching
    18.24 Metal stitching
    18.25 Soldering
    18.26 Paraffin
    18.27 Plastic materials
    18.28 Staples
18.3 *Packaging machinery*
    18.31 Filling machines
    18.32 Weighing machines (except scales and balances)
    18.33 Cartoning machines
    18.34 Wrapping machines
    18.35 Package, sealing, and stapling machines (including stitching machines, except hand-dispensing devices)
    18.36 Capping machines
    18.37 Labeling machines
    18.38 Combination machines (including units performing multiple functions of above)
18.4 *Packing and absorbent materials*
    18.41 Cotton and kapok
    18.42 Shredded materials
    18.43 Wood fiber (including loose excelsior and pads)
    18.44 Bracing devices, wood
    18.45 Suspension bracing (except wood)
    18.46 Corrugated paper
    18.47 Creped cellulose
    18.48 Rubberized curled hair

19. Materials and equipment not listed above
19.1 *Controls*
    19.11 Automatic loading and pick-up devices (for conveyors)
    19.12 Electronic controls
    19.13 Weighing machines (except packaging machinery)
19.2 *Man handling*
19.3 *Grasping devices* (including manipulative equipment)
    19.31 "Iron hand" devices
    19.32 Other hand grasping devices
    19.33 Charging machines (except monorail and bridge crane)
    19.34 Manipulators, forging type (except bridge cranes)
19.4 *Equipment adapted to handling from other activities*
    19.41 Bulldozer
    19.42 Road-grading machinery
    19.43 Earth scrapers (used for moving coal)

20. INDUSTRY
21. Basic industries
21.1 *Coal industry*
    21.11 Mining and extractive
    21.12 Processing
    21.13 Storage and handling
    21.14 Retail distribution
    21.15 Power-plant operations
21.2 *Other mining and extractive industries*
    21.21 Iron ore
    21.22 Other ores
    21.23 Stone quarries
21.3 *Primary reduction*
    21.31 Iron and steel smelting and processing
    21.32 Other smelting and reduction
    21.33 Foundry and casting operations (see 32.40)
    21.34 Oil refining and processing
    21.35 Rubber, natural and synthetic (except products)
    21.36 Chemicals

21.4 *Wood products*
    21.41 Logging and cutting (including timber and poles)
    21.42 Sawmill operations—lumber (all sizes and shapes)
    21.43 Plywood and wood bonding manufacture and fabrication
    21.44 Paper and pulp mills
21.5 *Sand and gravel plants*
22. Manufactured products
22.1 *Transportation equipment*
    22.11 Airplanes (including supplies, controls, and accessories)
    22.12 Automobiles (including passenger cars and trucks, tires, equipment, and accessories)
    22.13 Railroad equipment (including trains and locomotives)
    22.14 Railway repair shops
    22.15 Boat building (including lifeboats, motor boats and sail boats)
    22.16 Ship building (except naval construction)
    22.17 Barge construction (including tugs)
22.2 *Machinery*
    22.21 Machine tools
    22.22 Farm equipment
    22.23 Hand tools and equipment
    22.24 Office equipment
    22.25 Special processing machinery
    22.26 Material-handling equipment and supplies
22.3 *Household appliances*
    22.31 Washing machines
    22.32 Refrigerators
    22.33 Stoves and ranges
    22.34 Kitchen cabinets
    22.35 Toasters and mixing machines
    22.36 Sewing machines
    22.37 Metal furniture
22.4 *Electrical products*
    22.41 Motors
    22.42 Generating equipment (including turbines and power-station equipment)
    22.43 Controls

    22.44 Radio
    22.45 Television
22.5 *Wood products*
    22.51 Furniture
22.6 *Nonferrous metal products*
    22.61 Clocks and watches
    22.62 Jewelry
22.7 *Toys*
    22.71 Trains
22.8 *Stone, clay, and glass products* (except construction materials)
    22.81 Pottery (including all vitrified products except building materials)
    22.82 Glassware
    22.83 Marble, granite, and other stone products
22.9 *Other not listed*
    22.91 Metal-container industry
23. Food and clothing group
23.1 *Agriculture* (including farming of all kinds and types)
23.2 *Food products*
    23.21 Beverages
    23.22 Meat packing and animal products (including canned goods)
    23.23 Fresh vegetables and fruits
    23.24 Frozen foods
    23.25 Canned food products (except meat products)
    23.26 Tea, coffee, nuts, spices, and condiments
    23.27 Sugar and salt
    23.28 Wheat and grain products
23.3 *Dairy and poultry products*
    23.31 Milk
    23.32 Butter
    23.33 Cheese
    23.34 Poultry
23.4 *Clothing*
    23.41 Women's
    23.42 Men's
    23.43 Children's
    23.44 Textile manufacturing
23.5 *Leather goods*
    23.51 Tanning
    23.52 Men's and children's shoes
    23.53 Women's shoes
    23.54 Luggage

23.6 *Personal services*
   23.61 Hotels
   23.62 Restaurant and food service
   23.63 Laundry and dry cleaning
23.7 *Food processing*
   23.71 Bakery
   23.72 Fisheries
24. Building and construction
24.1 *Residential construction*
   24.11 Factory fabrication of houses
   24.12 Progressive assembly of houses on site
   24.13 Conventional construction methods
24.2 *Other construction*
   24.21 Office buildings
   24.22 Factories and industrial plant
   24.23 Other commercial structures
   24.24 Dams, bridges, harbor construction
24.3 *Concrete and tile materials*
   24.31 Concrete
   24.32 Precast concrete (including blocks, tile, and sections)
   24.33 Brick
   24.34 Clay products (including building, roofing, and lining tiles)
24.4 *Glass*
   24.41 Glass sheets
   24.42 Glass brick
24.5 *Structural steel and steel products* (building)
   24.51 Structural steel
   24.52 Steel flooring
   24.53 Wall sections and materials
   24.54 Plumbing
24.6 *Other building materials*
   24.61 Lumber
   24.62 Millwork
   24.63 Building board and plywood construction
25. Military (except aircraft and truck manufacturing, see 22.11)
25.1 *Quartermaster*
25.2 *Ordnance*
   25.21 Ammunition (including all types and sizes)
   25.22 Small arms (components and accessories)

25.23 Other ordnance
25.24 Tanks
25.25 Vehicles (except trucks, see 22.12)
25.3 *Air Corps*
   25.31 Airplane maintenance and repair
   25.32 Bombs and ammunition
   25.33 Military transport (including cargo handling; see 33.35)
25.4 *Navy*
   25.41 Shore operations (see 33.33)
   25.42 Ship construction (including repair and dry docking) (Includes battleships, submarines, and destroyers. Does not include cargo and passenger ships.)
   25.43 Ammunition (including torpedoes)
26. Merchandising
26.1 *Warehousing and distribution centers* (see 33.00)
26.2 *Retail distribution*
   26.21 Grocery stores
   26.22 Department stores
27. Transportation
27.1 *Railroad* (see 33.31)
   27.11 Bulkheads
   27.12 Special frames and racks
   27.13 Damage due to improper loading and shunting
   27.14 Lcl and package handling
   27.15 Carloading diagrams and instructions
27.2 *Trucking* (see 33.32)
   27.21 Trailers
27.3 *Ships* (see 33.33)
   27.31 Ferries
   27.32 River boats and barge lines (see 33.34)
   27.33 Lake steamers and cargo ships (including ore ships)
   27.34 Ocean-going ships
27.4 *Air transportation* (except military; see 33.35)
   27.41 Cargo handling
   27.42 Maintenance and repair
   27.43 Balancing cargo load

27.44 Tie-down devices and methods
27.45 Bulkheading and cargo compartments
27.46 Special frames and racks
27.47 Refrigeration
27.5 *Terminals*
   27.51 Air
   27.52 Railway
   27.53 Truck
   27.54 Ship and barge
   27.55 Combination of above
   27.56 Harbor facilities
28. Printing and publishing
28.1 *Lithoprinting*
28.2 *Newspapers*
28.3 *Magazine publishing*
28.4 *Book publishing*
29. Other industries not classified
29.1 *Postal service*
   29.11 Mail sorting
   29.12 Parcel section
30. TYPE OF OPERATION
31. Assembly
31.1 *Stationary assembly*
   31.11 Jigs
   31.12 Assembly station or workplace
31.2 *Progressive assembly*
   31.21 Continuous movement
   31.22 Cycle movement
   31.23 Assembly station or workplace
31.3 *Subassemblies*
   31.31 Assembly of small parts
   31.32 Large subassemblies
31.4 *Jigs and fixtures*
   31.41 Master tooling dock
   31.42 Multi-story jigs
   31.43 Wheeled jigs
   31.44 Wheeled or castered turn-over jigs
   31.45 Other turnover and positioning devices
   31.46 Wheeled assembly jigs
32. Processing
32.1 *Machining*
   32.11 Presses, all types
   32.12 Other metalworking machines
   32.13 Woodworking machines
   32.14 Special process machinery (not other listed)
32.2 *Dipping processes*
   32.21 Pickling, cleaning, and degreasing
   32.22 Galvanizing and electroplating
   32.23 Heat treating (including quenching and annealing)
   32.24 Painting and application of protective coating
   32.25 Bonderizing
   32.26 Product impregnation
32.3 *Other treating and protective processes*
   32.31 Sandblasting
   32.32 Spraying (where handling and movement of materials is involved)
   32.33 Ball peening and shot blast
   32.34 Bake and drying ovens (infrared and other radiant heating)
   32.35 Bake and drying ovens, other than above
32.4 *Foundry operations*
   32.41 Coremaking
   32.42 Molding
   32.43 Pouring
   32.44 Shakeout
   32.45 Cleaning
   32.46 Forging
   32.47 Inspection
33. Warehousing operations
33.1 *Receiving*
   33.11 Unloading in warehouse
   33.12 Checking and inspection
   33.13 Removing from container
   33.14 Documenting and record work
33.2 *Storage*
   33.21 High stacking
   33.22 Live storage, floor conveyors
   33.23 Live storage, overhead equipment
   33.24 Layout of storage areas
   33.25 Details of storage methods (corner devices, etc.)

33.3 *Loading*
    33.31 Railroad (see 27.10 and 27.52)
    33.32 Truck (see 27.20 and 27.53)
    33.33 Ship (see 27.30 and 27.54)
    33.34 Barge (see 27.32 and 27.54)
    33.35 Air (see 25.33, 27.41 and 27.51)
33.4 *Shipping* (except preparation and crating)
    33.41 Order filling
    33.42 Sorting, hand
    33.43 Sorting, machine
    33.44 Stock distribution (for outgoing shipments)
    33.45 Stock distribution (intraplant stock rooms)
34. Packing and packaging operations
34.1 *Packaging operations*
    34.11 Filling and weighing (see 18.31 and 18.32)
    34.12 Labeling (see 18.37)
    34.13 Wrapping (see 18.34)
    34.14 Sealing (including all methods; see 18.35)
34.2 *Packing and crating operations* (see 27.10)
    34.21 Making or assembling wood boxes or crates
    34.22 Making cartons or boxes (other than crates and wood boxes)
    34.23 Packing materials to cartons (paperboard, all types)
    34.24 Packing materials to crates
    34.25 Packing materials to solid wood boxes
    34.26 Packing materials to wood veneer or plywood boxes
34.3 *Export packing*
40. MATERIALS HANDLED
41. Bulk handling
41.1 *Lump materials*
    41.11 Coal and coke
    41.12 Ash
    41.13 Ores
    41.14 Gravel
41.2 *Free-flowing solids*
    41.21 Salt

41.22 Sugar
41.23 Grain
41.24 Chemicals
41.25 Sand
41.3 *Fine-particle materials*
    41.31 Cement
    41.32 Flour
    41.33 Starch
    41.34 Carbon
41.4 *Liquids*
    41.41 Extremely viscous materials
    41.42 Medium viscous materials (including lubricating and cutting oils)
    41.43 Nonviscous materials (including gasoline and other free-flowing liquids)
42. Materials weighing 10 tons and over
42.1 *Irregular shapes*
42.2 *Square or oblong shape*
42.3 *Long lengths*
    42.31 Structural steel
42.4 *Roll or coil shaped*
42.5 *Sheets or plates*
42.6 *Cylindrical*
43. Materials weighing over 1 ton
43.1 *Irregular shapes*
43.2 *Square or oblong shape*
43.3 *Long lengths*
    43.31 Structural steel
    43.32 Pipe
    43.33 Rails
43.4 *Roll or coil shaped*
    43.41 Wide metal coil stock
    43.42 Narrow metal coil stock (less than 18 inches wide)
    43.43 Wire or cable coils or reels
    43.44 Paper
43.5 *Sheets or plates*
    43.51 Metal
43.6 *Cylindrical*
44. Materials weighing over 500 pounds
44.1 *Irregular shapes*
44.2 *Square or oblong shape*
44.3 *Long lengths*
    44.31 Logs
44.4 *Roll or coil shaped*
44.5 *Sheets or plates*
44.6 *Cylindrical*

45. Materials weighing over 50 pounds
45.1 *Irregular shapes*
45.2 *Square or oblong shape*
    45.21 Bales
    45.22 Bags
    45.23 Cartons
45.3 *Long lengths*
    45.31 Structural steel
    45.32 Steel framing
    45.33 Bar stock
    45.34 Logs
45.4 *Roll or coil shaped*
45.5 *Sheets*
45.6 *Cylindrical*
    45.61 Barrels and drums
46. Materials weighing under 50 pounds
46.1 *Irregular shapes*
46.2 *Square or oblong shape*
    46.21 Cartons
    46.22 Wood boxes
46.3 *Long lengths*
    46.31 Pipe
46.4 *Roll or coil shaped*
46.5 *Sheets*
46.6 *Cylindrical*
    46.61 Barrels and drums
46.7 *Small parts*
    46.71 Rivets
47. Materials with special handling problems
    47.01 Scrap handling
    47.02 Chip removal
    47.03 Garbage and refuse
50. SYSTEMS AND ORGANIZATION
51. Materials-handling analysis
51.1 *Cost analysis and records*
    51.11 General analysis of handling costs
    51.12 Equipment operation costs (detailed)
    51.13 Equipment installation costs (detailed)
    51.14 Short cost studies
    51.15 Equipment cost records and forms
    51.16 Other cost records and forms
51.2 *Surveys*
    51.21 Sequence of operations—materials handling

51.22 Material characteristic and quantity surveys
51.23 Utilization of equipment
51.24 Equipment characteristic forms
51.25 Selection of equipment, factors of
51.3 *Time- and motion-study techniques*
    51.31 Timing of operations or elements
    51.32 Operation analysis
    51.33 PTPH or other prepared-symbol charts
    51.34 Multi-man charts
    51.35 Motion-picture techniques
    51.36 Other camera techniques
51.4 *Check sheets*
52. Approach to materials handling
52.1 *Place in the economy*
    52.11 Cost to the national economy
    52.12 Relationship to production costs
    52.13 Resale value (including used equipment)
52.2 *Planning* (includes over-all approach)
52.3 *Management, relationship to*
52.4 *Organization*
52.5 *Principles of materials handling*
    52.51 Use gravity where possible (see 12.42 and 15.10)
    52.52 Reduce terminal time of power units
    52.53 Standardization (including equipment standards and standard units)
    52.54 Avoid rehandling
    52.55 Move in unit loads (see 16.10, 16.20, and 17.12)
    52.56 Integrate handling equipment (indicates a complete system of handling)
    52.57 Utilize cubic space (including high stacking of pallets; see 11.20; also see high-lift industrial trucks)
    52.58 Straight-line flow
53. Operation
53.1 *Production control of materials-handling activities*

53.11 Scheduling (including load charts)

53.12 Dispatching

53.13 Coordinating equipment

53.2 *Intercommunication systems*

53.21 Telephone

53.22 Loudspeaker

53.23 Radio

53.24 Telautograph

53.25 Radio-visual

53.26 Pneumatic tube (see 12.63)

53.27 Trolley-basket

53.28 Messenger

53.3 *Job control*

53.31 Time studies

53.32 Procedure and instruction sheets (except safety)

53.33 Instruction manuals (including operating manuals)

53.34 Time standards (where not used for incentive plan)

53.35 Incentive plans

53.36 Job analysis (including job description and job evaluation)

53.4 *Safety*

53.41 Devices for equipment

53.42 Instructions

53.43 Programs and campaigns

53.44 Bulletins and instruction sheets

53.45 Demonstrations

53.46 Training the operator

53.5 *Maintenance*

53.51 Plant-wide for materials-handling equipment

53.52 Specific types of equipment

53.53 Floor repair and construction

53.54 Equipment details

53.55 Repair of equipment

53.56 Lubrication

53.6 *Operating methods*

53.7 *Tabulation of materials-handling equipment*

54. Layout planning (including general industrial buildings and design and techniques used in planning layouts)

54.1 *Information for layout*

54.11 Sequence of machine operations

54.12 Sequence of assembly operations

54.13 Manufacturing-data summary sheets

54.14 Machine-tool and equipment summaries

54.15 Workplace and machine space requirements

54.16 Steps for planning procedure

54.2 *Process charts* (see 51.32 and 51.33)

54.21 Operation process chart

54.22 Flow process chart

54.3 *Templets*

54.31 Background materials

54.32 Templets, handmade

54.33 Templets (furnished commercially or by equipment company)

54.34 Templets (transparent)

54.35 Templets (block or three-dimensional)

54.36 Templets (use of string to represent conveyors or to show flow lines)

54.4 *Scale models*

54.41 Machine tools and materials-handling equipment

54.42 Processing equipment

54.43 Office models

54.44 Other not classified

54.45 Use of transparent models

54.46 Commercial sources

54.47 Models of buildings

54.48 Working models

54.49 How to carve them

54.5 *Floor plans* (including layouts from scale drawings)

54.51 Floor plan of building only

54.52 Department drawings (no machines, no flow lines; shows major departments and areas only)

54.53 Department drawings (including flow lines; no machines)

BIBLIOGRAPHY OF MAGAZINE REFERENCES

Chapter 1. INTRODUCTION

CLARK, EZRA W.: Do Less Work and Cut Costs, *Nation's Business*, September, 1939, p. 27.

Conveyor Industry, *Iron Age*, Jan. 5, 1950, p. 247.

Handlers of Hardware, *Fortune*, March, 1949, p. 123.

Handling Organized for Mass Production, *American Machinist*, Oct. 23, 1947, p. 89.

Industrial Truck Shipments, 1935–1950, *Iron Age*, Jan. 4, 1951, p. 349.

Materials Handling in American Industry, 1950, *Management Review*, March, 1950, p. 144.

Materials Handling Is Vital to All Departments, *Textile World*, May, 1945, p. 97.

Materials Handling: The New Word in Industry, *Fortune*, June, 1948, p. 96.

Revolution in Mass Production, *Fortune*, February, 1943, p. 135.

WRIGHT, R. E.: Largest Single Item of Expense Other than Taxes, *Industrial and Engineering Chemistry*, April, 1950, Sup. 85A.

Chapter 2. HISTORY

BEAUMONT, W. WORBY: "Motor Vehicles and Motors," Constable & Co., Ltd., London, 1906.

CLARK, GRAHAM A.: "Textbook on Motor Car Engineering," Vol. 1, "Construction," D. Van Nostrand Company, Inc., New York, 1911.

FLANDERS, RALPH: "Construction and Manufacture of Automobiles," Industrial Press, New York, 1912.

HELDT, P. W.: "The Gasoline Automobile," P. M. Heldt, New York, 1920.

History of the Lift Truck in the Paper Industry, *Paper Industry and Paper World*, May, 1946, p. 226.

How They Began (the history of firms manufacturing mechanical handling equipment), *Mechanical Handling*, February, 1951, p. 70, and succeeding issues.

MORIARITY, T. F.: 35 Years of Fork Lift Truck Growth, *Paper Trade Journal*, Nov. 22, 1945, p. 76.

MOYER, JAMES A.: "Gasoline Automobiles," McGraw-Hill Book Company, Inc., New York, 1921.

New Ideas 20 Years Old; Studebaker Reverses Assembly Line, *Automotive and Aviation Industries*, Nov. 15, 1946, p. 21.

OWEN, C. B., and H. W. SLAUSON: "Machines, Tools, and Methods of Automobile Manufacture," Industrial Press, New York, 1910.

Chapter 3. PRINCIPLES

BEEBE, W. L.: The Handling and Transport of Materials in the Modern Factory, *Mechanical Handling*, May, 1947, p. 255.

GOENER, G. A.: Planning Avoids Unnecessary Handling, *Railway Age*, Feb. 8, 1947, p. 316.

MOTT, H. P.: Material Handling; A Résumé of General Principles, *Automobile Engineering*, June, 1950, p. 230.

New Parts Depots Do Cheaper, Faster Sales Job, *Business Week*, Aug. 7, 1948, p. 42.

Planned Materials Handling, *Mill & Factory*, June, 1944.

SCHIER, ARTHUR: Controlled Distribution, *Distribution Age*, November, 1946, p. 28.

Chapter 4. WORK SIMPLIFICATION

MOGENSON, ALLAN H.: Carry Out a Methods Improvement Program, *Factory Management and Maintenance*, July, 1949, p. 66.

WINKELMAN, CHARLES: Putting 105 Men to Work on Cost Reduction, *Factory Management and Maintenance*, July, 1949, p. 70.

Chapter 5. METHODS OF SHOWING FLOW

CARR, H. F.: Line Flow Requires only Five Days' Supply of Parts, *Factory Management and Maintenance*, September, 1948, p. 115.

Flow Handling of Materials, *Mill & Factory*, July, 1944.

Ford Redesigns for Straight Line Production of Radiators, *Automotive Industries*, July 15, 1947, p. 45.

Multi-product Assembly on a Straight Line, *Factory Management and Maintenance*, March, 1948, p. 74.

RYDER, FLORENCE: Relayout of 3-Story Warehouse Cuts Handling 30%, *Factory Management and Maintenance*, December, 1949, p. 112.

Chapter 6. TIME STUDY AND STANDARD TIMES

MUTHER, RICHARD: How to Use Pre-determined Motion Times to Material Handling Operations, *Modern Materials Handling*, 1951; March, p. 53; April, p. 64.

WEBB, W. J.: Methods, Motions and Time Study, *Automobile Engineering*, July, 1950, p. 254.

Chapter 7. FACTORS IN SELECTION OF EQUIPMENT

BLUM, F. M.: How to Evaluate a Crane Proposal, *Iron and Steel Engineering,* December, 1950, p. 125.

Materials Handling, Present and Future Use of Equipment, *Iron Age,* Jan. 4, 1951, p. 353.

Modern Materials Handling Equipment and Its Application, *Mechanical Handling,* running serially, January to June, 1949.

POOLE, W. E.: Survey Reveals Status of Materials Handling in Industry, *Industry and Power,* January, 1948, p. 80.

WISE, D. A., and L. N. BRAMLEY: Proposed Method of Specifying Travel-motion Performance to Steelworks Overhead Cranes, *Iron and Steel Institution Journal,* April, 1950, p. 439; discussion, November, 1950, p. 246.

WOODLEY, D. R.: Get the Best from Your Plant, *Mechanical Handling,* 1951; February, p. 61; March, p. 111; April, p. 149; May, p. 200; June, p. 232; October, p. 392.

1951 Production Preview: Plant Service Equipment, *American Machinist,* Jan. 22, 1951, p. 279.

Chapter 8. HORIZONTAL FIXED ROUTES

Battery-powered Monorail System, *Flow,* April, 1951, p. 44.

BRIGHT, JAMES R.: How to Provide for Traffic across Conveyor Systems, *Modern Materials Handling,* April, 1951, p. 49.

Conveyors Aid the Assembly of Motor Accessories, *Mechanical Handling,* February, 1947, p. 66.

Conveyors Handle Express Faster, *Railway Age,* July 1, 1950, p. 35.

DICKSON, B. A.: Ways to Get More Out of Your Freight Elevators, *Modern Materials Handling,* April, 1951, p. 37.

How to Figure Conveyor Belt Capacity, *Mill & Factory,* August, 1950, p. 101.

Merry-go-round System, *Steel,* Dec. 23, 1946, p. 59.

Perpetual Motion; Conveyor System Handles 1½ Million Pounds at Freight Terminal, *Steel,* Apr. 28, 1947, p. 124.

RICKER, C. A.: New Ideas in Conveyorized Assembly, *American Machinist,* Oct. 9, 1947, p. 96.

VON ROSEN, JOHN: Plymouth's Unique Conveyors, *Society of Automotive Engineering Journal,* March, 1948, p. 29.

SANDBERG, N. H.: New Roll Handling System at Waldorf, *Paper Industry and Paper World,* December, 1945, p. 1370.

STEEVES, ED.: Get Something Extra from Your Hoists, *Modern Materials Handling,* January, 1951, p. 21.

Take a Look at Your Freight Elevators, *Modern Materials Handling,* April, 1951, p. 34.

TORGERSON, R. S.: Move Cement with Air from Silos to Ships, *Rock Products,* January, 1943, p. 123.

WEBB, JERVIS B.: Flexibility of Chassis Assembly Widened by Suspended Conveying System, *Steel*, Sept. 8, 1947, p. 72.

Chapter 11. *HORIZONTAL MOVEMENT—NON-FIXED PATH*

At-a-Glance List of British-made Fork Lift Trucks, *Mechanical Handling*, 1951; May, p. 198; June, p. 240.

BRANDON, F. M.: Fork Trucks Double Storage Space; Halve Man Hours, *Factory Management and Maintenance*, November, 1947.

Industrial Trucks Move Heavy Loads Easily, *Mill & Factory*, October, 1948, p. 149.

LING, DAVID C.: The Potentialities of the Fork Truck and Pallet System, *Auto Engineer*, 1947; June, p. 213; July, p. 239; August, p. 287.

Materials Handling with Industrial Trucks, *Paper Industry and Paper World*, May, 1942, p. 152.

NILES, L. H.: Power Trucks Raise Effective Storage by 50%, *Factory Management and Maintenance*, December, 1947, p. 94.

Power Trucks Raise Effective Storage by 50%, *Railway Age*, June 26, 1948, p. 1278.

Truck for Each Job Achieves Smoother Materials Flow, *Steel*, Nov. 10, 1947, p. 120.

Unit Loads and Fork Trucks Save Time, *Railway Age*, June 26, 1948, p. 1278.

Chapter 12. *INDUSTRIAL STORAGE FACILITIES*

ASHLEY, E. H.: Saving in Freight Pays for Expendable Paper Pallets, *Factory Management and Maintenance*, March, 1947, p. 108.

BUCUSS, JOHN G.: Developing Unit Loads, *Modern Materials Handling*, May, 1951, p. 85.

Collapsible Metal Box Pallet, *Railway Age*, March, 1948, p. 478.

Corrugated Board Pallets Discarded after One Trip, *Textile World*, April, 1946, p. 160.

COVERT, ROYCE M.: Standard Palletized Loads, *Factory Management and Maintenance*, December, 1948, p. 108.

Dravo Develops New Shipping Container, *Marine Engineering*, September, 1947, p. 102.

GOLDWEITZ, SAUL: 41 Sources of Savings in Expendable Pallet Shipments, *Modern Materials Handling*, February, 1951, p. 53.

HENDRICKSON, B. M.: Tiering of Materials Conserves Valuable Floor Space, *Steel*, June 26, 1948, p. 123.

LEHN, H. V.: Palletizing Permits Stockpiling for Quick Shipment, *Factory Management and Maintenance*, September, 1947, p. 82.

LOEPER, B. R., and JOHN R. HUGHES: Practical Palletizing Pays Off, *American Machinist*, Nov. 21, 1946, p. 113.

MEREDITH, D.: New Container System on the L & N, *Manufacturing Record*, March, 1946, p. 39.

MILLER, HARRY J., JR.: More Pallet Loads in Less Space, *Modern Materials Handling*, February, 1951, p. 38.

Palletization, *Steel*, June 23, 1947, p. 127.

PALMER, T. O.: Light Weight Pallets for Easy Handling of Materials, *Mechanical Handling*, February, 1947, p. 100.

SITLER, RICHARD: How to Plan a Stockroom Layout, *Modern Materials Handling*, December, 1952, p. 51.

Standardization and the Use of Pallets, *Railway Age*, May 10, 1947, p. 936.

Standardization of Pallets, *Mechanical Handling*, April, 1947, p. 174.

Steel Strapping Methods for Bracing Carload Shipments, *Flow*, April, 1951, p. 56.

THOMPSON, J. I.: Palletized Handling—Uses and Misuses, *Food Industries*, June, 1947, p. 776.

Chapter 13. SHIPPING CONTAINERS

CLENDENIN, ROBERT G.: A Review of Cleaning and Rust Prevention, *University of Illinois Engineering Experiment Station Circular Series* 56, 1949.

PLASKETT, C. A.: Principles of Box and Crate Construction, U.S. Department of Agriculture *Technical Bulletin* 171.

SELLEI, HELEN: Rust Preventatives, *Chemical Industries*, January, 1948, p. 62.

Chapter 14. PACKAGING METHODS AND MATERIALS

ATKINSON, F. M.: Improvements in Flour Packing Machinery, *The Northwestern Miller*, Apr. 12, 1949.

Compression Packing, *Modern Packaging*, February, 1947, p. 118.

HOLDER, L. A.: Packaging Heavy Articles, American Management Association, Packaging Series 22, p. 23.

PATTERSON, MOOREHEAD: Outlook for Improved Packaging Machinery, *Modern Packaging*, April, 1947, p. 152.

What the Armed Forces Want, *Modern Packaging*, November, 1948, p. 93.

What's Wanted in Machinery, *Modern Packaging*, May, 1947, p. 104.

WOODROOF, J. G., and WILLIAM REBAK: Protective Packaging of Frozen Foods, *Refrigerating Engineering*, January, 1949, September, p. 34-R.

Chapter 15. RESEARCH IN PACKAGING AND MATERIALS HANDLING

Abraser Testing Set, Cylinder Beader, *Modern Packaging*, January, 1949, p. 144.

Boxes Put to Test, *Business Week*, Oct. 25, 1947, p. 41.

COUCH, ROBERT: Testing Package Materials and Packages, *Modern Packaging Encyclopedia*, 1949, p. 121.

GROSS, T. J.: The Compression Test, *Modern Packaging*, April, 1946, p. 147.

IMMER, JOHN R.: What Every Handling Engineer Should Know, *Flow*, September, 1951, p. 47.

Impact Tester, *Modern Packaging*, February, 1949, p. 136.

LAMBRECHT, R. C.: How Packaging Research Pays, *Railway Age*, Aug. 6, 1949, p. 246.

LINCOLN, W. B.: Shipping Container Study, *Modern Packaging*, April, 1948, p. 168.

NEWELL, W. C.: Materials Handling Show Draws Textile Men, *Textile World*, March, 1948, p. 114.

The Cause and Cure of Rough Handling, *Railway Age*, July 12, 1941, p. 61.

WEBB, J. L.: Loss and Damage Prevention through Improved Materials Handling, *Railway Age*, Feb. 28, 1948, p. 422.

WEBER, R. F.: Research in Materials Handling, *Mechanical Handling*, June, 1947, p. 322.

ZIEMBA, J. V.: Why a Packaging Laboratory, *Food Industry*, July, 1947, p. 924.

Chapter 16. HOW TO SOLVE A HANDLING PROBLEM

Better Materials Handling; A Special Section, *Factory Management and Maintenance*, January, 1949, pp. 65–111.

FARLEY, A. C.: Planning a Storeroom Operation, *Industrial Improvement*, October, 1948, p. 8.

HUDSON, W. G.: Evaluating Materials Handling Layouts, *Chemical Engineering*, August, 1947, p. 110.

IMMER, JOHN R.: Before You Mechanize!, *Mechanical Handling*, May, 1951, p. 180.

MALLICK, R. W., and A. T. GAUDREAU: Planning the Materials Handling Project, *Modern Materials Handling*, April, 1951, p. 38.

Chapter 17. METHODS OF ANALYSIS

FAULKNER, LEROY: How to Analyze Your Materials Handling Accident Problems, *Modern Materials Handling*, April, 1950, p. 22.

FAULKNER, LEROY: Accidents Cost Money, *Modern Materials Handling*, March, 1950, p. 13.

HARMAN, H. M.: Plant Layout for Materials Handling, *Mechanical Handling*, March, 1947, pp. 125–128.

IMMER, JOHN R.: Plant Layout Techniques, *Mechanical Handling*, running serially, June, 1949, to March, 1950.

Introduction, *Factory Management and Maintenance*, p. 88, January, 1948. Comparative Analysis (Westinghouse), pp. 90–96. Group Handling Analysis (Preben Jessen Company), pp. 97–98.

MALLICK, R. W., and J. H. SANSONETTI, Material Handling a Profit Factor, *Mechanical Handling*, June, 1947, p. 317.

Chapter 18. TYPES OF SURVEYS

BOYCE, CARROL: Adopt the Best in Plant Layout, *Factory Management and Maintenance*, September, 1949, p. 66.

Materials Handling, *Plant Engineering*, January, 1949 (16 pp.).

ROWAN, MILES J.: How Materials Handling Affects Plant Layout, *American Machinist*, Dec. 30, 1948, pp. 83–98.

Chapter 19. COST ACCOUNTING SYSTEMS

BOWER, MARVIN, and RICHARD D. ELWELL: The Chief Executive Looks at Materials Handling, *Modern Materials Handling*, November, 1946, p. 13.

BRINKERHOFF, H. W.: Three-dimensional Drawings Aid Plant Layout Visualization, *Chemical Industries*, Vol. 56, pp. 410–411, 1945.

Can You Spotlight Handling Wastes? *Modern Industry*, February, 1948, p. 40.

DELEHANTY, J. W.: How We Got the Boss to Say Yes to New Handling Ideas, *Factory Management and Maintenance*, June, 1950, p. 88.

MOFFAT, ALEX W.: A Fresh Eye (use of consultants), *Modern Materials Handling*, March, 1948, p. 27.

Chapter 20. DETERMINATION OF HANDLING COSTS

DIMMOCK, W. J.: Mechanical Handling in Industry and Its Effect on Costs, *Mechanical Handling*, June, 1951, p. 243.

LANDON, F. N.: Economics of Automatic Pallet Loader, *Modern Materials Handling*, May, 1951, p. 56.

Chapter 21. HOW TO SELL BETTER HANDLING METHODS

BAIRD, D. G.: Packard Knows the Operating Cost of Each Truck, *Mill & Factory*, October, 1950, p. 9799.

DOWD, C. R.: Material Handling Accounting Practices, *Flow*, March, 1951, p. 48.

FELL, R. F.: You Can Know How Much It Costs, *Flow*, April, 1947, p. 18.

McCLELLAND, W. B.: Management Pays the Bill, *Modern Materials Handling*, May, 1951, p. 81.

McLOUGHLIN, K.: New Approach to Handling That Will Cut Costs, *Factory Management and Maintenance*, June, 1950, p. 84.

OPSAHL, C. R.: Railroad Material Handling Problems, *Railway Age*, Feb. 14, 1948, p. 345.

WITHEY, S. T.: Depreciation and Maintenance of Mechanical Handling Plants, *Mechanical Handling*, 1942; May, p. 9; June, p. 109; July, p. 132; August, p. 153; September, p. 171.

WRIGHT, R. E.: Materials Handling Costs to Be Considered with Development of Process and Plant Layout, *Industrial and Engineering Chemistry*, May, 1950, Sup. 81A.

Chapter 22. ORGANIZATION

Establishment of a Materials Handling Program by General Electric, *Iron Age*, July 7, 1938, p. 30.

IMMER, JOHN R.: Management Responsibility in Materials Handling, *Produttività* (Rome), March, 1952, p. 205.

MACBETH, D. F.: Materials Handling Program Pays Off in Six Important Ways, *Modern Materials Handling*, January, 1951, p. 49.

NAKKULA, C. W.: How General Motors Keeps "Handling Minded," *Flow*, January, 1951, p. 50.

Chapter 23. PRODUCTION CONTROL

BRIGHT, JAMES R.: Radio Control, *Modern Materials Handling*, May, 1951, p. 40.

BROADY, J. M.: Two-way Radios Speed Handling of 10,000,000 Lbs. Daily, *Flow*, January, 1951, p. 44.

Mechanizing Inventory Control, *Modern Materials Handling*, May, 1951, p. 59.

Hammermill Traffic Control Speeds Its Operations, *Paper Trade Journal*, Mar. 20, 1947, p. 21.

Chapter 24. OPERATOR TRAINING AND INSTRUCTION

Army Trains Men for Better Loading Methods, *Railway Age*, July 7, 1945, p. 20.

HADFIELD, T. R., and J. L. ENGLISH: Mill Trains Fork Lift Truck Operators, *Textile World*, November, 1947, p. 112.

PENNOCK, D. W.: Training Courses for Fork Truck Drivers at Carrier, *Flow*, March, 1951, p. 39.

Chapter 25. INTEGRATION OF EQUIPMENT

ALLEN, A. H.: New Oldsmobile V-8 Engine Will Be Built in Remarkable Coordinated New Plant, *Steel*, Sept. 27, 1948, p. 69.

LONEY, M. N.: Material Handling in the Motor Industry, *Mechanical Handling*, April, 1947, p. 195.

Materials Handling Efficiencies Important Factor in Mass Production of Thunderbolt Fighter Bomber, *Storage Battery Power*, August, 1944, p. 3.

WHITMORE, EUGENE: New Building Cuts Handling Costs, *American Machinist*, June, 1946, p. 18.

Chapter 26. MAINTENANCE

Centralized Lubrication on Crane Pays for Itself in One Year, *Factory Management and Maintenance*, November, 1950, p. 91.

DUPUIS, F. L.: How to Keep Your Shop Trucks Rolling, *Mill & Factory*, December, 1950, p. 95.

Lubrication, Maintenance and Inspection of Belt Conveyors, *Mining Congress Journal*, December, 1950, p. 31.

Maintenance 'Round the Clock, *Flow*, March, 1951, p. 50.

Preventive Maintenance of Handling Equipment, *Flow*, April, 1951, p. 40.

ULDRICKS, C.: How We Keep Our Trucks Running 22 Hours a Day; Kellogg Company, *Factory Management and Maintenance*, December, 1950, p. 98.

Use and Maintenance of Battery Powered Trucks in Pulp and Paper Industry, *Paper Trade Journal*, Nov. 25, 1943, p. 52.

Chapter 27. SAFETY

Bigger Loads—Fewer Injuries, *National Safety News*, October, 1950, p. 82.

BLAKE, R. P.: "Industrial Safety," Prentice-Hall, Inc., New York, 1943.

BODEN, JACK: Automatic Safety Stops Improve Conveyor Efficiency, *American Machinist*, Sept. 25, 1947, p. 104.

CLEMENS, J. R.: Materials Handling Equipment in Action, *National Safety News*, April, 1951, p. 24.

First Safety Code for Power Trucks, *Standardization*, November, 1950, p. 288.

HEINRICH, H. W.: "Industrial Accident Prevention," 3d ed., McGraw-Hill Book Company, Inc., New York, 1950.

Industrial Trucks and Tractors, *National Safety News*, March, 1951, p. 133.

LIPPERT, F. G.: "Accident Prevention Administration," McGraw-Hill Book Company, Inc., New York, 1947.

Mechanical Handling for Safety and Savings, *Safety Engineering*, August, 1949, p. 25.

PANTAS, L. J.: Our Aging Plants—Mechanized Handling Overcomes Hazards, *National Safety News*, January, 1951, p. 18.

Safe Practices That Save Dollars, *Modern Industry*, October, 1949, p. 52.

Chapter 28. MACHINE OPERATIONS

ALLEN, H. H.: Chip Conveyors; Use of Abrasive-resisting Synthetic Rubber, *Steel*, June 3, 1946, p. 123.

CURTIS, H. C.: Transfer Presses Boost Output at A. C. Spark Plug, *American Machinist*, May 22, 1947, p. 100.

DIAMOND, E. L.: Characteristics of Scrap in Relation to Bulk Handling, *Iron & Steel Institution Journal*, April, 1950, p. 452; *Iron Age*, Sept. 21, 1950, p. 95; *Engineer*, May 12, 1950, p. 564; *Engineering*, May 5, 1950, p. 511.

Eight Methods for Handling Scrap, *Flow*, March, 1951, p. 44.

GESCHELIN, J.: Production of Body Hardware, *Automotive and Aviation Industries*, June 1, 1947, p. 38.

IMMER, JOHN R.: Handling Starts at the Workplace, *Mechanical Handling* (London), November, 1951, p. 457.

SOSS, CHARLES J.: Automatic Transfer between Machines, *Flow*, December, 1950, p. 44.

Chapter 29. WAREHOUSING ACTIVITIES

A Crane-and-cradle System and Low Cost Wood Racks (Bambergers), *Modern Materials Handling*, February, 1951, p. 40.

ARCHER, JOHN O.: Efficient Storage Saves Us $50,000 a Year, *Factory Management and Maintenance,* September, 1949, p. 111.

Automatic Warehouse—Johnson & Johnson, *Modern Packaging,* December, 1949, p. 110.

BROCLOW, J. R.: Material Handling and the Grocery Warehouse, *Journal of Marketing,* September, 1949, p. 30.

CHRISTIANSON, P. B., and D. O. HAYNES: Materials Handling in Multi-storied Cold Storage Warehouses, *Food Industry,* February, 1948.

CLOSE, G. C.: Receiving and Shipping Wheels; Douglas Aircraft Company, *Mill & Factory,* March, 1951, p. 109.

FISHER, G. M.: Covered Receiving Platform Is Heart of Plant Expansion, *Industry and Power,* October, 1946, p. 60.

FREY, E. H.: Warehouse Elevators and Palletized Freight, *Distribution Age,* July, 1949, p. 57.

GALLERY, JAMES J.: Palletization in Multi-story Warehouse, *Distribution Age,* June, 1948, p. 26.

HAINSWORTH, BRUCE A.: The Circular Warehouse, *Distribution Age,* January, 1947, p. 36.

HAINSWORTH, BRUCE A.: Warehouse Design and Construction, *Factory Management and Maintenance,* April, 1947, p. B-70.

Materials Handling in the Storehouse, *Textile World,* January, 1945, p. 128.

MELNITSKY, BENJAMIN: Handling in Cold-storage and Merchandise Warehouses, *Distribution Age,* September, 1949, p. 19.

MESEROLE, W. H.: Organization of Wholesale Operations for Low Cost, *The Journal of Marketing,* September, 1949, p. 192.

POTTS, MATTHEW W.: Material Handling Bonuses, *Distribution Age,* June, 1948, p. 35.

Revolution in the Warehouse; Lazarus, *Architectural Record,* December, 1950, p. 108.

Warehousing and Delivery Practices and Procedures, National Retail Dry Goods Association, Store Management Group, 1948.

WHEELER, W. S.: Planned Warehouse Handling Curtails Cost and Saves Space, *Factory Management and Maintenance,* July, 1948, p. 124.

When Should You Build a New Warehouse?, *Modern Materials Handling,* December, 1952, p. 56.

You're *Not* Too Small to Mechanize Your Warehouse, *Modern Materials Handling,* April, 1951, p. 46.

Chapter 30. ASSEMBLY

BAILEY, L. W.: Floor Layout and Materials Handling in the Light Engine Industry, *Mechanical Handling,* December, 1947, p. 620.

BIRD, FLOYD J.: Synchronizing Sub-assemblies to Main Line Needs, *Factory Management and Maintenance,* April, 1948, p. 56.

BOONE, A. R.: Perpetual Motion in Aircraft Assembly, *Mechanical Handling,* February, 1944, p. 51.

Conveyors Aid in the Assembly of Engines, *Mechanical Handling,* December, 1947, p. 637.

Double Productivity by Good Handling, *Factory Management and Maintenance,* December, 1946, p. 133.

DUPRE, F.: What! Assemble Instruments on a Conveyor? *Factory Management and Maintenance,* March, 1946, p. 113.

Engine Assembly, the System and Layout Employed by the Austin Motor Company, *Automobile Engineer,* March, 1947, p. 90.

Final Assembly of Mosquitoes, *Mechanical Handling,* January, 1945, p. 65.

GESCHELIN, JOSEPH: Delco-Remy Introduces New Facilities for High-volume Minimum Cost Production, *Automotive Industries,* Nov. 1, 1947, p. 36.

GESCHELIN, JOSEPH: Hudson Final Assembly Layout Quite Different from Others, *Automotive Industries,* Apr. 1, 1948, p. 28.

Put It [the stockroom] on the Line, *Modern Materials Handling,* May, 1951, p. 54.

RICKER, CHESTER S.: New Ideas in Conveyorized Assembly, *American Machinist,* Oct. 9, 1947, p. 96.

RYLANDER, A. E.: Automatic Hoppers Speed Assembly, *The Tool Engineer,* September, 1948, p. 17.

Chapter 31. AIR-CARGO HANDLING

Materials Handling Equipment, *Distribution Age,* October, 1949, p. 20.

SAPERSTEIN, CHARLES L.: Air Cargo Packing Problems, *Distribution Age,* October, 1946, p. 40.

Mechanical Handling of Freight at American Air Lines Chicago Terminal, *Traffic World,* Oct. 9, 1948, p. 63.

Chapter 32. RAILROAD AND TRUCK HANDLING

Railroad Handling

EIDSON, W. B.: What's New in Railroad Equipment? *Modern Materials Handling,* May, 1951, p. 49.

Express Agency Builds Largest Sorting Station at New York, *Railway Age,* Dec. 14, 1940, p. 897.

Freight Station Mechanization Helps Offset Trend of Rising Costs, *Railway Age,* May 8, 1948, p. 42.

Handling of Railway Freight, *Mechanical Handling,* September, 1948, p. 547.

HUDSON, N. C.: Modern Freight Handling with the Missouri-Pacific Lines in St. Louis, *Traffic World,* Dec. 13, 1949, p. 17.

Lawley Street Goods Shed, Birmingham, *Engineering,* Dec. 28, 1945, p. 533.

LYNCH, P. J.: Union Pacific Expedites L.c.l. Freight Handling, *Railway Age,* Aug. 28, 1948, p. 429.

Materials Handling Development on Great Western Railway, *Mechanical Handling,* August, 1947, p. 414.

MAYER, C. W.: Handling Railroad Materials, *Mechanical Engineering*, September, 1950, p. 741.

Mechanization of Freight Station Simplifies L.c.l. Handling, *Railway Age*, Sept. 13, 1947, p. 438.

MILLIKEN, J. W.: Carriers Plan Expanded Mechanization Program for Stations and Storehouses, *Railway Age*, Jan. 15, 1951, p. 186.

More Gains in Unit-load Handling Equipment, *Railway Age*, May 20, 1950, p. 100. (Includes list of freight stations with equipment for handling unit loads.)

VARNUM, G. W.: This New Freight House Has Everything, *Railway Age*, Mar. 6, 1948, p. 462.

Truck Handling

BRIGHT, JAMES R.: Devices for Meeting the Dock Height Problem, *Modern Materials Handling*, February, 1951, p. 21.

Boston Studies Truck Terminals, *American City*, February, 1948, p. 127.

HUDSON, N. C.: Trucking Terminals Embrace Mechanical Freight Handling, *Traffic World*, Mar. 13, 1948, p. 781.

JARMAN, HUGH G.: Shifting into High, *Distribution Age*, November, 1949, p. 26.

Planning Truck Shipping Areas, *Modern Materials Handling*, January, 1951, p. 26.

ROWE, ARTHUR E.: Adjustable Docks, *Modern Materials Handling*, January, 1951, p. 39.

WASIE, S. L.: Advantages of Overhead Conveyor System for Motor Truck Depots, *Traffic World*, Mar. 12, 1949, p. 69.

Chapter 33. SHIP AND BARGE HANDLING

Air Moves Cement from Barges to Batching Bins, *Rock Products*, February, 1948, p. 154.

Barge Transportation for Bulk Cement, *Rock Products*, August, 1947, p. 126.

Cargo Handling and Stowage, *Marine Engineering*, September, 1947, p. 102.

EICHENBERGER, R. W.: Self-unloading, *Marine Engineering*, August, 1948, p. 36.

Farrel Cargo Gear Demonstrated, *Marine Engineering*, November, 1949, p. 54.

First Technical Conference, International Cargo Handling Co-ordination Association, *World Ports*, July, 1952, p. 11.

GRINDROD, J.: Loading and Discharging Equipment at Dutch Ports, *Mechanical Handling*, October, 1948, p. 641.

Handling of Iron Ore, *Steel*, Dec. 19, 1949, p. 93.

LEDERER, E. H.: "Port Terminal Operations," Cornell Maritime Press, New York, 1945.

Package Ships on the Great Lakes, *Business Week*, Aug. 12, 1944, p. 76.

RANKIN, A. J., and A. J. ZUEHLKE: Conversion to Self-unloader, *Marine Engineering*, August, 1948, p. 36.

Rohn, A. C.: Cargo Handling with Crane Gear, *Marine Engineering*, October, 1947, p. 72.

Self-propelled Diesel and Diesel Electric Deck Whirleys, *Diesel Power*, March, 1947, p. 50.

Shipping Interests View Postwar Cargo-handling Devices, *Marine Engineering*, January, 1948, p. 74.

Chapter 34. HANDLING BULK MATERIALS

Belt Hoists Handle Coal Smoothly and Economically, *Coal Age*, March, 1948.

Bucket Elevators to Conserve Space, *Rock Products*, September, 1948, p. 95.

Coal Handling at Dalmarnack, *Canadian Mining Journal*, December, 1946.

Floating Pneumatic Grain Handling Plant, *Engineering*, March, 1947, p. 211.

Grain Discharging Plant at a Northern Port, *Mechanical Handling*, December, 1944, p. 516.

Grain Drying, Processing and Handling Equipment, *Mechanical Handling*, June, 1947, p. 291.

Hardy, A. F., Jr.: Better Way to Handle Dry Bulk Materials at Norton Company, *Factory Management and Maintenance*, November, 1950, p. 102.

Immer, John R.: Production Increased by Half in One Year!, *Mechanical Handling*, July, 1951, p. 269.

Mechanical Loading, *Coal Age*, June, 1948.

Miller, Fred: Unit Loads of Bulk Materials, *Modern Materials Handling*, December, 1952, p. 59.

Plant Layout for Conveyors, *Rock Products*, May, 1948, p. 78.

Push Button Operated Gravel Plant, *Rock Products*, May, 1946, p. 64.

Radial Conveyors, *Rock Products*, July, 1948, p. 118.

Tramway Handling of Materials, *Rock Products*, July, 1948, p. 74.

Use of Bulldozers at Generating Stations, *Electrical Review*, November, 1946.

APPENDIX D

REFERENCES TO SPECIFIC INDUSTRIES

FOOD

COLLINS, G. N.: Mechanizing Halves Handling Costs at Beardsley's Newark Plant, *Food Industries,* November, 1950, p. 1879.

Conveyor in the Food Industry, *Mechanical Handling,* April, 1946, p. 236.

Do's and Don'ts of Materials Handling, *Food Industries,* August, 1946, p. 1176.

Glued Pallet Loads Reduce Costs and Protect Crating, *Food Industries,* July, 1945, p. 750.

FILLIPPON, A. E.: How to Handle Corn Syrup, *Food Industries,* November, 1946, p. 82.

Handling of Foodstuffs, *Mechanical Handling,* September, 1945, p. 499.

Handling in a Food Factory, *Mechanical Handling,* September, 1947, p. 461.

JARMAN, H. G.: Handling and Packing Bottled Beer; National Breweries, *Mechanical Handling,* March, 1947, p. 259.

McCARTHY, F. W.: Modern Materials Handling: Special Food Industries Report, *Food Industries,* March, 1951, p. 107.

Packing, Grading and Handling of Fruit, *Mechanical Handling,* May, 1945, p. 272.

Pneumatics, *American Miller and Processor,* July, 1947, p. 28.

Whiskey Starts with the Grain, *American Miller and Processor,* January, 1947, p. 86.

FOUNDRIES

Foundry Using Fork Truck for Loading Its Annealing Oven, *Iron Age,* Dec. 7, 1944, p. 124.

HERRMANN, R. H.: Handling Materials in the Foundry Yard, *Foundry,* March, 1948, p. 70.

Mechanization in Magnesium Sand Foundry, *Mechanical Handling,* 1945; January, p. 2; February, p. 60.

Mechanized Grey Iron Foundry, *Mechanical Handling,* November, 1946, p. 668.

MITCHELL, W. K.: New Lifting Devices Simplify Mold Weight Handling, *Foundry,* March, 1947, p. 146.

MOELLER, C. H.: Handling Materials in the Foundry, *Foundry,* February, 1948, p. 222.

Production Jumps with Mechanization, *Mill & Factory,* February, 1951, p. 120.

HOUSE CONSTRUCTION

Assembly Line Methods Produce, *Civil Engineering*, August, 1947, p. 478.

Australian Pre-fab Resembles American Counterpart in Design, Fabrication, and Erection Techniques, *Architectural Forum*, March, 1947, p. 122.

British Firm Uses Line Production Methods in Pre-casting House Panels, *Concrete*, August, 1947, p. 3.

Equipment Developed for Mass Production of Pre-cast Concrete Houses, *Engineering News-Record*, May 2, 1946, p. 711.

Houses off the Line, *Architectural Forum*, October, 1946, p. 10.

OATES, J. A.: Handling of Pre-fabs, *Mechanical Handling*, October, 1946, p. 631.

Prefabricated Steel House, *American Builder*, November, 1946, p. 103.

Prefabrication in Buildings, *Mechanical World*, May 31, 1946, p. 610.

Steel Frame House Built on Assembly Line Basis, *Engineering News-Record*, June 12, 1947, p. 950.

PAPER AND PULP

COOK, C. B.: Paper Handling Methods Which Reduce Spoilage, *Paper Industry and Paper World*, August, 1944, p. 600.

Kimberly Mill of Kimberly-Clark Has Highly Developed Pulp and Paper Handling System, *Storage Battery Power*, February, 1943, p. 3.

Nekoosa-Edwards Paper Co. Has Highly Mechanized Material-handling System, *Storage Battery Power*, December, 1946, p. 3.

Routing Heavy Traffic Overhead, *Flow*, July, 1947, p. 20.

Truck Handling of Paper—Hammermill, *Paper Industry and Paper World*, April, 1948, p. 118.

CEMENT

Cement Handling and Storage Plant, *Mechanical Handling*, July, 1947, p. 349.

Palletizing of Portland Cement, *Compressed Air Magazine*, November, 1945, p. 286.

Three Methods of Handling Bulk Cement, *Rock Products*, July, 1946, p. 49.

AUTOMOTIVE

BRAZIER, H. E.: Flow Layout Means More Output at Less Than Estimated Cost (Crosley), *Factory Management and Maintenance*, October, 1947, p. 76.

Engine Assembly: System and Layout (Austin), *Automotive England*, March, 1947, p. 90.

FROST, E. R.: Profits from Cubic Inches, *Steel*, Dec. 4, 1950, p. 101.

GESCHELIN, J.: Completely Conveyorized Paint Shop Operation at DeSoto Body Plant, *Automotive Industry*, Dec. 1, 1950, p. 38.

GESCHELIN, J.: Handling Mechanization Boosts Shock Absorber Output, *Automotive & Aviation Industries*, Jan. 15, 1947, p. 24.

GESCHELIN, J.: Nash Prepares for 1949 Production, *Automotive Industry,* July 15, 1948, p. 32.

Handling in the New Vauxhall Factory, *Automobile Engineering,* January, 1951, p. 17.

Materials Handling in a Modern Automobile Factory (Vauxhall), *Mechanical Handling,* May, 1951, p. 185.

PATTON, G. W.: Chevrolet Assembly Plant Shows Way for Postwar Production, *Iron Age,* July 3, 1947, p. 80.

CONCRETE BLOCKS

Change Coring Room Layout to Speed up Handling, *Rock Products,* May, 1946.

Handling Aids Cut Unit Cost of Blocks, *Concrete,* 1946.

Lift Trucks and Conveyor Belts Reduce Handling Costs, *Rock Products,* April, 1948.

Transport Block from Machine to Rocks by Endless Cable Conveyor, *Rock Products,* June, 1948, p. 177.

Palletizing Block Handling, *Rock Products,* August, 1948, p. 207.

BRICK AND TILE

FRANCIS, W. C.: Fork Lift Truck Sets 20,000 More Brick Daily, *Brick and Clay Record,* April, 1947, p. 52.

HARTMAN, PETER: Works Visits—Brickmaking Plant, Denmark, *The British Clayworker,* Mar. 15, 1951, p. 326.

How Chicago Plants Handle Bricks, *Brick and Clay Record,* December, 1944.

Overhead Cranes May Be Used with Scove, Tunnel and Continuous Kilns, *Brick and Clay Record,* November, 1946, p. 47.

ELECTRIC MOTORS

LINSLEY, H. E.: Modern Motor Manufacturing Methods, *Iron Age,* May 8, 1947, p. 68.

LONEY, N. M.: Material Handling in the Motor Industry, *Mechanical Handling,* April, 1947, p. 195.

Quantity Production of Loom Motors, *Engineering,* Feb. 20, 1948, p. 176.

Work-handling Devices Simplify Motor Manufacturing, *American Machinist,* June 3, 1948, p. 88.

ORE HANDLING

Continuous Ore Transport: Belt Conveyor Design and Application, *Mining & Metallurgy,* December, 1947, p. 590.

HEUMANN, G. W., and W. C. RAUBE: Modern Ore Bridge Installation, *General Electric Review,* December, 1945, p. 7.

Mining Trends on the Mesabi, *Mining World,* September, 1947, p. 44.

Modern Equipment and Methods—Pictorial Review, *Engineering and Mining Journal*, November, 1947, p. 91.

COAL HANDLING

Coal and Coke Handling at Modern Gas Works, *Mechanical Handling*, July, 1942, p. 130.

Coal Handling with Earth Moving Equipment, *Mechanical Engineering*, July, 1947, p. 559.

Large Scale Material Handling in the Coal Industry, *Mechanical Handling*, January, 1947, p. 27.

Mechanized Handling of Domestic Fuel, *Mechanical Handling*, July, 1947, p. 375.

Mining and Loading, Past Progress and Future Prospects, *Coal Age*, June, 1947, p. 89.

MOYER, A. W.: Handling Coal Underground and by Conveyor Belt, *Coal Mining*, May, 1947, p. 26.

PEARSON, G. C.: Coal Handling, *Mechanical Handling*, July, 1947, p. 374.

Scraper Equipment Stock Piles Coal for Utility, *Power*, March, 1947, p. 102.

WELTON-CLARK, H.: Coal Mine Transportation, *Western Miner*, November, 1946, p. 55.

TEXTILE

BOWDEN, C. M.: Every Pick-up Adds to Handling Cost, *Textile World*, May, 1947, p. 104.

BOWDEN, C. M.: Materials Handling Cost Offers Opportunity for Saving, *Textile World*, January, 1947, p. 121.

Conveyors Deliver Spools to Spinning Room in Woolen Mill, *Textile World*, April, 1946, p. 120.

Electric Trucks in the Textile Industry, *Mechanical Handling*, November, 1946, p. 676.

Hand Tractor Aids Material Handling, *Textile World*, April, 1946, p. 160.

Improved Textile Handling Four Ways, *Flow*, April, 1951, p. 39.

Loading Industrial Machinery Pneumatically, *Compressed Air Magazine*, May, 1947, p. 124.

Materials Handling Reveals Mill Engineering Skill, *Textile World*, September, 1946, p. 125.

Mechanical Systems for Handling Textile Materials, *Rayon*, August, 1947, p. 447.

McGUIRE, W. B.: Better Handling Methods Offer Large Savings, *Textile World*, February, 1947, p. 117.

McGUIRE, W. B.: Mechanical Lap Handling System Produces Savings, *Textile World*, August, 1948, p. 109.

MOORE, J. C.: Beam Handling Facilitated by Fork Truck, *Textile World*, July, 1948, p. 125.

Profits through Efficient Materials Handling, *Rayon*, August, 1948, p. 91.

Schwartz, S.: Yarn Conveyors at May Hosiery, *Textile World*, October, 1943, p. 92.

Stevens, A. M.: Grapple Speeds Wool Handling, *Textile World*, July, 1947, p. 97.

Thomas, P. M.: Mechanical Handling Saves Time and Money; Avondale Mills, *Textile World*, December, 1946, p. 118.

AVIATION

Comprehensive Conveyor System, *Mechanical Handling*, December, 1945, p. 687.

Conveyor Production at Aeronca, *Aircraft Production*, September, 1946, p. 46.

Conveyor to Save Cost First Year, *Mechanical Handling*, September, 1944, p. 406.

Expediting Curtiss-Wright Heat-treating, Anodizing, and Plating, *Machinery*, July, 1944, p. 192.

Final Assembly of Mosquitoes, *Mechanical Handling*, January, 1945, p. 10.

Gerhauser, G. F.: Convair's Master Plan for Building the 204 Transport, *Automotive Industries*, July 15, 1947, p. 28.

New Overhead Conveyor System in Martin Bomber Plant, *Automotive & Aviation Industries*, May 15, 1942, p. 26.

Put Parts Where They Are Needed; Northrup F-89, *Aviation Week*, Mar. 12, 1951, p. 33.

Table Type Conveyor at North American, *Automotive & Aviation Industries*, Apr. 15, 1946, p. 34.

LUMBER AND WOOD PRODUCTS

Doubled Productivity by Good Handling, *Factory Management and Maintenance*, December, 1946, p. 133.

Mechanization Means Handling Five Times Faster; Grand Rapids Chair Co., *Factory Management and Maintenance*, August, 1947, p. 97.

Rudolph, W.: Handling Reduced 50% in Revamped Furniture Factory, *Mill & Factory*, July, 1948.

Upside Down Loading Benefits Dealer and Builders; Materials First Will Be on Top, *American Builders Journal*, February, 1948, p. 136.

Ziegler, W. H.: Conveyorized Handling Pays Its Way in 60 Days, *Factory Management and Maintenance*, September, 1947, p. 24.

LOGGING

Diesel Powered Log Loader, *Diesel Power*, September, 1947, p. 39.

Logging at Full Throttle, *Popular Science*, September, 1947, p. 99.

Lumberjack's Skyride, *Popular Mechanics*, August, 1945, p. 70.

Timber Rides Skyhook, *Popular Science*, May, 1947, p. 147.

PULPWOOD

HELVERSON, F. D.: Outstanding Materials Handling Practices in the Pulp and Paper Industry of the West Coast, *Tappi*, November, 1950, Sup. 14A.

McCARTHY, L. J.: Wood Handling at K.V.P., *Pulp and Paper of Canada*, October, 1946, p. 77.

PRATT, R. C.: How Hoberg Handles and Stores Pulpwood, *Paper Industry and Paper World*, May, 1947, p. 214.

LIST OF VISUAL AIDS

Most of the visual aids relative to materials handling have been produced by manufacturers of specific types of handling equipment. Many of these are of high quality and demonstrate principles and fundamentals of handling in addition to the use of equipment.

Most of these films are not listed in standard film catalogues, since they are issued by private organizations. They are generally available to schools and organized groups. In addition to the films listed, other visual aids may be obtained from university film libraries and by reference to film catalogues such as those listed on page 567.

The running time (min) and whether the film is silent (si) or sound (sd) are listed with each title. Unless otherwise stated, all titles are black and white 16-mm motion pictures.

GENERAL

GRQ Grand Rapids Metal Cabinet (Acme 10 min si). Plant operations and packing and strapping of knocked-down metal cabinets.

Life Stream of the City (GE 15 min sd color). This film illustrates the fundamental needs which good city transportation must fill and how it can be done. Modern streetcars, trolley coaches, rapid trains, and buses are shown in action.

Magazine Magic (Curtis 35 min sd color). An over-all review of the procedures involved in the production of five of the company's leading publications.

Materials Handling (GE 24 min sd color). Film AS-2622.

Safe Handling of Materials (NSC 15 min sd 35 mm film strip). Film shows how foremen can give effective instructions on how to lift and carry.

Trees to Tribunes (Chicago 30 min sd). Various steps required to produce a metropolitan newspaper, from logging to delivery of paper.

FARM APPLICATIONS

Gutter Cleaning Conveyor (Webb 12 min si). Shows dairy-barn conveyor system.

Harvest in a Hurry (Wooden 17 min sd color). Shows harvesting methods and handling of crops between field and processing plant.

Moving White Gold (Clark 25 min sd). A review of fork-truck handling methods, machines, and devices available to the cotton industry.

PAPER INDUSTRY

Haas-Baruch Towveyor (Webb 8 min si). Shows operation of Towveyor system.

Handling Rolls with the Bartel Device (Clark 12 min sd). Shows how Bartel device and fork truck unload rolls of newsprint from ship's hold at 80 tons per gang-hour and unload box car in 30 minutes.

Macon-Kraft Paper Company—Paper Roll Conveyors (Webb 8 min si). Inside views showing rolls conveyed through cutters, elevators, and scales automatically.

Macon-Kraft Paper Company—Pulpwood and Chip Conveyors (Webb 10 min si). Shows views in yard.

Paper Industry (Acme 20 min si). Packing and bracing carload shipments of paper.

Zellerbach Paper Company Towveyor (Webb 10 min si). Shows operation of Towveyor system.

TEXTILES

Textile Industry (Acme 24 min si). Packaging and handling by conveyor and truck all types of packages and bales within the textile industry.

Textiles Unlimited (GE 28 min sd color). Emphasizes the trend toward use of modern materials-handling equipment in the textile industry.

WOOD PRODUCTS AND BUILDING MATERIALS

Creosoted Poles (Acme 24 min si). Loading and bracing procedures for telephone poles on flatcars.

Flooring Industry (Acme 32 min si). Shows the handling of strapped bundles of hardwood flooring through warehousing and carloading operations with use of fork truck.

Getting the Most from the Labor Dollar (Liftall 16 min sd color). Illustrates the handling of bricks by one man with truck.

Liftall Trucks in Concrete Block Industry (Liftall 18 min si color). Shows yard handling of concrete blocks and mechanical delivery to job without hand labor.

Lumber (Acme 20 min si). Shows the handling of strapped bundles of hardwood flooring through warehousing and carloading operations with use of fork truck.

Mechanize for Profit (Building 45 min si). Pictures the handling of lumber and other building materials in retail and building supply yards and warehouses.

Moving Lumber at J. C. Turner Co. Yard (Ross 23 min sd color).

RAILROAD AND TRUCK HANDLING

Easy Does It! (AAR sd color). Illustrates effects of over-speed impacts with typical instances of damage to freight resulting therefrom.

Freight Handling Safety (NSC 11 min sd 16 and 35 mm sd). A training film showing how to handle and unload freight safely.

"Godsvard" (*Handling the Freight*) (AAR sd). This film, produced by the Swedish State Railways, shows the handling given to lcl freight in Sweden.

Handle With Care (B & O 18 min sd 35 mm slide film). Proper and improper methods of freight handling, checking, and stowing are shown. Its main purpose is to help freight handlers become more efficient in their jobs.

Handling of Materials, Methods and Equipment (Rock Island 20 min si). Rock Island shops at 51st Street (Chicago) and Silvis shops at Silvis, Ill.

Impact Tests (AAR si 20 min each). This series of films shows cars with sides and tops removed, loaded with the commodities indicated below, being impacted at various speeds. Effects on loading are portrayed through slow-motion.

Hot tops (clay pouring channels)
Machinery
Sewer pipe

Impact (S-P 18 min sd 35 mm film strip). Emphasizes proper car handling. Has views of damaged loading caused by rough handling. (Limited availability.)

It's a Deal (NYC 20 min sd). Shows damage which can result from improper loading of high-class freight. Is designed to educate freight-house employees in the handling of lcl merchandise.

Keep That Customer (S-P 13 min sd 35 mm film strip). Shows handling of lcl freight from pickup to delivery. Stresses proper handling, loading, and stowing. (Limited availability.)

Mystic Terminal, Boston, Mass. (Elwell si color).

On Time (Yale 40 min sd). Shows use of electric industrial trucks in railroad shops and yards. It covers handling of baggage, mail, and freight, locomotive and car overhauling, and general shop handling.

Problem No. 1, the $20,000,000 *Challenge* (ATA 22 min sd 35 mm film strip). Points out the high cost of loss and damage claims.

Railroads Speed the Freight (Waugh 15 min sd color). Portrays railroad progress, showing various methods of handling the nation's freight.

Testing Devices (AAR 18 min si). Shows use of Conbur Incline Impact Tester.

Think Twice (B & O 16 min sd color). An animated cartoon designed to be shown to operating, freight-house, and mechanical employees.

Unit Load Methods (Acme 28 min si). Tests conducted by the American Association of Railroads on open-sided car, showing impact tests on sewer pipe, both rigidly braced and floating loads. Loading and bracing methods used on acid carboys and washing machines.

Wheels of Progress (C, RI & P sd color). Includes interesting close-ups of classification yards.

Who Done It? (U-P 20 min sd color). Good and bad practices of freight handling are shown in a manner both interesting and educational.

BULK MATERIALS

Added Values (Harnischfeger 35 min sd color—English or Spanish dialogue). Shows the assembly of excavators from the bare steel to on-the-job applications.

Bucket Loaders (Barber-Greene si color 16 min).

Coal Handling Machines (Barber-Greene si color 36 min).

Portable Conveyors (Barber-Greene si color 12 min).

Lorains for Irrigation and Drainage (Thew 17 min sd color). Devoted primarily to draglines on drainage-ditch, levee, and dam construction.

Lorains in Pits, Quarries and Mines (Thew 20 min sd color). Uses of shovels, clamshells, and draglines in gravel pits, stone quarries, supply yards, and iron-ore and coal mines.

The Story of River Sand and Gravel (Dravo 30 min color). Dredging and distribution of sand and gravel on the Ohio River.

WATER TRANSPORTATION

Freight Terminal Operations (Mercury 10 min si). Shows scenes of loading and unloading of barge freight.

King Edward Pier, Montreal, Canada (Mercury 8 min si). Shows tractor-trailer method of handling transshipment of freight from rail terminal to ocean-going ships.

Power behind the Nation (Norfolk 38 min sd color). Mining procedure in Appalachian field is shown. Transportation of bituminous coal and the work of the coaling terminal at Norfolk is covered.

Timber Head (Dravo 30 min color). Shows operation of barge tows on inland waterways.

BASIC INDUSTRIES

Die Casting (New Jersey 35 min sd color). Technical film showing all phases of die-casting process.

Handling Materials in the Steel Industry (Link-Belt 22 min sd color). The efficient mechanical handling and transferring of coils of hot or cold steel strip.

Manufacturing Anchor Chain (MHS 20 min sd).

Modern Coal Mining (Goodyear 20 min sd). Shows how laborsaving machinery has replaced old methods.

Steel (British 34 min sd color). Describes the steel industry in Britain from the digging of ore to the finished product.

This Is Aluminum (ALCOA 35 min sd). Shows steps in mining bauxite, chemical processes used in refining the ore, electrolytic production of aluminum, and the principal fabricating methods.

This Is Steel (Bethlehem 28 min sd). Shows production of pig iron in the blast furnaces, refining of iron into steel, and the shaping of steel.

This Moving World (Malleable 30 min color sd 16 and 35 mm). Story of how malleable iron is made, tested, and used.

MOTION STUDY

A Pictorial Study of Methods Improvement Principles (Saginaw 45 min si color). Shows principles relating to operation combination, automatic ejection, multiple processing, and barrier elimination on typical grinding, drill press, assembly, heat-treat, and packaging operations.

Correct Working Methods (MEC 33 min si).

Effective Working Methods (MEC 9 min si).

Flow Process Chart (ITA 20 min sd).

If the Shoe Fits (Institute 30 min sd). Presents a study of the flow of materials through varied operations that results in the production of finished shoes.

Material Handling Methods (MEC 25 min si). Pictorial demonstration of material-handling methods used by present-day industry.

Motion Study Economy (Saginaw 67 min si color). An excellent presentation of various ways of improving efficiency by building motion-economy principles into standard or special machinery.

Motion Study Principles (Iowa 21 min sd).

MASS PRODUCTION

Bombs by Mass Production (MHS 20 min sd). Materials-handling processes carried to the *n*th degree in war production work.

Building the B-29 (Clark 27 min sd). Outlines the types of handling done by fork trucks at Boeing during the Second World War.

Chevrolet-Flint Power and Free Conveyor System (Webb 15 min si).

Fairfax and Fork Trucks (Clark 24 min sd). A pictorial story of the handling methods employed in the Fairfax Industrial District, Kansas City, Kan.—a planned industrial community.

Ford Motor Company (Mercury 24 min si). Shows fork trucks and tractor-trailer trains.

Ford Rouge Plant (Ford 30 min sd). Illustrating the control and simplicity in the world's greatest industrial unit.

Helping America Deliver the Goods (ACIA 30 min sd color). Depicts the manufacture of wooden barrels and kegs, providing a comprehensive treatment of the cooperage industry.

Material Handling Newsreel 2 (Clark 12 min sd color). Truck loading and unloading in yard of manufacturing plant.

Material Handling Newsreel 3 (Clark 14 min sd). Rotating device on fork truck handling scrap metal.

Materials on the Move (Yale 30 min sd). Industrial fork lift trucks shown in operation at the International Harvester Tractor Works with important cost savings outlined.

Shipways (Bethlehem 40 min sd). Advances in art of shipbuilding from days of clipper ships; the building of a Victory ship from drawing board to trial run; repairing and reconditioning certain types of vessels.

U.S. Rubber Company Power and Free Conveyor System (Webb 12 min si).

FOOD AND BOTTLED PRODUCTS

Blatz Brewing Company (Acme 20 min si). Conveyor system for handling of bottles and cases and loading of trucks.

Bottling without Bottlenecks (Clark 25 min sd). A survey of handling methods in bottling plants—old and new. Shows operations in large and small plants and how new methods increase profits.

Handling Groceries the "Certified" Way (Clark 12 min sd). Story of Certified Grocers of California, Ltd. Use of tractor train in order selection.

Quaker Oats, Akron, Ohio (Mercury 8 min si). Shows fork trucks handling and stacking bagged products.

The Connecting Link to Customer Satisfaction (Great Atlantic 20 min 16 mm slide film).

The Pallet System of Case Handling (Yale 10 min sd). Shows handling by gasoline fork truck of Coca-Cola cases on pallets on the production line and into and out of storage, and the loading and unloading of delivery trucks.

WAREHOUSING

Materials Handling in Receiving, Warehousing and Shipping (GE 30 min sd color).

Modern Material Handling Methods (Clark 17 min sd). Shows fork-truck handling methods in loading and in warehousing operations. Shows some obsolete equipment, but methods are sound.

Operation Frigid (Yale 15 min sd). Battery-powered fork trucks shown in the Quincy Market and Cold Storage Warehouses in Watertown, Mass. Shows complete handling operations.

INDUSTRIAL TRUCKS

Clark Modern Material Handling Methods (Clark 23 min sd). Wartime film made for the instruction of operators in Air Force depots. Some obsolete equipment is shown, but proper use of equipment is demonstrated.

Fork Trucks (Lewis si color 8 mm). Shows use of fork trucks and walkie electric equipment.

Here's Your Worksaver (Yale 15 min sd color). Shows one line of electric industrial trucks, including for trucks, platform trucks, and tractors.

It's Your Money (Yale 38 min sd). This film covers the complete range of the company's electric industrial trucks, showing the basic types in operation in several different industries.

Liftall Forks in Action (Liftall 30 min sd color).

Man Behind the Wheel (NSC 25 min sd 35 mm film strip). Demonstrates safest and most efficient operation of tractor-trailer units.

Material Handling in Exide Plant (Electric 22 min sd). Palletized unit loads and battery-powered fork and hand trucks.

Material Handling Newsreel 1 (Clark 29 min sd). Mechanized handling methods in various industries.

Material Handling Newsreel 4 (Clark 20 min sd). Diversified modern materials-handling methods and equipment in six different installations.

Modern Battery Shop Practice (Edison 26 min sd). How to design, equip, and operate battery shops in connection with industrial trucks.

Modern Material Handling (Edison 34 min sd). The use of the unit-load method of handling for reducing unit costs of production and distribution. Advantages of storage-battery power.

Payloads Pay Off (Automatic 35 min sd). Theme that material loads efficiently handled with electric equipment are payloads, and that such loads pay off in profits for management and result in upgrading for labor.

Skylift Newsreel (Automatic 35 min sd). Presents operation and features of first of company's postwar line of high-pressure hydraulic power trucks.

Storage Battery Power (Edison 20 min sd). How Edison came to invent and perfect the nickel-iron-alkaline type of storage battery; where it is used and how it is manufactured.

The One Man Gang (Towmotor 35 min sd). Shows materials-handling sequences in various manufacturing plants and a complete line of fork lift trucks and accessories.

Top Performance (Yale 24 min sd color). Yale & Towne's famous road show.

Transporter Newsreel (Automatic 18 min sd). Shows progress from hand trucks pushed or pulled by human strength to motorized units effortlessly moving heavy loads by electric power.

You and Your Tractor (NSC 15 min sd 35 mm film strip). Explains the safe operation of industrial power trucks and their proper loading and maintenance.

What Makes It Tick? (Towmotor 15 min sd 35 mm film strip). Shows basic construction features of fork truck.

CRANES

Crane Called Krane Kar (Silent Hoist 12 min si). An industrial rubber-tired gasoline-powered crane.

Giant Hands of Industry (NSC 15 min sd film strip). Points out the main causes of crane accidents and illustrates standard hand signals and safety tips.

Heavy Duty Materials Handling (Silent 12 min si). Shows use of combination crane and lift truck in industrial and utility operations.

Lorains at Work (Thew 13 min sd color). Covers general construction uses of Lorain shovels, draglines, and hoes.

Lorains in Industry (Thew 27 min sd color). Application of rubber-tired and crawler cranes. Includes use of crane-and-trailer combination.

Roll to Profits on Rubber (Thew 17 min sd color). General uses of rubber-tire mounted cranes and shovels, as the equipment is applied to various types of industry.

The Changing World (Power Crane 45 min 35 mm film strip). This film strip covers the functional design, job analysis, and job application of power cranes and shovels.

Thew-Lorain "Pipeliners" (Thew 20 min sd color). Use of wide-gauge crawler and rubber-tired cranes in cross-country pipe-line construction.

CONVEYORS

Bauer & Black (Acme 10 min si). Export cartons of surgical dressings being strapped on a conveyorized line setup.

Careers in Conveyors (CEMA 28 min sd 35 mm film strip).

Composite Conveyor Installations (Lamson 30 min sd). This film shows a wide range of types of conveyors in several manufacturing plants.

Conveying Systems (Rapids 12 min si).

Golden Valley (Goodyear 20 min sd). Conveyor used in construction of Shasta Dam.

Pacemakers for Industry (Webb 30 min sd).

Permanent Belt Conveyors (Barber-Green 36 min si color).

Rapids Standard Conveying Systems—What They Will Do for You (Rapids 12 min si).

Up and Over (American Monorail 20 min sd). Complete story of monorail material-handling equipment.

Yours to Command (CEMA 23 min sd 35 mm film strip). Starts with the first installation of conveying equipment in 1783 and shows more than a score of modern applications.

OTHER HANDLING EQUIPMENT

Automatic Pallet Loader (Lamson 15 min sd). Describes the working and application of the pallet loader.

How to Seal It Right with Gummed Tape (GIA 15 min sd 35 mm film strip). Proper methods of sealing cartons with gummed paper sealing tape.

Material on the Move (Caterpillar 25 min sd). The operational and mechanical advantages of Caterpillar scrapers.

The Dempster-Dumpster (Dempster 10 min si). Explains the mechanical principles of the "Dumpster."

The Talking Hoist (Yale 12 min sd color). An up-to-the-minute description of the integral parts of a hoist with a unique interest-holding setting.

SOURCES OF FILMS LISTED ABOVE

AAR—Association of American Railroads, Secretary, Freight Claim Division, 59 E. Van Buren St., Chicago 5, Ill.

ACIA—Associated Cooperage Industries of America, 408 Olive St., St. Louis 2, Mo.

Acme Steel Co., Strapping Division, 2840 Archer Ave., Chicago 8, Ill.

ALCOA—Aluminum Company of America, Motion Picture Dept., Gulf Bldg., Pittsburgh 19, Pa.

American Monorail Company, Advertising Manager, 13107 Athens Ave., Cleveland 7, Ohio.

Automatic Transportation Co., 141 West 87th St., Chicago 20, Ill.

Barber-Greene Co., Advertising Dept., Aurora, Ill.

Bethlehem Steel Co., Bethlehem, Pa.

B & O—Baltimore & Ohio Railroad Co., General Freight Claim Agent, Baltimore, Md.

British Information Services, 30 Rockefeller Plaza, New York 20, N.Y.

Building Supply News, 5 Wabash Ave., Chicago 3, Ill.

Caterpillar Tractor Co., Advertising Dept., Peoria, Ill.

CEMA—Conveyor Equipment Manufacturers Assn., 1129 Vermont Ave., Washington 5, D.C.

Chicago Tribune, Film Bureau, 33 W. Madison St., Chicago 2, Ill.

Clark Equipment Co., Industrial Truck Division, Advertising Dept., Battle Creek, Mich.

C, RI & P—Chicago, Rock Island and Pacific Railroad Co., Public Relations Dept., Chicago 5, Ill.

Curtis Publishing Co., Motion Picture and Speakers Bureau, Rm. 1223, Public Ledger Bldg., Philadelphia, Pa.

Dempster Brothers, Inc., Springdale Ave., Knoxville 17, Tenn.

Dravo Corp., Dravo Bldg., Liberty and Fifth Aves., Pittsburgh 22, Pa.

American Trucking Association, Freight Claims Dept., 1424 16th St., Washington, D.C.

Edison, Thomas A., Inc., Storage Battery Division, West Orange, N.J.

Electric Storage Battery Co., 42 South 15th St., Philadelphia 2, Pa.

Elwell-Parker Electric Co., 4237 St. Clair Ave., Cleveland 3, Ohio.

Ford Motor Co., 3000 Schaefer Rd., Dearborn, Mich.

GE—General Electric Co., Advertising and Sales Promotion Division, 1 River Rd., Schenectady 5, N.Y.

GIA—Gummed Industries Assn., Inc., 19 W. 44th St., New York 18, N.Y.

Goodyear Tire & Rubber Co., Motion Picture Dept., Akron 16, Ohio.

Great Atlantic and Pacific Tea Co., New York, N.Y.

Harnischfeger Corp., Advertising Dept., Milwaukee 14, Wis.

Institute of Visual Training, 40 E. 49th St., New York 17, N.Y.

Iowa, State University of, Bureau of Visual Instruction, Iowa City, Iowa.

ITA—Industrial Truck Assn., 3701 N. Broad St., Philadelphia 40, Pa.

Lamson Corporation, Syracuse 1, N.Y.

Lewis-Shepard Products, Inc., 159 Walnut St., Watertown 72, Mass.

Liftall Corporation, 2007 Baltimore, Kansas City, Mo.

Link-Belt Co., Advertising Dept., 307 N. Michigan Ave., Chicago 1, Ill.

Malleable Founders Society, Union Commerce Bldg., Cleveland, Ohio.

MEC—Methods Engineering Council, Wood and Franklyn Sts., Pittsburgh, Pa.

Mercury Manufacturing Co., Sales Manager, 4044 S. Halstead St., Chicago 9, Ill.

MHS—Mechanical Handling Systems, Inc., 4600 Nancy Ave., Detroit 12, Mich.

New Jersey Zinc Co., 160 Front St., New York 7, N.Y.

Norfolk & Western Railway Co., Roanoke, Va.

NSC—National Safety Council, 425 N. Michigan Ave., Chicago 11, Ill.

NYC—New York Central Railroad Co., Prevention Bureau, Property Protection and Freight Claim Dept., 466 Lexington Ave., New York 17, N.Y.

Power Crane and Shovel Assn., 74 Trinity Pl., New York 6, N.Y.

Rapids-Standard Co., Inc., 685 Rapistan Bldg., Grand Rapids 2, Mich.

Rock Island Lines, 139 W. Van Buren St., Chicago 5, Ill.

Ross Carrier Co., Miller and Second Sts., Benton Harbour, Mich.

Saginaw Steering Gear Division, General Motors, 628 N. Hamilton St., Saginaw, Mich.

Silent Hoist & Crane Co., 841–877 63d St., Brooklyn 20, N.Y.

S-P—Southern Pacific Co., Freight Protection and Station Service Dept., 65 Market St., San Francisco 5, Calif.

Thew Shovel Co., Loraine, Ohio.

Towmotor Corp., Advertising Dept., 1226 E. 152d St., Cleveland 10, Ohio.

U-P—Union Pacific Railroad Co., General Freight Claim Agent, 1416 Dodge St., Omaha 2, Neb.

Waugh Equipment Co., 420 Lexington Ave., New York, N.Y.

Webb, Jervis B., Co., 8951 Alpine Ave., Detroit 4, Mich.

Wooden Box Institute, 55 New Montgomery St., San Francisco 5, Calif.

Yale & Towne Manufacturing Co., General Sales Manager, Philadelphia 15, Pa.

OTHER LISTINGS OF VISUAL AIDS

American Society of Mechanical Engineers, 29 W. 39th St., New York 18, N.Y. Available to sections of the ASME.

McGraw-Hill Book Company, Inc., Text-film Dept., 330 W. 42d St., New York 36, N.Y.

British Information Services, 30 Rockefeller Plaza, New York 20, N.Y. Catalogue of films from Great Britain available in the United States.

Business Screen Magazine, 812 N. Dearborn St., Chicago 10, Ill. An index of training films is issued annually.

Castle Films, 30 Rockefeller Plaza, New York 20, N.Y. Catalogue contains a complete listing of all U.S. Office of Education visual aids.

INDEX

A

A frame (*see* Rack, A-frame)
Abrasive materials (*see* Materials)
Accident, causes of, 373
  elimination of, by overhead handling, 420
Account numbers, handling shown by, 244
  need of, for cost information, 245, 279
  as setup for costing, 30
Accountant for handling cost, 245
Acetate, 214
Acid, danger in handling, 268
  shipped in drums, 188
Act-breakdown chart, 40
Activity chart, man and machine, 72
  multi-man, 71
Agricola, G., early handling, 16
Air cargo, 440
  equipment built in planes, 29
  terminal time reduced, 29
Air-operated hoist, 125, 388
Airplane industry, chain conveyor assembly line, 434
  machining of cylinder blocks, 402
  movement of assemblies, 320
  use by, of channel tracks, 435
  of pneumatic-tube system, 333
Airslide conveyor, 509
Aisles, effect of, on safety, 375
  not needed for cranes, 174
  overhead handling and width of, 105
  for storage areas, 417
  survey needs, 262
Alkali, hot solution, 196
Aluminum drum, 188
Aluminum foil to prevent corrosion, 195
Amortization, effect of depreciation and obsolescence rates on, 83
  principle of, 30
Analysis, of aisle space, 417
  of equipment costs, 254
  annual, 282
  flow, 249
  flow-chart, 239
  of functions involved in handling, 307

Analysis, graphic, 250
  operation, 241
  safety, 252
  symbols for, 57
Annealing operation, cold-roll mill, 357
Annuity method of depreciation, 276
Applied percentage for costs, 280
Approval of projects, 318
Apron conveyor (*see* Conveyors)
Architect, warehouse study by, 264
Ashes, air conveyor to move fly, 509
  sluice used for, 98
Assembly, factor of equipment, 429
  hydraulic lift section for, 120
  movement of, 320
  parts kit for, 430
  progressive, 433
  rail track, for, 88
  slat conveyor for, 92
  stationary, 433
  trolley conveyor, for, 395
  250-ton sections, 306
  work at conveyor positions, 35
Associations, reference to trade, 339
Attachments (*see* Trucks, fork lift)
Authorization, of repairs, 367
  of studies, 317
Automobile industry, assembly in, 93, 435
  monorail for, 107
  early handling methods, 429
  machining of cylinder blocks, 402
  standard times, 65
  straddle truck to move frames, 151

B

Baggage truck (*see* Trucks)
Bags, burlap, 214
  canvas, on wheeled frame, 144
  conveyors for, flat-belt, 91
    portable loading, 131
    slat, 91
    V-belt, 103
  cotton, 214
  expendable pallet, shipped on, 475
  glassine, 203

571